STP 1226

Lead in Paint, Soil and Dust: Health Risks, Exposure Studies, Control Measures, Measurement Methods, and Quality Assurance

Michael E. Beard and S. D. Allen Iske, Editors

ASTM Publication Code Number (PCN)
04-012260-17

ASTM
1916 Race Street
Philadelphia, PA 19103
Printed in the U.S.A.

Library of Congress Cataloging-in-Publication Data

Lead in paint, soil, and dust : health risks, exposure studies, control
    measures, measurement methods, and quality assurance / Michael
    E. Beard and S.D. Allen Iske, editors.
        (STP ; 1226)
    "Texts from . . . presentations given at the 1993 Boulder
Conference on Lead in Paint, Soil, and Dust . . . sponsored by
ASTM Committees . . . held at the University of Colorado, Boulder,
Colorado, between 25-29 July 1993"—Intro.
    "ASTM publication code number (PCN) 04-012260-17."
    Includes bibliographical references and indexes.
    ISBN 0-8031-1884-8
    1. Lead poisoning—Congresses. 2. Lead—Environmental
aspects—Congresses.   I. Beard, Michael E., 1940-   .   II. Iske,
S. D. Allen, 1950-   .   III. Conference on Lead in Paint, Soil, and
Dust (1993 : Boulder, Colo.)   IV. Series: ASTM special technical
publication ; 1226.
RA1231.L4L3785   1995
615.9′25688—dc20   95-17787
                                                                CIP

Photocopy Rights

Peer Review Policy

Each paper published in this volume was evaluated by three peer reviewers. The authors
addressed all of the reviewers' comments to the satisfaction of both the technical editor(s) and
the ASTM Committee on Publications.

To make technical information available as quickly as possible, the peer-reviewed papers in
this publication were printed "camera-ready" as submitted by the authors.

The quality of the papers in this publication reflects not only the obvious efforts of the
authors and the technical editor(s), but also the work of these peer reviewers. The ASTM
Committee on Publications acknowledges with appreciation their dedication and contribution
to time and effort on behalf of ASTM.

Printed in Ann Arbor, MI
June 1995

Foreword

This publication, *Lead in Paint, Soil and Dust: Health Risks, Exposure Studies, Control Measures, Measurement Methods, and Quality Assurance,* contains papers presented at the 1993 Boulder Conference on Lead in Paint, Soil, and Dust held in Boulder, Colorado at the University of Colorado on 25–29 July 1993. The conference was sponsored by ASTM Committees D-22 on Sampling and Analysis of Atmospheres, E-6 on Performance of Buildings, D-1 on Paint and Related Coatings, Materials and Applications, and D-18 on Soil and Rock. Michael E. Beard, U.S. Environmental Protection Agency, and S. D. Allen Iske, Ph.D., CIH, Miles, Inc., presided as conference cochairmen and editors of this publication.

Contents

CONTROL MEASURES

Overview

Introduction

This special technical publication (STP) compiles the texts from a series of presentations given at the 1993 Boulder Conference on Lead in Paint, Soil, and Dust. The conference was sponsored by ASTM Committees D-22 on Sampling and Analysis of Atmospheres, E-6 on Performance Buildings, D-1 on Paint and Related Coatings, Materials, and Applications, and D-18 on Soil and Rock and was held at the University of Colorado, Boulder, Colorado, between 25–29 July, 1993. This was the tenth in a series of biannual conferences to advance the science and knowledge in various topics concerning environmental and atmospheric measurements.

Specifically, this 1993 Boulder Conference provided an opportunity to review the latest results in research on monitoring and controlling environmental exposures to lead in paint, soil, and dust. The program for the conference was arranged to provide a multidisciplinary overview of environmental lead-monitoring research programs and the status of analytical methods as well as certification programs for analysis of environmental samples. The primary goal for the conference was to provide an up-to-date review of technical topics relating to lead monitoring while bringing the disciplines of exposure assessment and analytical chemistry together to promote a better understanding of their mutual interests, needs, and limitations for monitoring of lead.

The ASTM committees sponsoring this conference provided a forum for the presentation of state-of-the-art research by a selected group of distinguished researchers as well as for formal and informal discussions between all attendees. The technical presentations provided the experienced professional in lead monitoring with an up-to-date review of research while for the newcomer to the lead area an introduction of current status of knowledge. The conference was a benefit to industrial hygienists, health researchers, chemists, agronomists, building management and operations personnel, laboratory managers, governmental regulatory authorities (federal, state, and local governmental officials), anyone interested in the lead monitoring issues, and academic researchers.

The publication of the papers will serve to extend the information and experience presented during the conference to those in attendance and to serve as a resource for all to use.

Summary of Presentations

Papers in this publication summarize the presentations and discussions given by the authors during the conference. The manuscripts support the discussions held during the week covering the topics of Health Risks, Exposure Studies, Control Measures, Measurement Methods, Quality Assurance, and Laboratory and Field Measurement Accreditation. The following is a brief summary of each of the presentations made at the conference.

Although all presenters were requested and expected to submit a formal paper to be included in this special publication, all authors did not submit finished written papers. In addition, a few submitted papers had to be rejected for publication based on technical issues. All papers published in this text have been fully approved after a thorough "peer review" process by selected expert reviewers and the editors for this publication. A designation of an

"*" after a paper's reference in this summary section indicates that the paper was presented at the conference but a formal paper is not published in this book.

Health Risks

Three papers were presented on the health effects and risks of environmental lead exposure to open the conference. *Mahaffey** presented the opening paper with an overview of adverse health effects of lead as the basis for establishing soil and dust standards. She presented research regarding pediatric lead poisoning and on the implications of biokinetics (that is, internal redistribution of lead) in assessing health effects from environmental exposures.

Weis et al. discussed their work on determining the gastrointestinal absorption of lead using immature swine as a plausible mammalian model for juvenile children. The experimental design of a series of investigations to understand the bioavailability of lead using a lead reference substance and a residential soil from a mining and smelter area were discussed.

The session closed with *Marcus and Elias* leading a discussion on the significance of different sources and pathways in childhood lead exposure. Different methods and models for predicting the factors for a child's total lead exposure are detailed from three cross-sectional studies.

Exposure Studies

Several papers were arranged on this topic to review the pathways and extent of exposure to lead. *Clickner and Rogers* began the session with a review of the findings from a national survey of lead-based paint in housing. The estimates on the amount and hazards of lead-based paint as well as the sources and pathways in residential homes were described.

Kinateder et al. presented data to assess the long-term efficacy of various abatement methods for lead-based paint with findings from an earlier U.S. Department of Housing lead-based paint abatement demonstration. Results from soil and dust samples were reported as well as compared with corresponding data from other abatement efficacy studies.

Eberle highlighted a demonstration project using multifamily public housing to examine the problems and opportunities associated with lead-based paint abatement in conjunction with scheduled modernization of these structures.

Limited capability of the lead isotope ratio technique to determine the source of lead for blood lead content was shown by *Rabinowitz*. The potential benefits using this technique for clues to the origin and transport of lead pollution were noted; however, the limitations and variations in the isotope ratios must be considered.

Burgoon et al. reported on information derived from an EPA scientific literature search investigating the sources of lead contamination of soil. The authors strived to make some global evaluations for the sources for soil contaminations, geographic variations in soil lead levels, and correlating these lead-contaminated soils with elevated levels in children's blood.

A paper summarizing the statistical evaluation of the relationship between lead in environmental media (dust, soil, water, and air) and blood-lead levels using data from infants from late pregnancy to two years of age (Brigham and Women's Hospital Longitudinal Lead study) was presented by *Menton et al.* The goal was to assess statistically the environmental pathways of lead exposure.

Further studying the impact of abatement of lead in soil with a reduction of blood lead content of children was reported by *Elias and Grant**. Preliminary evidence for a quantifiable reduction in blood lead for the population of children that received intervention in their homes through abatement was presented.

With the other papers concerning lead exposures, *Farfel and Lim* outlined a planned study to compare full lead-paint abatement techniques with three different levels of repair and maintenance (R&M) intervention. The authors cited the importance of this new R&M approach to reduce lead in dust since lead-contaminated dust has been noted to be one major source of exposure for children.

As an appropriate closing paper to this session, *Burgoon et al.* summarized the efficacy of lead abatement in reducing children's lead exposure. Key studies were used to provide results and conclusions.

Control Measures

Control measures are used to reduce or eliminate exposure to lead (such as removal, encapsulation, and so forth) to meet lead action levels or "clean" standards. This session was opened with a paper by *Sussell et al.* discussing the hazard evaluation of crews using three different methods of "cleaning" the rooms of a building contaminated with lead-based paint. Correlation of worker esposure data to paint-lead concentrations were drwan.

As a second in the three-part series of papers on the long-term efficacy study of abatement methods, *Buxton et al.* presented the statistical modeling results as well as the performance of the studied lead-based paint abatement methods. Observed correlations of the lead levels in the household dust and soil measured at different locations were made.

*Lefkowitz and Harris** led a discussion on the engineering considerations and design of a decontamination needlegun system with local exhaust. Applications and safety/health requirements were cited.

*Weaver** commented to the attendees about atmospheric lead from automobiles (gasoline). Weaver cited that the estimation of lead from gasoline's environmental fate is urgent and must be primary to all lead control. Control of lead in a child's environment should be the focus. A somewhat contradictory paper to Weaver was next presented by *Jacobs*. Jacobs reviewed historical, epidemiological, and analytical evidence to support his presentation that lead-based paint constitutes a major source of lead poisoning in young children today in the United States. Jacobs further described the principal pathway of childhood lead exposure from lead paint in soils along with the direct ingestion path. Jacobs also noted soil contains lead from other sources such as residues from leaded gasoline and industrial sources in some locations.

Measurement Methods

An expanded session was necessary to accommodate the papers concerning the evaluation of measurement methods for determining lead levels using various instrumental techniques. *Harper et al.* summarized the research efforts in progress to evaluate the performance of measurement methods for lead in paint and paint-contaminated medias. The methods were evaluated for reliability and cost-effectiveness. The development of reference standards was discussed.

*Binstock et al.** discussed surface sampling using the wipe collection method to collect dust samples. The development of a field sample collection design was presented with laboratory and field validation data. *Grohse et al.** continued the discussion for field sampling using portable X-ray fluorescence (XRF) instruments or field test-kits for lead assessment. Grohse described the development of performance parameters to compare the methods.

Bernick et al. presented data supporting the use of field-portable XRF instruments for analyzing lead in soils and sediments as near real-time data with cost savings. *Vincent and Boyer* continued the session comparing the results for "real world" soil and dust samples from an abatement project using XRF with other instrumental (atomic absorption spectroscopy [AAS] and inductively coupled plasma [ICP]) data. Factors for variance in data as well as the importance of sample preparation were discussed.

Dewalt et al. completed the series of papers on the EPA's long-term efficacy study of abatement methods by presenting the sampling and analysis methods used for the study. Dewalt also provided the quality control measures implemented for the study from the field as well as in the laboratory. The results were statistically analyzed and sources of variability found.

Demyanek et al. investigated the use of adhesive lift-sampling technology for evaluation of lead in surface dust. This paper compared the use of this adhesive lift technique compared to other traditional surface-monitoring methods such as vacuum and wipes during field studies.

Scanning electron microscopy (SEM) and XRF used to determine lead levels in house dust samples collected as a post-lead abatement clean-up process following lead-paint removal or encapsulation was presented by *Mamane et al.* An analysis of the lead data results with particle size, morphology, and chemistry was developed.

The session closed with *Johnson and Hunt* presenting initial data for a new approach to lead in soil analysis. Johnson described the use of individual particle analysis (IPA) with SEM and EDX to characterize particles in size, shape, and elemental composition in a timely, efficient manner. Results suggested soil lead from paint undergoes a relatively rapid transformation and redistribution.

Quality Assurance

Quality assurance procedures are essential to ensure reliable lead measurements including the use and development of reference and performance audit measures. *Watters and DeVoe* introduced this topic with information on the design, development, and application of Standard Reference Materials (SRMs) and primary methods of measurements. The importance of these SRMs and primary methods to develop traceability to a U.S. national system of measurement as well as a potential worldwide acceptance was emphasized. *Hartwig* outlined that the goal of any "legitimate" analytical laboratory is to provide data of the highest quality possible. The componenets of a quality assurance/quality control program to minimize errors and control analytical variables were outlined.

Binstock et al. discussed the work required to develop method evaluation materials (MEMs) to support environmental lead studies. MEMs must meet target concentrations for regulatory levels and real-world data as well as meet homogeneity criteria for instrumental use.

Pella et al. updated the current status of NIST efforts to generate standard reference materials (SRMs) for both field paint-screening techniques and for laboratory quantitative analyses. Reference standards at various concentrations were and are being required.

Vincent et al. finished the session on quality assurance with a presentation on the submission of quality assurance double-blind samples during a lead abatement project. These audit samples included soils and dusts and were submitted for quality assessment of the analytical laboratories. Statistical interpretation of data results were summarized.

Laboratory and Field Measurement Accreditation

Accreditation or certification programs or both are key in providing performance criteria for programs and laboratories. *Scalera* reviewed the National Lead Laboratory Accreditation

Program (NLLAP) objectives and requirements of the program and the goal to assure that their recognized laboratories have the capability of analyzing for lead in paint, soil, and dust.

Unger discussed that accreditation of lead-testing laboratories through the American Association for Laboratory Accreditation (A2LA) program has been recognized by the EPA for the NLLAP program. The essential elements of the accreditation process were described. Next, *Peters and Hurley* detailed the American Industrial Hygiene Association's Environmental Lead Laboratory Accreditation Program (AIHA's ELPAT) program to accredit laboratories analyzing environmental samples for lead content. Hurley cited the key elements in this proficiency performance program as well as its recognition by EPA for the NLLAP program.

The last paper of the conference was given by *Cada** on state certification programs for laboratories completing lead analyses. The role of the Association of State and Territorial Public Health Laboratory Directors to represent the needs and difficulties of public health laboratories was discussed.

Final Comment

The cochairs for this conference sincerely hope the publication of the proceedings from the 1993 Boulder Conference will be beneficial to the scientific world. This STP reviews the current status of research as well as hopefully stimulates future work to understand this complex lead issue.

S. D. Allen Iske, Jr., Ph.D., CIH
Miles, Inc.,
Kansas City, MO; Conference cochairman and coeditor.

Michael E. Beard
US EPA,
Research Triangle Park, NC;
Conference cochairman and coeditor.

Health Risks of Lead in Paint, Soil, and Dust

Christopher P. Weis[1], Robert H. Poppenga[2], Brad J. Thacker[3], Gerry M. Henningsen[1] and Allan Curtis[4]

DESIGN OF PHARMACOKINETIC AND BIOAVAILABILITY STUDIES OF
LEAD IN AN IMMATURE SWINE MODEL

REFERENCE: Weis, C. P., Poppenga, R. H., Thacker, B. J., Henningsen, G. M., and Curtis, A. "Design of Pharmacokinetic and Bioavailability Studies of Lead in an Immature Swine Model," LEAD IN PAINT, SOIL, AND DUST: HEALTH RISKS, EXPOSURE STUDIES, CONTROL MEASURES, MEASUREMENT METHODS, AND QUALITY ASSURANCE. ASTM STP 1226, Michael E. Beard and S. D. Allen Iske, Eds., American Society for Testing and Materials, Philadelphia, 1995.

ABSTRACT: We have designed and implemented a series of investigations aimed at estimating the range and extent of gastrointestinal absorption of lead from various mineralogical matrices following oral and intravenous reference substance doses and oral test substance doses. Using pharmacokinetic information from our previous work [1,2] we are employing immature swine as a plausible, in vivo mammalian model for lead absorption in juvenile children [3]. This paper describes the rationale for the experimental design used to characterize the dose and time dependence of lead absorption over a subchronic (~30 day) period. Four dose groups ranging from 25 μg/kg/day to 675 μg/kg/day were used to validly characterize the oral absorption of a soluble lead reference substance, lead acetate (PbAc$_2 \cdot$3H$_2$O). Based on those results, oral doses ranging from 90 μg/kg/day to 1400 μg/kg/day, were planned to characterize the absorption of a test soil substance derived from residential soil in an active non-ferrous mining and historical smelting area of the Rocky Mountain west. Test substances employed were fully characterized as to lead concentration, geochemistry, and mineral matrix.

KEYWORDS: lead, bioavailability, absorption, pharmacokinetics, gastrointestinal, uptake, swine, metal, mining, smelting, soil, contamination

---

[1]Regional Toxicologist, U.S. Environmental Protection Agency-Region VIII, 8HWM-SM, 999 18th Street, Ste 500, Denver, CO.

[2]Assistant Professor, Dept. of Pharmacology and Toxicology, Michigan State University, East Lansing, MI 48824.

[3]Associate Professor, Dept. of Large Animal Clinical Sciences, Michigan State University, East Lansing, MI 48824.

[4]Chief, Laboratory Services Section, U.S. Environmental Protection Agency-Region VIII, 8ESD, 999 18th Street, Ste. 500, Denver, CO 80202.

INTRODUCTION

Estimation of exposure to environmental lead with the objective of providing adequate protection for public health is a continuing goal of the U.S. Environmental Protection Agency (EPA). Considering the extent of soil and dust lead contamination, the potential social costs of childhood lead poisoning, and the economic importance of avoiding over-regulation, the adequate assessment of lead bioavailability is both prudent and cost effective. Remedial costs are highly sensitive to adjustments in lead bioavailability estimates. On a national scale the cost implications of adjustments in lead bioavailability are staggering.

Biophysical aspects of the lead absorption process as it relates to soil lead absorption are described elsewhere [4]. To better address the uncertainties of bioavailability estimates for lead, we have designed a series of applied investigations to characterize the dose and time dependence of lead absorption in the immature swine model. Investigations into the bioavailability of lead in mature rats have been completed by others [5,6]. The rat, however, may not be an optimal model for lead absorption in human children for a variety of reasons [3]. Understanding the comparative physiology of the absorption process for lead is an important and on-going effort [7]. Immature swine afford a number of advantages for estimating the absorption of lead across the gastrointestinal (GI) tract: (1) Immature swine are similar in weight and size to human children; (2) the digestive system of swine, evolutionarily adapted to omnivorous behavior, is more like the human digestive system compared with the rodent or lagomorph models. The swine GI tract has been used for a variety of biomedical investigations into this complex organ system and is relatively well characterized; (3) immature swine remain in the prepubertal state throughout the test period thus allowing an assessment of lead absorption at the correct developmental stage; and (4) swine afford the opportunity for relatively extensive serial blood sampling without the risk of anemia or exsanguination.

DEFINITION

Bioavailability of a substance may be defined in a variety of ways, depending upon the interests of the investigator and the specific objectives of the study. For the purpose of this study design, we have used an operational definition of bioavailability which is derived from the medical sciences: the rate and extent of gastrointestinal lead absorption into the central (blood) compartment. Absorption and transport of lead into other compartments such as bone or liver may also provide useful comparisons and will be assessed.

OBJECTIVES

Phase I Objectives

In the simplest terms, the object of the overall study is to obtain a reliable estimate of the percent of lead in a defined residential soil that is likely to be absorbed across the gastrointestinal tracts of young children. More specifically, the Phase I study is designed to characterize immature swine as an appropriate and valid model for lead-uptake in children. Phase I study objectives are:

1) to determine the **absolute** oral absorption of lead from both a commonly employed, soluble lead compound (lead acetate) and from a lead-contaminated residential soil, and to establish a quantitative comparison of **relative** oral absorption for these defined lead types under the proposed experimental conditions;

2) to determine the **concentration-dependence** of the absorption for

the lead-contaminated residential soil and a reference substance (lead acetate) in the characterized experimental model;

3) to determine the **slope** of the time vs whole-blood lead (Pb) concentration curve for the defined lead contaminated residential soil and for the reference substance (lead acetate);

4) if possible, to determine the extent that a specific **skeletal sample** (tibia or femur) correlates with the absorbed fraction and total body burden of administered lead;

5) to establish an **optimal range** of doses and dosing period for lead to validly determine the relative or absolute absorption of lead from various environmental sources using the characterized immature swine model.

Phase II Objectives

A second phase of the study will be undertaken following completion of Phase I characterization studies. Phase II study objectives have been adjusted from phase I findings and will be finalized following discussion and interaction with end-users of the information to be obtained.   In general terms, the objective of Phase II is to employ Phase I information to establish the effectiveness of a simplified protocol for assessing relative bioavailability of various types of lead-contaminated substrates associated with two or more contaminated sites in the intermountain west.   Proposed Phase II objectives are:

(1) To firmly characterize the dose dependence and time dependence of the biological responses to lead exposures initially observed in Phase I studies;

(2) To establish a quantitative or semi-quantitative understanding of the effect of the fed vs fasted state on GI absorption of environmental lead;

(3) (the main objective of Phase II): To establish dose dependence and time dependence of lead absorption across the GI tract of the immature swine model for a wide spectrum of fully characterized environmental media.

The desire/intent of this second phase is to validate the ability of the model to sensitively distinguish relative and absolute bioavailability of lead from a range of environmental lead samples and to account for differences in bioavailability based upon geophysical-chemical properties of the lead in the samples. Dose-responsiveness, limits of detection, and variability of Pb uptake from various defined environmental samples will be established to adequately characterize the immature swine model for future studies.

METHOD

Nutritional Status

Nutritional status and the presence of active ionic ligands in the gut are likely to have important impacts on the bioavailability of lead [8,9]. This investigation is not intended to assess the relationship between nutritional status and the bioavailability of lead.   The animals employed in the study are supplied with 100% of their recommended food requirements as suggested by the National Research Council [10].   Food with adequate calories was provided twice per day, and water was supplied *ad libitum*. The feed did not contain common swine medicines, such as tetracycline (a lead ligand) or organic arsenicals which could interfere with lead absorption. During the course of the study, animals were fed a relatively low-lead feed (~0.1 ppm). Custom feed which meets these requirements of the study is available from Ziegler, Inc., PA.

<u>Dosing Regimen</u>

Pigs were randomly assigned to experimental groups, with litter mates being assigned equally throughout all groups. Doses were delivered as indicated in Tables 1 and 2. Prior to conducting Phase I, Part 2a, dose-range finding studies were performed for this animal model as Phase I, Part 1 investigations. Only healthy, growing immature swine were used. Disease-free status was confirmed before and at the end of the study, by testing for pathogens that could affect GI absorption or other pertinent physiological functions, using routine veterinary hematology and/or microbiology tests.

Tables 1 and 2 describe the details of experimental design. The study was conducted in two parts (parts 2a and 2b) which were run sequentially.

The first study part (2a) established dose and time dependence of soluble lead absorption ($PbAc_2 \cdot 3H_2O$). The second part (2b) compared the absorption of a lead contaminated residential soil with the benchmark lead acetate absorption. Five dose groups and three control groups were employed in part 2a (Table 1). All dose groups received lead acetate ($PbAc_2 \cdot 3H_2O$) mixed with control (< 50ppm lead) soil. Control group number 7 received lead acetate with no control soil to assess the possible influence of soil matrix mineralogy on lead absorption. Both a naive vehicle reference and an intravenous lead acetate group were included in part 2a to define untreated baseline and 100% Pb absorption respectively.

Table 2 represents detailed study design for the second study part (part 2b). Four dose groups and three control groups were employed in part 2b. Lead-contaminated residential soil (<250μm particle size) which was fully characterized for size, matrix, metal speciation and lead concentration was delivered at doses indicated in table 2 groups 1 through 4. Quantitative dose verification was established by acid digestion of duplicate doses at the termination of the study. Pigs were dosed with increasing soil mass as indicated (column 4 of table 2) which resulted in the estimated intake of ionic lead (Pb^{2+}) presented (column 5 of table 2). Control groups 5 and 6 were included to confirm physiological comparability of lead absorption between study parts (parts 2a and 2b).

For the purpose of estimation, uptake of lead delivered as lead acetate was assumed to be linear at a fraction of 1/3 that of intake. Uptake of lead from soil was assumed to be linear at a fraction of 1/10 that of intake (columns 6-9 in tables 1 and 2). This information, coupled with estimates of apparent distribution volume, was used to determine necessary analytical sensitivity for the study.

Oral dosing substances (both soil and lead acetate)were prepared in five gram pellets of the low lead feed. Intravenous doses were delivered via IV catheters which were installed aseptically approximately 7 days prior to dosing. Catheters were flushed with heparinized saline solution to maintain viability throughout the study.

<u>TABLE 1</u>

SOIL DOSE AND ESTIMATED Pb^{2+} UPTAKE FOR PHASE I-PART 2a

Group[~] #	N #	Daily Administered Oral Dose[*]			Nominal Pb^{++} Uptake[°], µg/kg/d			
		Control Soil, mg	Lead Soil, mg	Lead as Ac, µg/kg	Soil	Diet	Acetate	Total
1	5	200	0	0	≤.5	≤2	0	≤3
2	5	200	0	25	≤.5	≤2	7.5	10
3	5	200	0	75	≤.5	≤2	22.5	25
4	5	200	0	225	≤.5	≤2	67.5	70
5	5	200	0	675	≤.5	≤2	202.5	205
6	4	200	0	IV: 100	≤.5	≤2	100	103
7	4	0	0	225	0	≤2	67.5	70
8	3	0	0	0	0	≤2	0	≤2

*   The total daily dose of lead acetate ($PbAc_2 \cdot 3H_2O$) was divided into two equal doses and administered as above according to the daily schedule in Table 3; 30% oral bioavailability and linear absorption was presumed.

∞   **Experimental Control:** <u>Group #1</u> (vehicle only); **Experimental Dose-Response:** <u>Groups #2-5</u> (increasing $PbAc_2 \cdot 3H_2O$ in constant amount of control soil);
IV Reference Dose: <u>Group #6</u> (for groups 4 and 7 comparisons - 100 µg of $PbAc_2 \cdot 3H_2O$ in 1 cc PS administered as divided doses of 1/2 cc each);
Control Soil Reference: <u>Group #7</u> (to compare with potential soil interactions with Pb uptake in experimental group 4);
Naive Control Reference: <u>Group #8</u> (for normal, untreated baseline reference data).

☼   Assumes feed (at ~ 0.1 ppm Pb++) and control soil (at ~ 50 ppm Pb^{++}) contribute about 60 µg/day to the total intake of Pb^{++} in the immature swine, respectively accounting for ≤20 µg and ≤5 µg of Pb^{++} UPTAKE per day for a 10 kg pig at the start of the study; Also assumes that 30% of the administered oral dose (and 100% of the IV dose) of $PbAc_2 \cdot 3H_2O$ is bioavailable (enters the blood).

TABLE 2

SOIL DOSE AND ESTIMATED Pb^{2+} UPTAKE FOR PHASE I, PART 2b

Group #	N #	Daily Administered Oral Dose[*]			Nominal Pb^{++} Uptake, $\mu g/kg/d$[☼]			
		Control Soil, mg	Lead Soil, mg/kg	Dosed Pb^{2+} $\mu g/kg$	Soil	Diet	Acetate	Total
	5	0	11.0	90	9	≤2	0	11
2	5	0	27.5	225	25	≤2	0	27
3	5	0	68.5	560	55	≤2	0	57
4	5	0	171.4	1400	140	≤2	0	142
5	4	Vehicle	0	IV: 100	0	≤2	100	102
⁻6	4	Vehicle	0	oral: 225	0	≤2	40	42
7	4	Vehicle	0	0	0	≤2	0	≤2

*   The total daily dose of lead was divided into two equal doses and administered at times according to Table 3. The parent (source) lead soil had about <u>8170 ppm Pb^{++},</u> with an estimated bioavailability of 10% which was used to calculate the nominal estimated levels for daily uptake. <u>Incremental doses were calculated as log 2.5 based on doses above and below a study - standard 225 $\mu g/kg$ reference dose.</u> Group 5 is a common IV reference control group as used in the prior study, Phase I - Part 2a, and outlined in Table 1. Group 7 is the vehicle control which will be used for statistical comparisons between the 4 dose groups numbered 1-4. Column 4 (Lead Soil) represents the mass of lead-contaminated soil delivered to the animals. Column 5 (Dosed Pb) represents the delivered ionic Pb dose.

**   **Oral reference dose group** derived from Group 7 in Table 1 above: 225 $\mu g/kg$ $PbAc_2 \cdot 3H_2O$ administered orally as split doses in <u>no soil</u>; planned to link relative soil concentrations and the IV reference dose for $PbAc_2 \cdot 3H_2O$ in Table 1.

☼   Assumes feed (at ≈ 0.1 ppm Pb^{++}) contributes about 50 $\mu g/day$ to the total intake of Pb^{++} in the immature swine, accounting for ≤20 μg of Pb^{++} UPTAKE per day for a 10 kg pig at the start of the study; Also assumes that 10% of the administered oral soil dose, 100% of the IV $PbAc_2 \cdot 3H_2O$ dose, and 17% of the oral dose of $PbAc_2 \cdot 3H_2O$ is bioavailable (enters the blood) based on earlier experiments. Daily uptake amounts in the far right column are estimated on a per kg basis.

It is likely that human children receive doses of lead episodically. While it is not possible to exactly mimic temporal patterns of childhood lead exposure with the proposed study, a repetitive dosing schedule should more closely follow likely childhood exposures. Therefore, animals were dosed two times daily. The first dose was delivered following an overnight fast and followed approximately two hours later by the first feeding. The second dose was given four hours after the first feeding, and the animals again received food at approximately two hours post dosing (Table 3). This regimen was chosen to minimize confounding interactions of feed with dosed lead.

Table 3. DAILY EXPERIMENTAL ROUTINE

Time	8:00	9:00	11:00	15:00	17:00
Event	Bleed	Dose	Feed	Dose	Feed

Whole blood samples were collected aseptically from the anterior vena cava, with minimal stress or excitation, by using a closed blood collection system (Vacutainer, Bectin-Dickinsen, Rutherford, NJ). Blood collection systems were determined to be lead free prior to initiation of the study by rinsing with weak acid and analysis of the rinsate with graphite furnace atomic absorption spectroscopy (GFAA). Whole blood collection tubes contained calcium EDTA as the anticoagulant. Whole blood samples were split into four smaller aliquots for: 1) whole blood lead determinations by GFAA at the U.S. EPA laboratory in Lakewood, CO; 2) submission of 5% of samples to the Centers for Disease Control (CDC) to perform a random independent check on the accuracy of the analytical blood lead measurements; 3) archiving by freezing (-80°C), and; 4) 5% split sample analyses by interested outside parties. In summary, three (3) types of quality control samples were submitted for analysis: a) sample splits at field collection (5-10%) of the total number of tissue samples) coded to evaluate reproducibility of sample preparation within the MSU laboratory; b) sample splits at analysis (5-10%) to evaluate reproducibility and precision of laboratory methods; and c) 8 weekly spiked-blood samples containing either background, low, medium or high levels of lead (two samples for each level), in relation to levels found in blood from dosed pigs, to serve as analytical reference samples for determining laboratory accuracy. Samples were spiked at the MSU laboratory prior to preparation and shipping. Each sample was assigned a separate EPA tag number.

Soils Characterization

Residential soils for use as dosing material in part 2 of Phase I were a subset of archived samples obtained from the California Gulch site in Leadville, Colorado. Archived samples with appropriate lead concentrations (high-lead, and low-lead control samples) were composited and screened, such that all dosing material passed through a 250 μm screen. No material was ground prior to or following the sieving procedure. Thoroughly mixed dosing material was then characterized for: 1) total lead concentration under conditions of acceptable precision and accuracy; 2) total lead as characterized by X-ray fluorescence (XRF-microprobe) at the University of Colorado Department of Geology, 3) scanning electron microscopy for qualitative morphologic characteristics (including matrix), and 4) particle size distributions and speciation of the lead phase. Duplicate samples of the soil dosing material were retained in sufficient quantities for independent analysis and archiving.

CONCLUSION

Results of the above study design will be presented upon completion of the work. Specific aspects that were tailored to better model children included: species, intact sex, age, health, diet, low dose, soil ingestion rates, and residential soil source. Stringent experimental controls were incorporated into the design. A parallel designed study using weanling rats by the National Toxicology Program has been initiated to be able to better compare responses in the two species.

Upon completion of this characterization, the work described should allow for confident development of a simpler and more efficient bioassay for assessing lead absorption in the test system described.

REFERENCES

[1]   LaVelle, J.M., Poppenga, R.H., Thacker, B.J., Giesy, J.P., Weis, C.P., Othoudt, R. and Vandervoort, C., Bioavailability of lead in Mining Waste: an oral intubation study in young swine. In: The Proceedings of the International Symposium on the Bioavailability and Dietary Uptake of Lead. Science and Technology Letters Vol. 3,(1991) pp. 105-111.

[2]   Weis, C.P., Henningsen, G.H., Poppenga, R.H., and Thacker, B Pharmacokinetics of lead in blood of immature swine following acute oral and IV exposures. The Toxicologist Vol. 13, (1993) pp.175.

[3]   Weis, C P. and LaVelle, J.M. Characteristics to consider when choosing an animal model for the study of lead bioavailability. In: The Proceedings of the International Symposium on the Bioavailability and Dietary Uptake of Lead. Science and Technology Letters Vol. 3, (1991) pp. 113-119.

[4]   Mushak, P., Gastrointestinal absorption of lead in children and adults: Overview of biological and biophysico-chemical aspects. In: Proceedings of the Symposium on the Bioavailability and Dietary Exposure of Lead Science and Technology Letters Vol. 3, (1991) pp. 87-104.

[5]   Johnson, J.D., Freeman, G.B., Liao, S.C., Feder, P.I., Killinger, J.M. Bioavailability of lead in mining waste soil: a dosed feed study using Sprague-Dawley rats. Battelle Columbus Operations, Laboratory ID #SC9000006 (1991).

[6]   Freeman, G.B., Johnson, J.D., Liao, S.C., Feder, P.I, Killinger, J.M., Chaney, R.L., and Bergstrom, P.D. Effect of soil dose on bioavailability of lead from mining waste soil in rats. Proceedings of the Symposium on the Bioavailability and Dietary Uptake of Lead. Science and Technology Letters Vol. 3, (1991) pp. 121-128.

[7]   Matthews, H.B. (1993) National Institutes of Environmental Health Sciences (NIEHS), National Toxicology Program (NTP). Personal Communications

[8]   Mahaffey, K.R. Role of nutrition in prevention of pediatric lead toxicity. In: Increased Lead Absorption in Children: Management, Clinical and Environmental Aspects. Chisholm, J.J. Jr., O'Hara, D.M. (eds.) Urban and Schwartzberg, Baltimore, MD (1982).

[9]   Mushak, P., Interactive relationships as modifiers of metal toxicity with special reference to those of lead and those of

selenium. In: <u>Selected Aspects of Exposure to Heavy Metals in the Environment. Joint Workshop of the National Academy of Sciences. USA and Council of Academies of Sciences and Arts</u>, Yugoslavia, April 1985, (1987) pp. 36-41, National Academy Press, Washington, D.C.

[10] National Research Council. Nutrient Requirements of Swine. Ninth Revised Edition. National Academy Press, Washington, D.C. (1988).

Allan H. Marcus[1] and Robert W. Elias[2]

ESTIMATING THE CONTRIBUTION OF LEAD-BASED PAINT TO SOIL LEAD, DUST LEAD, AND CHILDHOOD BLOOD LEAD

REFERENCE: Marcus, A. H., Elias, R. W., "Estimating the Contribution of Lead-Based Paint to Soil Lead, Dust Lead, and Childhood Blood Lead", Lead in Paint, Soil, and Dust: Health Risks, Exposure Studies, Control Measures, Measurement Methods, and Quality Assurance, ASTM STP 1226, Michael E. Beard and S.D. Allen Iske, Eds., American Society for Testing and Materials, Philadelphia, 1995.

ABSTRACT: Young children are particularly susceptible to lead carried in fine particles of surface soil (exterior dust) and in household dust. Multi-media environmental and biological samples may allow causal inferences about the relative importance of different sources and pathways in childhood lead exposure, and about the effectiveness of intervention strategies. Methods include: (1) statistical inferences about pathways using structural equation modeling; (2) inferences about pathways using physical tracers of sources; (3) inferences based on mass balance estimates.

    Structural equation modeling allows estimation of both direct and indirect exposures to lead-based paint. For example, chips of exterior lead-based paint may be ingested directly, may contribute to surface soil lead which is ingested, and may also be transported into household dust which is ingested. It is often possible to identify soil and dust exposure from elevated lead levels on the child's hands. We use structural equation models in cross-sectional field studies in some Western communities, to demonstrate the role of lead paint as a source of lead exposure. Stronger causal inferences about sources and pathways can be made when there are physical identifiers of the source, such as an unusual ratio of some stable lead isotopes. Another approach is to carry out an intervention, such as removal or encapsulation of the lead-based paint, or removal of the contaminated soil and dust associated with the paint. If lead-based paint is not removed and there is some recontamination of these media over time after the intervention, then we can attribute the exposure to lead paint.

KEYWORDS: lead, soil lead, dust lead, lead-based paint, hand lead, blood lead, environmental pathways, exposure assessment, structural equation model, nonlinear regression, repeated measures analysis, stable lead isotope, lead tracer, dust mass transport, lead abatement.

INTRODUCTION

    Any particular source of environmental lead may have several pathways leading to undue exposure for a child or for other targets. Identification and quantification of these pathways may be very helpful in determining the most effective and/or cost-effective interventions or abatements for preventing childhood lead exposure. Young children are especially vulnerable to excessive lead exposure in the home. Because of their size and activity, they are likely to inhale more air and consume more tap water per body weight than are adults. Young children are particularly susceptible to ingesting lead carried in fine particles of surface soil (exterior dust) and in household dust particles. Fine particles adhere to the child's hands and skin and are swallowed during the course of normal childhood hand-to-mouth activity. Charney et al. [1] have shown that effective

---

[1]Senior Research Scientist, Statistics and Data Analysis Systems, Battelle Memorial Institute, Durham, NC; now Statistician, Environmental Criteria and Assessment Office, U.S. Environmental Protection Agency, MD 52, Research Triangle Park, NC 27711.

[2]Health Scientist, Environmental Criteria and Assessment Office, U.S. Environmental Protection Agency, MD 52, Research Triangle Park, NC 27711.

control of household dust was sufficient to keep blood lead levels of heavily lead-burdened children from increasing to pre-treatment levels when they returned to the same residential unit after treatment. Blood lead levels in treated children were still high, possibly from other exposure media inside or outside the home, but also from the large burden of lead stored in the child's skeleton. Rosen et al. [2] have shown that endogenous lead sources in a child's cortical bone are only partially removed by chelation therapy, and decrease very slowly after environmental abatement without chelation. There is thus a built-in limitation in the effectiveness of lead abatement in reducing blood lead levels or body lead burdens of lead-exposed children. It is clearly preferable to prevent exposure by removing the source, or by preventing exposure to media contaminated by that lead source.

Lead-based paint (abbreviated as LBP in this paper) may be available to the child in several media: as chips or flakes of deteriorating LBP, chewed directly from the painted surface; as a contributor to lead contamination of the surface soil near a LBP painted surface; as a contributor to dust in window wells, on window sills, and at entry areas; and as a contributor to household dust, both from exterior LBP to soil to dust and from interior LBP to interior dust. When sufficient data are available to characterize the lead levels in all relevant exposure media, then it may be possible to attribute certain fractions of the total exposure to differences in lead levels in the various media, and thence to a primary source of the exposure such as LBP. Several physical and statistical methods have been used to do this. We will show how these methods may be applied when there is enough information to adequately define the child's total lead exposure.

PHYSICAL IDENTIFICATION OF ENVIRONMENTAL LEAD PATHWAYS

MASS BALANCE ESTIMATES

A few simple calculations will demonstrate that lead-based paint can make significant contributions to household dust and to exterior soil near the house. The amount of lead-based paint on walls can be estimated from the HUD National Hazard Survey [3]. The area covered by LBP depends on the age of the house. The average interior LBP area on houses with LBP is 157 square feet for houses built between 1960 and 1979, 463 square feet for houses built between 1940 and 1959, and 1250 square feet for houses built before 1940. The average exterior LBP area on houses with LBP is 521 square feet for houses built between 1960 and 1979, 851 square feet for houses built between 1940 and 1959, and 1384 square feet for houses built before 1940. (One . ft^2 = 0.0929 m^2.) The average XRF levels also depend on the age of the house, with a geometric mean XRF of 0.59 mg Pb/cm^2 for houses built between 1960 and 1979, 0.70 mg Pb/cm^2 for houses built between 1940 and 1959, and 1.1 mg Pb/cm^2 for houses built before 1940. One may thus estimate the amount of lead on a typical (roughly, median) house built between 1960 and 1979 as 0.1 kg inside and 0.4 kg outside, for houses built between 1940 and 1959 as 0.3 kg inside and 0.6 kg outside, and for houses built before 1940 as 1.3 kg inside and 1.4 kg outside. Thus, for analysis purposes, we may take about 1 kg lead paint each on the interior and the exterior.

Lead-based paint deteriorates slowly over time, by design. We may assume that a typical lead-painted interior surface (about 1 mg Pb/cm^2) will lose all of its paint in, say, 100 years, so that the rate of accumulation of lead from interior LBP in household dust may be about 0.01 kg Pb/year.

The typical amount of household dust in older housing is about 5 kg. For example, in the Baltimore houses selected for the Three-City Study, the mean dust loading is about 49 g/m^2. With a typical floor area of about 1100 ft^2 (100 m^2) the estimated total dust content is about 4900 g = 4.9 kg in these houses.

The contribution of interior LBP to this dust load depends on the rate of removal of leaded dust (presumably the same as the rate of removal of total dust) from the house. Farfel et al. [4,5] found that there was significant dust recontamination of Baltimore houses after LBP abatement by traditional or modified abatement methods, with a first-order time constant that we have estimated as about 2 to 3 months. Allott et al. [6] showed that the rate of removal of the radioactive isotope ^{137}Cs in dust from British homes following the Chernobyl explosion was closely exponential with a time constant of 9 to 12 months. We assume a rapid rate of dust removal, at a rate of 4 times per year (time constant 0.25 years). The steady-state level of lead in floor dust from LBP is therefore equal to (0.01 kg Pb/year) * 0.25 years = 0.0025 kg. The steady-state contribution of interior LBP to dust lead concentration is 0.0025 kg Pb / 5 kg dust = 500 µg Pb /g dust. Roughly similar levels may be expected to characterize LBP contributions to lead in surface soil near the house perimeter or dripline. These levels are very similar to those we have observed in a number of studies.

USE OF STABLE LEAD ISOTOPES TO IDENTIFY PATHWAYS

Several studies have use the isotopic composition of lead to identify source contributions. While ^{208}Pb is the most common isotope, smaller quantities of ^{207}Pb, ^{206}Pb, and ^{204}Pb characterize lead with different radiogenic or cosmogenic origin. Lead added to gasoline or paint during manufacture will usually come from a single location, such as Broken Hill in Australia or from the Missouri Lead Belt, will have different ratios of these isotopes. Yaffee et al. [7] studied 12 children in Oakland, CA in 1978. The children lived in 2 dwelling units. The authors conclude that "the isotopic ratios of lead in the blood of these children were close to the average lead ratios of paints from exterior walls and to the lead ratios of surface soils in adjacent areas where the children played. In both case studies, the data suggest that the lead in soil was derived mainly from the weathering of lead-based exterior paints and that the lead-contaminated soil was a proximate source of lead in the blood of the children." The children were not pica-prone and probably did not ingest large paint chips directly, since the blood lead levels were not excessively elevated (maximum 43 µg/dl). The children spent much time playing in the lead-contaminated soil (1050 to 1370 µg Pb/g soil). Indoor dust samples were collected and had isotopic compositions similar to soil lead and to paint, but higher lead concentrations (1200 to 3300 µg Pb/g dust). The total exposure to lead derived from LBP included the otherwise indistinguishable contributions from soil and dust.

Rabinowitz [8] used stable lead isotope ratios to evaluate the environments of 3 lead-poisoned Boston children in the early 1980's. Lead isotopes and concentrations were studied in blood and fecal samples, and in air, soil, dust, and paint. He concludes that "In each case, the isotopic composition (IC) of the child's blood lead was identical with the IC of lead paint taken from the child's residence at a site accessible to the child. Fecal lead samples were also identical to that particular paint. Soil lead IC did not always match the IC of local paints. ... Dust in homes that never had lead paint contained lead that resembled lead in urban soils. Dust lead IC did not necessarily have the same IC as current [1981] automobile lead emissions, but appeared to reflect the long-term accumulation of several sources of urban lead fallout. ... These findings may not be directly representative of the sources of lead among children with lower but still excessive blood lead levels (i.e., in the range of 15-30 µg/dl), The lead in the dust in their homes appears to be coming from a large reservoir in the urban soil, which has accumulated over many decades of using lead additives in gasoline ..."

PATHWAYS OF LEAD EXPOSURE

A number of authors have developed statistical models for total lead exposure, including important behavioral variables such as the relative frequency of child mouthing behavior or eating non-food items. These were discussed in detail in EPA's 1986 document on Air Quality Criteria for Lead [9]. Lead paint was banned for use in housing by the 1971 Lead-Based Paint Poisoning Prevention Act. For most children in the U.S., residual lead in LBP and subsequent contamination of soil and household dust are the most important remaining sources of environmental lead exposure [10]. Intact LBP surfaces will produce fine particles by "chalking", which is intentional. Deteriorating LBP surfaces can contribute much larger quantities of particles to soil and household dust while flaking, peeling, or chipping.

While LBP remains a significant potential source of lead exposure if left in place, its improper removal may be at least as hazardous. A number of studies [4,11] have shown that when LBP is removed by older "conventional" methods such as scraping, sanding, or burning, there is a large transient increase in the surface loading of leaded dusts on nearby floors and windows. The large increase in dust lead loading produces substantial increases in blood lead levels in adults, children, and household pets who live in the dwelling unit, and cases of symptomatic lead toxicity are not uncommon. For this reason, most epidemiologic studies of residential lead exposure now ask whether there has been any recent removal of paint or refinishing of furniture on the premises.

The conceptual pathways for childhood lead exposure from LBP are thus well defined. When epidemiologic data are available for measuring exposure (lead in LBP, soil, dust, air, and recent LBP removal), external burden (lead on hands), internal burden (lead in blood), and mitigating behavioral variables (mouthing behavior) or surrogate demographic variables for behavior (age, socio-economic status, household income), multivariate statistical methods may be used to estimate the importance of each of the pathways from LBP to blood lead.

STATISTICAL MODELS FOR CHILD BLOOD LEAD

Many statistical models have been proposed for relating blood lead concentrations (denoted PbBlood) to environmental lead levels (denoted PbPaint, PbSoil, PbDust, PbAir etc.). The environmental lead levels may be either concentrations or surface loadings, depending on available data, and studies are in progress to determine which of the field measurements are the most predictive of blood lead levels. A review of statistical modelling approaches in EPA's Air Quality Criteria for Lead [9] suggested that the following issues must be addressed in any modeling exercise:

(1) lead exposures from different media are additive, and total lead exposure and lead intake should be expressed as the sum of contributions from each medium;

(2) blood lead levels at low to moderate levels of exposure (total lead intake) are approximately linear functions of intake from each medium, but the coefficients reflect differences in the quantity of medium ingested, the availability of lead in ingestion media (soil, dust, paint, food) for dissolution in the stomach, and the absorption or uptake of lead at the entry portal (gut or lung);

(3) at higher levels of lead intake, blood lead levels show less than linear increases with increasing exposure, reflecting biokinetic factors such as limited binding of lead to red blood cells and lower absorption of lead from the gut;

(4) in most epidemiologic studies, the distribution of both environmental lead levels and blood lead levels is highly skewed and may be approximated by a log-normal distribution.

These issues suggested that a consistent method for estimating the contribution of different media would use the following equation for relating blood lead to environmental lead:

$$PbBlood = B_0 + B_1 \, ExteriorPbPaint + B_2 \, Interior \, PbPaint + B_3 \, PbSoil + B_4 \, PbDust + etc. \quad \text{(Equation 1)}$$

The actual estimation of parameters would be carried out using a logarithmic transformation of both sides of Equation 1:

$$\ln(PbBlood) = \ln(B_0 + B_1 \, ExteriorPbPaint + B_2 \, Interior \, PbPaint + B_3 \, PbSoil + B_4 \, PbDust + etc.)$$
$$+ \text{residual} \quad \text{(Equation 2)}$$

The use of Equation 2 in estimation implies that the estimand is the <u>geometric mean blood lead level</u>. Note that Equation 2 is intrinsically nonlinear in its parameters B_0, B_1 etc., even though it expresses a linear relationship between biological and physical variables, and so must be fitted using nonlinear regression techniques. Examination of regression residuals shows that Equation 2 both normalizes the residuals and stabilizes their variances, which are desirable statistical properties.

STATISTICAL ANALYSIS OF MULTI-MEDIA PATHWAY MODELS

Unfortunately, Equations 1 or 2 do not allow estimation of the effects of different primary sources such as LBP on blood lead, since they combine both the direct effects of LBP ingestion with the indirect effects of ingesting soil and dust contaminated by LBP. These may be expressed by additional equations for PbDust and PbSoil, similar to Equation 2:

$$\ln(PbDust) = \ln(D_0 + D_1 \, PbSoil + D_2 \, Interior \, PbPaint + etc.) \quad \text{(Equation 3)}$$

$$\ln(PbSoil) = \ln(S_0 + S_1 \, Exterior \, PbPaint + etc.) \quad \text{(Equation 4)}$$

Thus the total effect of exterior LBP is not simply B_1, but is:

$$\text{Total Exterior LBP effect} = B_1 + B_3 \, S_1 + B_4 \, D_1 \, S_1 \quad \text{(Equation 5)}$$

Equations 2, 3 and 4 should not be fitted individually, since the output of Equation 4 is defined as an input variable for Equations 2 and 3, etc. The statistical problems inherent in fitting coupled systems of equations was first used in studies on environmental lead by R. Bornschein, S. Clark, K. Dietrich, P. Succop and their co-investigators at the University of Cincinnati [12-15]. We have used somewhat different specifications of the SEM than these investigators, in order to account for the biological and physical processes discussed previously in deriving Equations 1 and 2. Equation 1 and related linear models were fitted without transformation using the asymptotically distribution-free AGLS procedure in the EQS program [16]. Equations 2, 3, 4 and related log-transformed linear models were fitted using the program PROC MODEL in the SAS/ETS statistical system [17]. Other analyses of lead data are described by Menton et al. [18].

We will discuss three examples of structural equation modelling (SEM). The first example is an analysis of the data collected in 1989 by the University of Cincinnati investigators around the lead-contaminated community of Midvale, Utah. The second example looks at a cross-sectional study carried out in the active lead smelter community of East Helena, MT in 1983. The third example looks at the study in Butte. MT, carried out by the University of Cincinnati investigators.

DATA FROM THREE CROSS-SECTIONAL STUDIES

These data were provided to us by the Principal Investigator, Dr. Robert Bornschein. Midvale is on the outskirts of Salt Lake City. Metal processing operations have occurred at Midvale for over a century, producing large tailings piles at the edge of the town. Family recruitment, environmental sampling, blood lead and behavioral data collection, and preliminary statistical analyses are reported in [15]. Additional analyses were carried out using methods described above [19,20]. The available data set includes information for 166 children in 128 families.

The other data sets contain similar variables, but are not quite identical. The study at East Helena, Montana, in 1983 was carried out by EPA, CDC, state and local health agencies. The data set used here was that available for the 1989 Office of Air Quality Planning and Standards (OAQPS) staff paper on lead exposure analysis [21,22], supplemented by some additional child and family socio-demographic data. There were some problems in dust measurement from vacuum cleaner samples, with many missing values. These were imputed for this analysis from air and soil lead. The information on lead-based paint was quantitatively uncertain and was replaced by a dummy variable that indicated either presence or absence of lead-based paint anywhere in the house. There was no variable that was directly comparable to the socio-economic status variable (SES) used in the Midvale and Butte studies, so a dummy variable to indicate family income > $15,000 was used. Also, air lead was an important contributor to lead in blood and in soil and dust media, since there was and is an active primary lead smelter at the south edge of the community. These differences illustrate some of the problems in the naive comparison of lead regression coefficients across different studies.

The 1990 Butte study was also carried out by the Univ. of Cincinnati investigators [23] and is in general very similar to the Midvale study, with similar variables. Butte, MT, has been the site of lead mining and smelting activities for over a century. Although these activities are currently inactive, mine waste piles dominate some parts of the community. These analyses are for children whose residences were inside the area closest to the largest mine waste piles. The data set included XRF measurements for both exterior and interior paint.

RESULTS

The results for three very similar analyses at different sites are shown in Table 1, and graphically in Figures 1, 2, and 3. It is seen that there are statistically significant pathways from paint to soil lead to blood lead at all three sites, but that other factors differ from one place to another. The total effect on blood lead of lead in soil or dust for a typical child is the sum of the coefficients of the coefficient for that medium and the coefficient for the product of concentration and mouthing or ingestion of non-food objects. Thus, from Table 1, the blood lead equation for East Helena has terms

1.30* dust lead + 0.73 * dust lead * (Mouthing Score) =2.03 * dust lead * { 0.64 + 0.36 * (Mouthing Score)}.

TABLE 1. REGRESSION COEFFICIENTS FOR BLOOD LEAD, DUST LEAD AND SOIL LEAD EQUATIONS IN STRUCTURAL EQUATION MODELS FOR THREE WESTERN COMMUNITIES. ASYMPTOTIC STANDARD ERRORS IN PARENTHESES.

EQUATION:	BLOOD (μg/dL)			DUST (1000 μg/g)			SOIL (1000 μg/g)		
STUDY:	EAST HELENA	MIDVALE	BUTTE	EAST HELENA	MIDVALE	BUTTE	EAST HELENA	MIDVALE	BUTTE
DUST LEAD (1000 μg/g)	1.30*** (0.41)	0^CON	0^CON						
SOIL LEAD (1000 μg/g)	0^CON	0.44 (0.77)	0^CON	0.815*** (0.117)	0.546*** (0.084)	0.380*** (0.055)			
AIR LEAD (μg/m³)	0.76** (0.33)	NA	NA	0.361*** (0.040)	NA	NA	0.35*** (0.04)	NA	NA
LEAD PAINT ON HOUSE (0 or 1)				0.116+ (0.081)	NA	NA	0.23* (0.11)	NA	NA
XRFI (mg/cm²)				NA	0.002 (0.008)	0.012 (0.034)			
XRFX (mg/cm²)							NA	0.27* (0.13)	0.070* (0.04)
PAINT REMOVAL (0 or 1)	NA	0.67+ (0.49)	NA	NA	-0.016 (0.038)	NA	NA	-0.192*** (0.052)	NA
DUST LEAD * MOUTHING NON-FOOD (1000 μg/g)	0.73* (0.40)	0^CON	0^CON						
SOIL LEAD * MOUTHING NON-FOOD (1000 ppm)	0^CON	2.12** (0.90)	0.65** (0.24)						
MOUTHING NON-FOOD (Median=1)	0^CON	0.00 ((0.06)	0.03 (0.32)						
SES (0 TO 1)	NA	-8.9*** (1.7)	-3.1*** (1.26)	NA	-0.257* (0.127)	0.047 (0.210)	NA	-0.750* (0.304)	0.12 (0.21)
HIGH INCOME (0 or 1)	-1.00* (0.60)	NA	NA	-0.069+ (0.048)	NA	NA	-0.11 (0.052)	NA	NA
POST WW2 (0 or 1)							NA	-0.12 (0.20)	NA
HOUSE AGE (100 YEARS)							NA	NA	0.47 (0.46)

Code for statistical significance for one-tailed tests: + = 0.05<P<0.10; *=0.01<P<0.05; **= 0.001<P<0.01; ***= P<0.001; con= Estimate constrained to be non-negative; NA= Not Available; Blank cells indicate no direct pathway (see Figures 1-3).

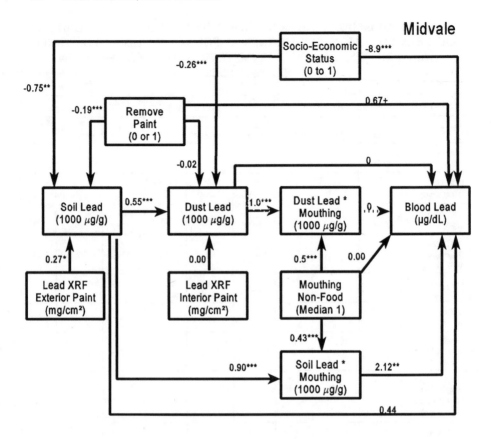

Figure 1. Environmental lead pathways for 1989 Midvale Study. Code for statistical significance: + = 0.05<P<0.10; * = 0.01<P<0.05; ** = 0.001<P<0.01; *** = P<0.001.

Since the typical child has standardized mouthing score = 1, the total effect is 2.03 ug/dl blood lead per 1000 ppm lead in dust. The coefficients for soil lead are 0 when constrained to non-negative values. Thus, for East Helena, air lead and dust lead are significant direct pathways.

The indirect pathways for the East Helena study are important. There is a strong statistically significant dependence of dust lead on both air lead and soil lead. There is a marginally significant relationship of lead-based paint on household dust lead (one-tailed P < 0.10). However, the relationship of soil to lead-based paint is statistically significant, about 230 ppm additional lead in soil for houses with lead paint above 1 mg/cm². This is then readily transferred from soil to house dust to the child. It is interesting that an independent effect of lead-based paint on blood lead can be detected even when there a great deal of lead exposure from airborne sources.

The Midvale and Butte community studies did not have high air lead concentrations. There are some differences in the relative importance of environmental pathways among the three communities. In the Midvale

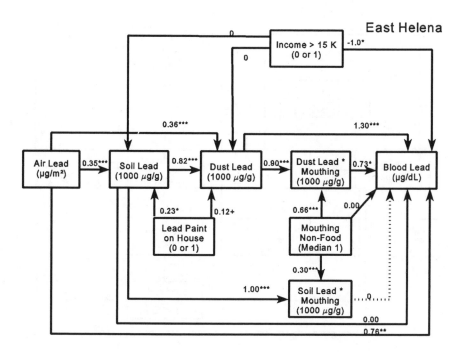

Figure 2. Environmental lead pathways for 1983 East Helena Study. Code for statistical significance: + = 0.05<P<0.10; * = 0.01<P<0.05; ** = 0.001<P<0.01; *** = P<0.001.

study, the direct soil lead pathway is not statistically significant, but the product of soil lead and standardized frequency of mouthing of non-food objects is highly significant. The combined soil lead effect is given by:

0.44 * soil lead + 2.12 * soil lead * (Mouthing Score) = 2.56 * soil lead * { 0.16 + 0.84 * (Mouthing Score)}.

Interior lead-based paint is not significantly correlated with household dust in this study, nor is household dust correlated with blood lead. Perhaps the dust effect is subsumed by the direct and indirect soil lead effect. Recent removal of lead-based paint is marginally associated with a 0.67 μg/dL increase in blood lead. However, there is a very strong statistical relationship between soil lead and exterior lead-based paint (270 μg/g per mg/cm^2) and between soil lead and recent paint removal (190 μg/g less in soil near house with recent paint removal). The effects of socio-demographic factors such as SES and house age may also account for the disappearance of an apparent dust lead effect, which dust lead is confounded with SES and house age.

The results of the Butte study are also shown in Table 1. In the Butte study, the direct soil lead pathway is also not statistically significant, but the product of soil lead and standardized occurrence of mouthing of non-food objects is highly significant. The combined soil lead effect is given by:

0.00 * soil lead + 0.65 * soil lead * (Mouthing Score) =0.65 * soil lead * { 0.00 + 1.00 * (Mouthing Score)}.

Interior lead-based paint is not significantly correlated with household dust in this study, nor is household dust correlated with blood lead. Perhaps the dust effect is subsumed by the direct and indirect soil lead effect. There is a statistical relationship between soil lead and exterior lead-based paint (70 μg/g per mg/cm^2) and between soil lead and dust lead. The effects of socio-demographic factors such as SES and house age may also account for the disappearance of an apparent dust lead effect.

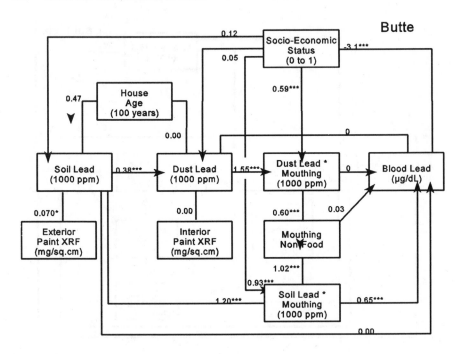

Figure 3. Environmental lead pathways for 1990 Butte Study. Code for statistical significance: + = 0.05<P<0.10; * = 0.01<P<0.05; ** = 0.001<P<0.01; *** = P<0.001.

The relationship of soil lead concentration to dust lead concentration is strong and highly significant in all three studies, largest at an active lead smelter site (0.82 at East Helena), smaller at an inactive lead smelter site (0.55 at Midvale), and smallest -- but not small -- at an inactive lead mining and smelting site (0.38 at Butte). The relationship of blood lead to the most predictive medium is about the same at East Helena and Midvale, 2.03 and 2.56 μg/dL per 1000 μg/g respectively.

DISCUSSION

Lead-based paint is a source of lead in soil in residential yards near houses, whether or not air lead point sources are present. Lead from exterior lead-based paint may thus enter the house as the soil contribution to household dust. Recent studies in other small communities and in urban areas have found quantitatively similar relationships.

The relationship of interior lead-based paint to household dust is harder to detect. The large quantity of paint on the exterior surfaces of an older house with lead-based paint (ca. 8 kg) weathers fairly rapidly and is deposited on the soil near the house. Interior paint deteriorates more slowly and may not be a quantitatively significant component of interior dust, except perhaps in wet rooms such as the kitchen or bathroom. However, detailed studies of individual lead-poisoned children have often found deteriorating lead-painted surfaces nearby, so one must assume that interior lead-based paint can also be a significant source of childhood lead exposure in some cases, even if it is not the most significant source of lead in household dust.

The relationship between blood lead and dust lead or soil lead concentration has two components. The first is the blood lead attributable to dust lead or soil lead without adjustment for mouthing behavior, and the second is the blood lead attributable to the product of dust lead or soil lead and mouthing behavior. The mouthing behavior variables are different among the studies, and have been normalized to mean value = 1 for comparison. These two components vary considerably in relative importance, with substantial differences between communities. In the East Helena study, the larger coefficient for dust lead was connected to the dust lead main effect (1.30 $\mu g/dL$, not to the dust lead * mouthing score interaction term (0.73 $\mu g/dL$). In the Midvale study, the estimated regression coefficient on soil lead being 0.44 µg/dl per 1000 ppm, but the regression coefficient on soil lead <u>times</u> mouthing frequency being 2.12 µg/dl per 1000 µg/g in Midvale. Children with frequent ingestion or mouthing of non-food items would show an even larger response.

The income level variable is much less predictive in the 1983 studies than was the SES variable used in the 1989-1990 studies. We suspect that parental education and household hygiene practices that affect infant and toddler lead exposure and nutrition are described better by SES than by income. There is an increase in blood lead after age 6 to 12 months.

These studies also confirmed that even in communities where lead deposition from historical mining and smelter activities is a very significant source of lead contamination of soil, there is also a detectable contribution to soil lead from exterior lead-based paint. Direct evidence of the importance of the exterior lead paint to soil to blood pathway was provided by stable lead isotope studies [7,8]. The apparent lack of a detectable pathway from interior lead-based paint to household dust requires further study.

It is obvious that some of the most highly elevated child blood leads in these communities are associated with the ingestion of deteriorating lead paint, but some of the other elevated blood leads are associated with elevated dust lead concentrations when XRF levels are low. Thus, ingestion of non-LBP components of soil and dust must also be substantial.

REFERENCES

[1]   Charney E., Kessler B., Farfel M. and Jackson D., "Childhood Lead Poisoning: A Controlled Trial of the Effect of Dust-Control Measures on Blood Lead Levels," <u>New England Journal of Medicine</u>, 1983, 309(18):1089-1093.

[2]   Rosen J.F., Markowitz M.E., Bijur P.E., Jenks S.T., Wielopolski L., Kalef-Ezra J.A., Slatkin D.N., "Sequential Measurements of Bone Lead Content by L X-Ray Fluorescence in $CaNa_2EDTA$-Treated Lead-Toxic Children," <u>Environmental Health Perspectives</u>, 1991, 91:57-62.

[3]   U.S. Department of Housing and Urban Development, <u>Comprehensive and Workable Plan for the Abatement of Lead-based Paint in Privately Owned Housing: A Report to Congress</u>, U.S. Department of Housing and Urban Development, Washington, DC., December 7, 1990.

[4]   Farfel M.R., Chisolm J.J., "Health and Environmental Outcomes of Traditional and Modified Practices for Abatement of Residential Lead-Based Paint," <u>American Journal Public Health</u>, 1990, 80(10):1240-

[5]   Farfel M.R. and Chisolm J.J.. "An Evaluation of Experimental Practices for Abatement of Residential Lead-Based Paint: Report on a Pilot Project[1]," <u>Environmental Research</u>, 1991, 55:199-212.

[6]   Allott R.W., Hewitt C.N., and Kelly M.R., "The Environmental Half-Lives and Mean Residence Times of Contaminants in Dust for an Urban Environment: Barrow-in-Furness", <u>The Science of the Total Environment</u>, 1990, 93:403-410.

[7]   Yaffe Y., et al., "Identification of Lead Sources in California Children Using the Stable Isotope Ratio Technique," <u>Archives of Environmental Health</u>," 1983, 38(4):237-245.

[8]   Rabinowitz M.B., "Stable Isotope Mass Spectrometry in Childhood Lead Poisoning," <u>Biological Trace Element Research</u>, 1987, 12:223-229.

[9]   U.S. Environmental Protection Agency. 1986. Air Quality Criteria for Lead Volume I-IV. Environmental Criteria and Assessment Office, Office of Research and Development, RTP, NC. EPA-600/8-83-028 a-d.

[10]   Mushak P., "Defining Lead as the Premier Environmental Health Issue for Children in America, 1992, Environmental Research, 59:281-309.

[11]   Amitai Y., Graef J.W., Brown M.J., Gerstle R.S., Kahn N., "Hazards of Deleading Homes of Children with Lead Poisoning," 1987, American Journal of Diseases of Childhood," 1987, 141:758-760.

[12]   Bornschein R.L., Succop P.A., Dietrich R.N., Clark C.S., Que Hee S., and Hammond P.B., "The Influence of Social and Environmental Factors on Dust Lead, Hand Lead, and Blood Lead Levels in Young Children," Environmental Research, 1985, 38:108-118.

[13]   Bornschein R.L., Clark C.S., Grote J., Peace B., Roda S., Succop P.A., "Soil Lead - Blood Lead Relationship in a Former Lead Mining Town.". In: Environmental Geochemistry and Health, Monograph Series 4, Lead in Soil: Issues and Guidelines. B.E. Davis and B.G. Wixson (Eds). Science Review Limited, Northwood, England, 1988, pp. 149-160.

[14]   Clark C.S., Bornschein R.L., Succop P.A., et al., "Condition and Type of Housing as an Indicator of Potential Environmental Lead Exposure and Pediatric Blood Lead Levels," Environmental Research, 1985, 38:46-53.

[15]   Bornschein R.L., Clark C.S., Pan U.W., Succop P.A., et al., "Midvale Community Lead Study", Department of Environmental Health, University Cincinnati Medical Center, July 1990.

[16]   Bentler P.M., EQS Structural Equations Program Manual. BMDP Statistical Software, Los Angeles CA, 1989.

[17]   SAS (Statistical Analysis System). ETS (Econometric and Time Series Analysis Programs) Ver. 6.03, 1991, SAS Institute, Cary, North Carolina.

[18]   Menton R.G., Burgoon D.A., and Marcus A.H., "Pathways of Lead Contamination for the Brigham and Women's Hospital Longitudinal Lead Study", Lead in Paint, Soil and Dust: Health Risks, Exposure Studies, Control Measures, Measurement Methods, and Quality Assurance, ASTM STP 1226, Michael E. Beard and S.D. Allen Iske, Eds., American Society for Testing and Materials, Philadelphia, 1994.

[19]   Marcus, A.H., "Inter-site Comparisons of Environmental Lead Uptake." Presented at Symposium on the Bioavailibility and Dietary Uptake of Leak, ECAO/USEPA. Chapel Hill, NC, September 24-27, 1990. Report from Battelle Columbus Division, Arlington Office, to USEPA Office of Toxic Substances. Contract No. 69-02-4246.

[20]   Marcus, A.H., "Use of Site-Specific Data in Models for Lead Risk Assessment and Risk Management." In: An Update of Exposure and Effects of Lead, B.Beck (Ed), Fundamental and Applied Toxicology, 1992, 18:10-16.

[21]   U.S. Environmental Protection Agency. 1989. Review of the National Ambient Air Quality Standards for Lead: Exposure Analysis Methodology and Validation. USEPA Office of Air Quality Planning and Standards. RTP, NC. EPA-450/2-89/011.

[22]   Centers for Disease Control. 1986. East Helena, Montana child Lead Study. 1985. Lewis and Clark county Health Department and Montana Department of Health and Environmental Sciences.

Centers for Disease Control, Public Health Service, US Department of Public Health and Human Services, Atlanta, GA.

[23]   Bornschein, R.L., Clark, C.S., Pan, U.W., Succop, P.A.. 1991.   The Butte-Silver Bow Environmental Health Lead Study. Department of Environmental Health, University of Cincinnati Medical Center. June, 1991.

Exposure Studies

Robert P. Clickner[1] and John W. Rogers[2]

HUD NATIONAL SURVEY: FINDINGS ON THE LEAD PAINT HAZARD IN HOMES

REFERENCE: Clickner, R. P., and Rogers, J. W., **"HUD National Survey: Findings on the Lead Paint Hazard in Homes,"** Lead in Paint, Soil and Dust: Health Risks, Exposure Studies, Control Measures, Measurement Methods, and Quality Assurance, ASTM STP 1226 Michael E. Beard and S.D. Allen Iske, Eds., American Society for Testing and Materials, Philadelphia, 1995.

ABSTRACT: The U.S. Department of Housing and Urban Development sponsored a national survey of lead-based paint in housing, with technical support from the U.S. Environmental Protection Agency. In that sample survey, 381 housing units were inspected for lead in paint on interior and exterior surfaces, lead in interior dust, and lead in exterior soil. National estimates of the extent of the lead paint hazard in homes are presented. Data are presented on the prevalence, condition and amount of lead-based paint in housing. Also presented are findings from the national survey on the sources and pathways of lead in homes.

KEYWORDS: lead, lead-based paint, dust lead, soil lead

INTRODUCTION

The 1987 amendments to the Lead-Based Paint Poisoning Prevention Act required the Secretary to Housing and Urban Development (HUD) to prepare and transmit to Congress "a comprehensive and workable plan" for the abatement of lead-based paint in housing and "an estimate of the amount, characteristics and regional distribution of housing in the United States that contains lead-based paint hazards at differing levels of contamination." In response, HUD sponsored a national survey of lead-based paint in housing [1] to obtain data for estimating:

- The number of housing units with lead-based paint;

---

[1] Associate Director and Senior Statistician, Environmental Studies, Westat, Inc., 1650 Research Boulevard, Rockville, MD 20850

[2] Senior Statistician, Westat, Inc., 1650 Research Boulevard, Rockville, MD 20850

- The surface area of lead-based paint in housing, to develop a national estimate of abatement costs;

- The condition of the paint; and

- The incidence of lead in house dust and in soil around the perimeter of residential structures, to analyze the sources and pathways of lead in the residential environment;

SURVEY DESIGN AND METHODOLOGY

The study population consisted of nearly all housing in the United States constructed before 1980. Newer houses were presumed to be lead-free because, in 1978, the Consumer Product Safety Commission banned the sale of lead-based paint to consumers and the use of such paint in residences. The survey was conducted between December 1989 and March 1990 in 30 counties across the 48 contiguous states, selected to represent the entire United States housing stock, both public and privately-owned. The total sample size is 381 dwelling units, 284 privately owned and 97 publicly owned.

The sample was stratified into privately-owned single family housing, privately-owned multi-family housing, and publicly owned units and further divided into three age strata. Age strata, based on differences in historical patterns in lead-based paint use, were needed to analyze the associations between age of structure, condition of paint and substrates, and lead in dust and soil. Table 1 displays the estimated national distribution of housing units across the nine strata and Table 2 displays the distribution of the sample across the strata. Privately-owned multifamily housing and public housing were over-sampled, relative to their national representation, in order to ensure that acceptable sample sizes would be achieved. Within housing types, construction year strata were proportionately sampled.

Inspection Protocol

Interior rooms were inventoried and classified into wet and dry rooms according to the presence or absence of plumbing. One wet room and one dry room were randomly selected for inspection. In each of these two rooms, field technicians inventoried painted surfaces, measured their dimensions, and assessed the condition of the paint; they measured the lead concentration in randomly selected painted surfaces; and they gathered samples of dust.

Paint lead concentrations were measured using *in situ* X-ray fluorescence (XRF) analyzers. This non-destructive protocol was chosen to eliminate the destructive technique of collecting paint scrapings from occupied homes for laboratory analysis. The analyzers measured lead loadings, milligrams of lead per square centimeter of painted surface (mg/cm^2).

Exterior painted surfaces were inventoried and measured and lead readings taken according to protocols similar to those used in the

TABLE 1 - - NATIONAL DISTRIBUTION OF
DWELLING UNITS BUILT BEFORE 1980

	Number of Pre-1980 Dwelling Units (000)			
	Construction Year			
Type	1960-1979	1940-1959	pre-1940	Total
Privately Owned, Occupied				
Single Family	29,137	18,782	18,499	66,418
Multifamily	6,548	1,690	2,521	10,759
Sub-Total	35,685	20,472	21,020	77,177
	1960-1979	1950-1959	pre-1950	Total
All Public, Family Units	182	278	346	807
Total	35,867	20,750	21,366	77,984

Source: 1987 American Housing Survey.

TABLE 2 - - DISTRIBUTION OF COMPLETED INSPECTIONS
BY CONSTRUCTION YEAR AND DWELLING UNIT TYPE

	Completed Inspection Visits			
	Construction Year			
Type	1960-1979	1940-1959	pre-1940	Total
Privately Owned, Occupied				
Single Family	94	72	61	227
Multifamily	26	15	16	57
Sub-Total	120	87	77	284
	1960-1979	1950-1959	pre-1950	Total
All Public, Family Units	30	24	43	97
Total	150	111	120	381

interior. Soil samples were also taken at selected locations around the building exterior. Common areas, if present, were also sampled and inspected.

Dust samples were collected by vacuuming randomly selected floor locations, window sills and window wells in the wet room and again in the dry room. In addition, a dust sample was collected from the floor just inside the main entrance to the dwelling unit. Soil samples were taken outside the main entrance to the building, at a randomly selected location along the drip line of the sampled exterior painted surface, and at a remote location away from the building but still on the property. Further details of the dust and soil sampling protocols may be found in [1] and [2]. Soil and dust samples were sent to laboratories and analyzed by inductively coupled plasma-atomic emission spectrometry (ICP-AES) and by graphite furnace atomic absorption (GFAA) spectroscopy, respectively.

CONCLUSIONS

The national survey found that lead-based paint is widespread in housing. Fifty-seven million homes, or 74 percent of the privately-owned housing units built before 1980, have lead based-paint somewhere in the building. Nearly ten million of these homes are occupied by families with children under the age of seven years old. No significant differences were observed in the prevalence of lead-based paint by type of housing, market value of the home, amount of rent payment, household income, or geographic region.

While no statistically significant association was found between the presence of lead-contaminated dust and the presence of lead-based paint, excessive dust lead levels were found to be associated with the presence of *damaged* lead-based paint. Fourteen million homes, 18 percent of the pre-1980 housing stock, have more than five square feet of damaged lead-based paint. Nearly half of them have excessive dust lead levels.

Excessive soil lead levels are also associated with the presence of damaged lead-based paint. While 18 percent of all pre-1980 homes have excessive soil lead levels, nearly half of the 10 million homes with damaged lead-based paint on exterior walls have excessive soil lead levels.

Although a large majority of pre-1980 homes have lead-based paint, most of them have relatively small amounts of it. However, the amounts of lead-based paint per housing unit vary with the age of the dwelling unit. Pre-1940 units have, on average, about three times as much lead-based paint as units built between 1960 and 1979.

SOURCES OF ERROR IN THE DATA

Nonresponse--An analysis was conducted to estimate the potential for nonresponse bias. It was necessary because intrusive studies that

impose significant burdens on the respondents tend to have lower
response rates than less burdensome studies and, therefore greater
potential for nonresponse biases [3]. In the national survey, 50% of
the homes asked to permit the inspection visits cooperated with the
study. There was no significant association between the response rate
and measures of wealth (rent, home value, and income), suggesting that
there is little likelihood of significant nonresponse biases.

Measurement bias--The XRF measurement equipment tends to yield
biased readings. Validation data collected daily during the national
survey field period enabled the estimation of the XRF bias. XRF
readings were made on shims of known lead concentration placed over
substrate materials (wood, drywall, steel, and concrete) selected to
represent the typical range of substrate materials encountered in
residential construction. Regression equations were developed to relate
the substrate lead concentrations to the XRF readings. These equations
were inverted to generate equations to statistically calibrate the XRF
readings.

The soil lead and dust lead data were subject to similar
measurement errors. However, because the samples were analyzed in
laboratories (not in the field) the measurement errors were much
smaller. Laboratory recoveries for soil samples ranged from 81 percent
to 96 percent; those for dust samples ranged from 82 percent to 114
percent [2]. All dust and soil data were therefore corrected for
recovery.

Misclassification errors--There are two major factors that induce
misclassification errors. First, the XRF equipment has random
variability in its measurements. This variation can induce a
classification bias, that is, a bias in the estimated prevalence of
housing units with lead-based paint. Second, the protocol for
inspecting a housing unit for lead-based paint provided for sampling
painted surfaces for XRF measurement, rather than measuring the lead in
every painted surface in the housing unit. It is therefore possible for
a housing unit to have some surfaces with lead-based paint, other
surfaces with lead-free paint, and only the lead-free surfaces selected
for XRF measurement. Such housing units would be incorrectly classified
as not having lead-based paint. To correct for these classification
biases, and more accurately predict the prevalence of housing units with
lead-based paint, it was necessary to develop a mathematical simulation
model based on data from the survey and other sources. The model was
used to statistically extend the results from the measured surfaces to
all surfaces in the unit, based on: data on the number of rooms in the
unit; data on the number of surfaces per room; and assumptions about the
relationship of the lead concentrations on unmeasured surfaces to those
on the sampled and measured surfaces. The misclassification rates were
estimated, and used to adjust the prevalence estimates accordingly.

NATIONAL ESTIMATES OF THE LEAD-BASED PAINT HAZARD

Selected data for privately-owned housing is reported here;
findings for public housing will be reported later. More extensive

findings may be found in [1]. (Data reported in [1] do not reflect the effects of XRF measurement error discussed above.) Following the Federal standard, housing units are considered to have lead-based paint if the average lead concentration across any painted surface is 1.0 mg/cm^2, or greater [4]. This Federal standard is not a health-based standard; it is not a threshold for determining safe or unsafe conditions.

Lead-Based Paint

Table 3 summarizes data collected and analyzed for the National Survey. Fifty-seven million homes, 74% of the pre-1980 stock, have lead-based paint somewhere in the home. Nearly 10 million of the homes with lead-based paint are occupied by families with children under the age of seven. This is an important statistic because childhood lead poisoning is thought to be the most common and preventable public health concern in our country today [5]. Figure 1 shows the prevalence of lead-based paint by location in privately-owned occupied housing. An estimated 51% of the 77 million pre-1980 homes have lead-based paint on interior surfaces, while 60% have it on exterior surfaces. While these numbers are vast, they do not necessarily suggest that each home is an immediate hazard to its occupants. There are many potential factors which determine the hazards posed by lead-based paint. Several are discussed below.

The risk of hazards potentially increase as the amount of lead in the paint increases. The estimated national geometric mean paint lead loading is 0.1 mg/sq. cm. on interior surfaces and 0.3 mg/sq. cm. on exterior surfaces. Figure 2 displays the breakdown by building age. The highest loadings are on the exteriors of pre-1940 homes. While 74% of pre-1980 homes have some lead-based paint, most have relatively little of it. The estimated average amount of lead-based paint per home is 53 square meters of on interior surfaces and 84 square meters on exterior surfaces.

The condition of the paint is also a factor in determining the hazards from lead-based paint. Intact lead-based paint generally poses little immediate risks to occupants; however, peeling, chipping, or deteriorating paint may present an immediate danger to occupants. An estimated 14 million or 18% of pre-1980 private housing units have non-intact lead-based paint on their surfaces. This is significant not only because peeling and chipping paint may be ingested by children, but it is likely to contaminate house dust and soil. Young children (generally less than seven years old) ingest dust and soil every day through normal hand-to-mouth contact. Because of this normal activity, dust and soil are considered to be the most significant routes of lead exposure to children. Therefore, understanding lead pathways resulting in exposure is essential to preventing childhood lead poisoning.

Soil and Dust Lead

Guidelines for excessive dust lead levels have been set by HUD [4] for declaring an abated residence ready for re-occupancy after lead paint abatement, not for determining health hazards. The current HUD

**TABLE 3 - - ESTIMATED NUMBER OF PRIVATELY OWNED OCCUPIED HOUSING UNITS
BUILT BEFORE 1980 WITH LEAD-BASED PAINT, BY SELECTED CHARACTERISTICS**
(Paint Lead Concentration > = 1.0 mg/sq cm)

Characteristic	Total Occupied Housing Units (000) (1)	Housing Units With Lead-Based Paint Anywhere in Building		Number of Housing Units in Sample
		Percent	Number (000)	
Total Occupied Housing	77,177	74%	57,370	284
Units Built Before 1980		(6%)	(4,705)	
Construction Year:				
1960-1979	35,681	62%	22,149	120
		(10%)	(3,407)	
1940-1959	20,476	80%	16,381	87
		(9%)	(1,824)	
Before 1940	21,018	90%	18,916	77
		(10%)	(2,056)	
Housin Single Family	66,418	74%	49,476	227
		(7%)	(4,520)	
Multifamily	10,759	73%	7,894	57
		(13%)	(1,358)	
One or More Children	13,912	71%	9,900	90
Under Age 7		(9%)	(1,302)	
Owner-Occupied	52,894	72%	38,251	179
		(8%)	(4,160)	
Market Value of Home				
Less than $40,000	11,885	79%	9,399	39
		(15%)	(1,820)	
$40,000 to $79,999	10,228	53%	5,442	46
		(17%)	(1,770)	
$80,000 to $149,999	5,582	65%	3,641	45
		(17%)	(932)	
$150,000 and up	7,405	87%	6,474	42
		(12%)	(891)	
Renter-Occupied	24,285	79%	19,120	105
		(9%)	(2,281)	
Monthly Rent Payment				
Less than $400	16,339	69%	11,334	59
		(14%)	(2,314)	
$400 and up	8,395	87%	7,324	40
		(12%)	(1,042)	
Household Income				
Less than $30,000	46,126	76%	35,124	156
		(7%)	(3,091)	
$30,000 and up	31,048	72%	22,345	107
		(9%)	(2,642)	

(1) Total units data are from the 1987 American Housing Survey.

Note: Numbers in parentheses are approximate half-widths of 95% confidence intervals for the estimated percents and numbers. For example, the approximate 95% confidence interval for the percent of housing units with some lead-based paint is 74% + / -5% or 68% to 80%.

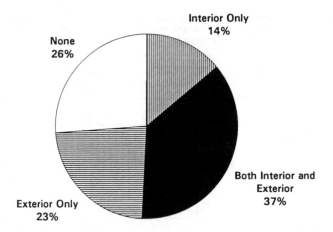

FIG. 1 - - Prevalence of Lead-Based Paint by Location in Privately Owned Occupied Housing Units

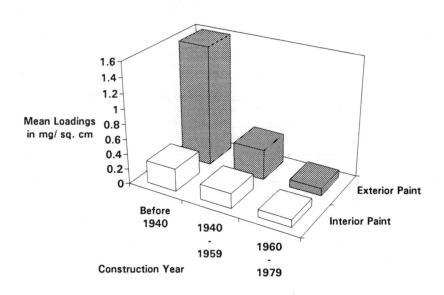

FIG. 2 - - Geometric Mean Paint Lead Loadings in Privately Owned Housing

guidelines state that no more than 2154 $\mu g/m^2$ (200 $\mu g/ft^2$) on floors, 5386 $\mu g/m^2$ (500 $\mu g/ft^2$) on window sills and 8617 $\mu g/m^2$ (800 $\mu g/ft^2$) on window wells is allowed inside a home after lead paint abatement takes place. The current guidelines for excessive soil lead used in this report, 500 ppm, were derived from EPA Superfund guidance on establishing soil lead cleanup levels [6] and also do not necessarily reflect the potential exposures to occupants near residential structures. (New guidelines will be promulgated by EPA in 1994.)

There is no one widely-accepted dust sample collection protocol. Consequently, different researchers may use different methods; which means that data reported by two different researchers may not be comparable. In particular, some researchers use wet wipes to collect dust samples. There is evidence that wipe samples tend to yield higher dust lead levels than vacuuming. Consequently, caution must be taken in comparing these results with other studies.

An estimated 11 million or 14% of private housing units have dust lead levels above Federal guidelines. Similarly, 14 million or 18% of private housing units have soil lead levels above guidelines. Table 4 displays summary statistics for soil lead concentrations. While every soil sample collected in the national survey had measurable lead levels, most had low levels, well below the guideline. Table 5 displays summary statistics for dust lead loadings in dry rooms (wet rooms are similar). Windows tend to have significantly higher dust lead levels than floors.

Figure 3 relates dust lead loadings to the condition and location of lead-based paint. Housing units with *intact* lead-based paint are less likely to exceed dust lead guidelines than units with *non-intact* lead-based paint. In fact, more than half of the homes with exterior non-intact lead-based paint are estimated to have dust lead loadings above HUD's Guidelines. Figure 4 shows similar information for soil lead. Again, about half of the 10 million homes in the United States with non-intact exterior lead-based paint have excessive soil lead concentrations.

SOURCES AND PATHWAYS

This section summarizes selected findings on the sources and pathways of dust and soil lead. Further detail on the findings and methodology may be found in [2].

Sources of Soil Lead

Regression equations were developed to relate soil lead levels to a number of potential sources of soil lead, including exterior and interior paint lead loadings, percentage of damaged paint, and surface areas covered with paint; dwelling unit age and other descriptors of the housing unit; number of rooms, local traffic volumes, county of residence, and 1920-1990 decennial Census populations. Combined, these potential sources of soil lead account for 47% to 59% of the statistical variation in the lead in soil data, as measured by the adjusted R^2.

TABLE 4 - - Descriptive statistics for soil lead measurements

Set of data	Entrance samples	Drip line samples	Remote Samples
Number of Measurements	260	249	253
Arithmetic Mean (ppm)	327	449	205
Percentiles (ppm)			
maximum	6,829	22,974	6,951
upper quartile	225	230	119
median	64.6	56.3	39.9
lower quartile	28.4	21.2	18.5
minimum	2.84	1.16	1.45
Geometric mean (ppm)	85	74	47

TABLE 5 - - Descriptive statistics for dust lead loadings in dry room

Set of data	Floor	Window sill(1)*	Window well(2)*
Number of Measurements	273	233	84
Arithmetic Mean (ug/sq.ft.)	6.6	65.1	981
Percentiles (ug/sq.ft.)			
maximum	205	2,638	40,455
upper quartile	3	25	475
median	1	5	86
lower quartile	0	1	15
minimum	0	0	0
Geometric mean (ug/sq.ft.)	1.11	4.73	74.6

(1)* A window sill is the lower part of the window inside the room.

(2)* A window well is the bottom of the window between the screen and the glass.

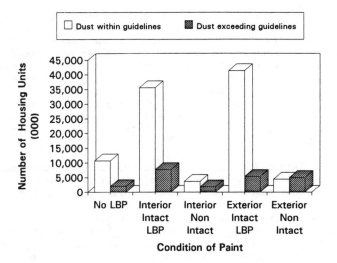

FIG. 3 - - Privately Owned Housing Units with Interior Dust Lead Levels
Above Guidelines by Presence and Condition of Lead-Based Paint

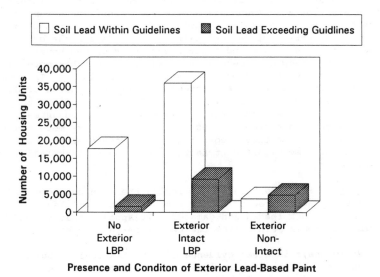

FIG. 4 - - Privately Owned Housing Units with Lead in Soil by Presence and Condition of
Exterior Lead-Based Paint

The strongest predictors of soil lead are dwelling unit age and county of residence, for all three soil sample locations. Both are highly significant (p < 0.01). Dwelling unit age measures the length of time since the construction of the building and, in most cases, the last major disturbance of the soil. Thus, dwelling unit age measures the length of time lead deposits - from whatever source - have been accumulating on the soil. The county of residence effect may be due to many factors including regional variations in population density, population growth, traffic, and home building and painting practices. Local traffic volumes are significantly related to soil lead at all three locations.

Overall, lead concentrations at the two close-in soil samples (entrance and drip line) were more closely related to paint lead concentrations than was the remote soil sample. This finding was expected because entrance and drip-line samples are closer to painted structures than are remote samples. Interior paint lead is significantly associated (p < 0.05) with soil lead at all three locations when the paint is damaged but generally not when it is intact. In contrast, exterior paint lead is significantly associated (p < 0.05) with soil lead regardless of its condition.

Sources of Dust Lead

The statistical relationships were studied between interior dust lead levels, for all seven dust sample locations, and a number of possible sources of dust lead, including housing unit paint lead loadings, percentage of damaged paint, and surface areas covered with paint; dwelling unit age and other descriptors of the housing unit; and all three soil samples. Generally, house dust lead has more variation than soil lead, with windows more variable than floors. This makes it more difficult to identify and assess significant sources of dust lead. The dust lead equations account for only 16% to 27% of the statistical variation in the dust lead data, as measured by the adjusted R^2. The findings regarding sources of dust lead are therefore more tentative and less conclusive than those regarding the sources of soil lead. Nevertheless, some significant factors relating to dust lead have been identified.

Floors--Floor dust lead just inside the main entrance is statistically associated primarily with exterior soil lead and exterior paint that is both leaded and damaged. It appears that the soil lead contribution comes mainly from the two close-in samples.

While there is clear evidence of a statistical association between soil lead at the two close-in locations and floor dust lead, the evidence is less clear of a direct association between floor dust lead and paint lead. There is one exception to this: floor dust lead in the wet room is significantly associated with wet room paint lead. However, as described above, soil lead is related to exterior and damaged interior paint lead. This suggests that lead migrates from exterior paint to soil to floor dust.

FIG. 5 - - Dust and Soil Lead Pathways

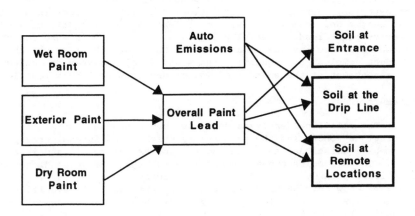

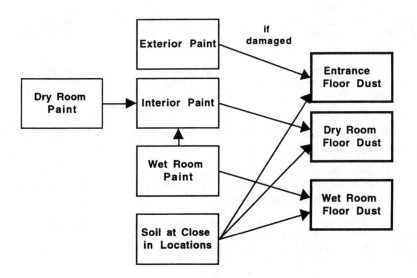

Windows--Soil lead concentrations at the close-in locations are significant predictors of dry room window sill dust lead. Interior, but not exterior, paint lead is also associated with dry room window sill dust lead. Wet room window sill dust lead is significantly related to interior paint lead, especially in the wet room. There were fewer window well dust samples to analyze and these are the most variable of the dust samples; consequently, the statistical analyses do not permit any assessment of the sources of wet or dry room well dust lead levels.

Pathways

The relational analyses described above suggest certain conclusions concerning the pathways by which lead migrates from paint, automobile emissions, and other sources to exterior soil and interior dust. These conclusions are summarized in Figure 5, which diagrams the identified pathways of lead from these sources to floor dust. The diagrams show only pathways identified as statistically significant in the analysis of the national survey data. Additional pathways, not identifiable from the national survey data, may exist.

REFERENCES

[1]   U.S. Department of Housing and Urban Development, Comprehensive and Workable Plan for the Abatement of Lead-Based Paint in Privately-Owned Housing: A Report to Congress, 1990. (Available from HUD USER, 1-800-245-2691.)

[2]   U. S. Environmental Protection Agency, Data Analysis of Lead in Soil and Dust, EPA 747-R-93-011, 1993. (Available from Toxic Substances Control Act (TSCA) Assistance Information Service 202-554-1404.)

[3]   Cox, B.G., Mage, D.T., and Immerman, F.W., Sample Design Considerations for Indoor Air Surveys. Journal of the Air Pollution Control Association Vol. 38, 1988, pages 1266-1270.

[4]   U.S. Department of Housing and Urban Development, Lead-Based Paint: Interim guidelines for Hazard Identification and Abatement in Public Housing, Federal Register 55 (April 18, 1990): 14557-14789.

[5]   U.S. Department of Health and Human Services, Public Health Service, Center for Disease Control, Preventing Lead Poisoning in Young Children, 1991. (Available from Superintendent of Documents, U.S. Government Printing Office, Washington, D.C. 20402.)

[6]   U. S. Environmental Protection Agency Interim Guidance on Establishing Soil Lead Cleanup Levels at Superfund Sites, OSWER Directive #9355.4-02, September 7, 1989. (Available from CERCLIS-Helpline 703-538-7234.)

John G. Kinateder[1], Priti Kumar[1], Bruce E. Buxton[1], Steve W. Rust[1], John G. Schwemberger[2], Benjamin S. Lim[2], Frederic G. Dewalt[3], and Paul Constant[3]

COMPREHENSIVE ABATEMENT PERFORMANCE STUDY: PART I -- STUDY DESIGN AND CHARACTERIZATION OF SOIL-LEAD AND DUST-LEAD LEVELS

REFERENCE: Kinateder, J.G., Kumar, P., Buxton, B.E., Rust, S.W., Schwemberger, J.G., Lim, B.S., Dewalt, F.G., and Constant, P., "Comprehensive Abatement Performance Study: Part I -- Study Design and Characterization of Soil-Lead and Dust-Lead Levels", Lead in Paint, Soil, and Dust: Health Risks, Exposure Studies, Control Measures, Measurement Methods, and Quality Assurance, ASTM STP 1226, Michael E. Beard and S.D. Allen Iske, Eds., American Society for Testing and Materials, Philadelphia, 1995.

ABSTRACT: The Comprehensive Abatement Performance (CAP) Study [1] was a U.S. Environmental Protection Agency (EPA) project designed to follow up on the FHA Lead-Based Paint Abatement Demonstration [2] conducted by the U.S. Department of Housing and Urban Development (HUD). The primary objective of the CAP Study was to assess the long-term efficacy of the various abatement methods employed during the HUD Demonstration. To address this objective, the U.S. EPA collected dust and soil samples at each of the 52 HUD Demonstration houses in Denver, Colorado, approximately two years after the abatements had been completed. This paper is the first in a series of three papers [3],[4] describing the CAP study. We present the experimental design employed to collect data in the study, provide a characterization of lead levels in dust and soil at these houses two years after abatement, and, finally, compare these levels with those in other abatement efficacy studies.

KEYWORDS: Comprehensive Abatement Performance Study, CAPS, HUD FHA Abatement Demonstration, dust lead, soil lead

[1] Research Scientist, Researcher, Projects Manager, and Research Leader, respectively, Battelle, 505 King Avenue, Columbus, OH 43201.

[2] Statistician and Chemist, respectively, U.S. Environmental Protection Agency, 401 M Street, S.W., Washington, DC 20460.

[3] Senior Research Chemist and Program Manager, respectively, Midwest Research Institute, 425 Volker Boulevard, Kansas City, MO 64110.

INTRODUCTION AND BACKGROUND

In response to requirements mandated by the Lead-Based Paint Poisoning Prevention Act (as amended by Section 566 of the Housing and Community ' Development Act of 1987), the Residential Lead-Based Paint Hazard Reduction Act of 1992, and other legislation, the U.S. Environmental Protection Agency (EPA), U.S. Department of Housing and Urban Development (HUD), U.S. Department of Health and Human Services, and other federal agencies are conducting a broad-based program of research, demonstration, and policy actions aimed at reducing the incidence of childhood lead poisoning in the U.S. An important part of the federal program is to identify and abate lead-based paint hazards in privately-owned and public housing. Toward this end, the HUD initiated two important studies in 1989, the HUD National Survey of the incidence of lead-based paint in housing [5], and the HUD Lead-Based Paint Abatement Demonstration [2].

The HUD National Survey sampled both public and private housing in order to estimate the number of housing units with lead-based paint, the total housing surface area covered with lead-based paint, the condition of the paint, and the incidence of lead in household dust and surrounding soil. The National Survey found that approximately 57 million homes, or 74 percent of all occupied housing units built before 1980 have some lead-based paint. Older homes are more likely to be contaminated; 90 percent of housing units built before 1940 have lead-based paint. Within the 57 million contaminated homes, there are on average 580 square feet of interior surfaces and 900 square feet of exterior surfaces covered with lead-based paint [5].

The HUD Abatement Demonstration was a research program in ten cities assessing the costs and short-term efficacy of alternative methods of lead-based paint abatement. A variety of abatement methods was tested in approximately 120 multi-family public housing units in three cities -- Omaha, Cambridge, and Albany. Similar methods have already been tested in 172 single-family housing units in the FHA inventory in seven metropolitan areas -- Baltimore, Birmingham, Denver, Indianapolis, Seattle, Tacoma, and Washington [2]. This demonstration evaluated the following two classes of abatement methods: encapsulation and enclosure methods, and removal methods. The study found that the cost of encapsulation and enclosure abatements ranged from about $2000 to $8000 per housing unit, while the cost of removal abatements ranged from about $2000 to $12000 per housing unit [5].

Although the HUD Abatement Demonstration did assess the short-term efficacy of certain lead-based paint abatement strategies (via clearance testing of lead levels in dust), it was not intended to evaluate the longer-term performance of these approaches. Therefore, in 1990, the EPA Office of Pollution Prevention and Toxics (formerly the Office of Toxic Substances) decided to conduct the Comprehensive Abatement Performance (CAP) Study to further evaluate the abatement strategies used in the HUD Abatement Demonstration.

STUDY OBJECTIVES

The CAP Study was designed to examine the long-term performance of the abatement methods after the residences had been re-occupied. A long-term study was therefore necessary to preclude spending large sums of money abating lead-based paint using methods that may prove in the long term to be ineffective at maintaining low lead levels in household dust.

High levels of lead in household dust pose health risks to occupants regardless of the source. Therefore the CAP Study also collected information regarding the potential source(s) of lead in household dust. It is possible that even for those houses in which the lead-based paint has been removed or covered, lead can reappear in the dust after the house is reoccupied. Prior to or during the abatement process, leaded dust may be deposited in the ventilation system or other parts of the house which, when reoccupied by new residents, may spread throughout the house. Also, activity patterns of the occupants may re-introduce lead from exterior soil.

Therefore, to help address these concerns, the specific objectives of the CAP Study were as follows:

1.   Characterize levels of lead in household dust and exterior soil at the abated and control (residences identified in the Demonstration to be free of lead-based paint hazards) HUD Demonstration houses.
2.   Compare abatement methods or combination of methods relative to performance. Assess whether there are differences in performance.
3.   Investigate the relationship between lead in household dust and lead from other sources, in particular, exterior soil and air ducts.

The HUD Demonstration intended to eliminate the lead-based paint from housing environments either by containing the lead-based paint with encapsulation or enclosure methods, or by eliminating the lead-based paint with removal methods. Encapsulation and enclosure methods attempt to chemically bond or mechanically affix durable materials over painted surfaces, while removal methods attempt to either scrape or chemically strip lead-based paint from painted surfaces, or to completely remove and replace painted components (e.g., windows, doors, baseboards).

There are two primary performance concerns with these abatement methods. First, conducting the abatement methods themselves might generate large amounts of leaded dust that could significantly contaminate the housing environment. And second, the performance of the abatement measures might degrade over several months or years following abatement, allowing the lead hazard to be reintroduced to the housing environment. Encapsulation and enclosure methods do not attempt to remove lead-based paint from housing surfaces and therefore may have a lesser potential to disperse lead to the housing environment during the actual abatement process. However, these two types of abatement may be more susceptible to degradation over time. In contrast, removal methods do attempt to remove lead-based paint from housing surfaces and therefore may have a greater potential to disperse lead during abatement. This might be seen shortly after abatement, or its effects might be seen more gradually over time.

The approach in the CAP Study was to collect environmental samples about two years after abatement from inside and outside housing units abated by HUD and from control houses known to be relatively free of lead-based paint, and measure the concentration of lead in these samples. The performance of the abatement methods was assessed by comparing the lead concentrations at abated houses with those at control houses. Sampling at control houses provided a measure of the amount of lead introduced to the housing environment from sources other than lead-based paint abatement. If the environmental-lead concentrations at abated houses were found to be significantly higher than those at control houses, this was viewed as an indication that abatement failed to completely eliminate the lead hazard because lead was introduced to these environments either immediately through inadequate dust control during abatement, or more gradually through recontamination over time. This paper is the first in a series of three papers describing the CAP Study. Here, we address the first objective of the CAP Study, i.e., provide a characterization of lead in dust and soil in the HUD Demonstration homes two years after abatement. While the second paper [3] in this series compares the performances of the encapsulation/enclosure and removal methods for lead-based paint abatement, the third paper [4] discusses the sampling and chemical analyses techniques employed during the study.

STUDY DESIGN

In 1989 and 1990, HUD conducted abatement demonstrations in 172 single-family dwellings from the inventory of FHA repossessed houses in seven urban areas. Three of these houses had only pilot abatements performed, while the other 169 were completely abated. The distribution of these 169 houses at each city is presented in Table 1. The specific units for abatement were selected by first identifying older housing likely to contain lead-based paint and then testing painted surfaces for lead using portable x-ray fluorescence (XRF) instruments. Not all tested units were abated; units were only abated when they were found to have a large number of structural components covered by lead-based paint. When surveying houses for lead-based paint, HUD considered all painted surfaces both on the interior and exterior of the house.

The HUD Demonstration evaluated six different abatement methods: encapsulation, enclosure, and four removal methods (chemical stripping, abrasive stripping, heat-gun stripping, and complete removal or replacement of painted components). Because of the diversity of housing components containing lead-based paint, it was generally true that no single abatement method could be used uniformly throughout a given housing unit. One important consideration in the CAP Study was the appropriate way in which to summarize and classify the abatement activities conducted at each house. Detailed information was collected by HUD which listed each type of interior and exterior structural component abated in the Demonstration, along with the linear or square footage abated and the abatement method used. For the CAP Study, each house was then classified as encapsulation/enclosure (E/E) or removal according to the abatement category accounting for the largest square footage of interior abatement. However, at many HUD Demonstration houses, a great deal of exterior abatement was also performed, and another objective of the CAP Study was to assess the performance of this exterior abatement. Therefore, the data interpretation also distinguished between the specific methods used on both the interior and exterior of the house.

TABLE 1--Number of houses abated in the HUD Demonstration.

City	Primary Interior Abatement Category		Exterior Abatement Only[1]		Total
	Encap/Enclos	Removal	Encap/Enclos	Removal	
Baltimore	11	9	...	...	20
Birmingham	8	12	2	1	23
Denver	33	18	5	1	57
Indianapolis	17	10	3	4	24
Seattle/Tacoma	12	10	1	3	26
Washington	6	3	...	...	9
Total	87	62	11	9	169

[1] These houses had abatement performed only on exterior surfaces.

Initial plans for the CAP Study included selection of housing units from all seven urban areas in the FHA portion of the HUD Demonstration. However, after conducting a pilot sampling and analysis program [6], and subsequently developing a cost estimate for the CAP Study, it was decided that the CAP Study would only be conducted in Denver, where 57 of the 169 abated units were located (see Table 1). The reoccupied houses in Denver were prioritized for recruitment in the CAP Study based on the amount of abatement performed by each method (E/E and removal). Results from a preliminary statistical power analysis indicated that approximately 40 abated houses and 20 control houses would be sufficient to detect two-fold differences between the dust-lead levels in abated and control houses. Given the initial set of 57 abated houses in Denver, 70% of these units had to be successfully recruited into the study.

In order to use the lead levels measured in dust and soil samples at abated houses as a measure of the performance of abatement, they must be compared to their respective pre-abatement lead levels. Since very few data on pre-abatement lead levels were available, we decided to use lead levels at control houses (houses that were previously tested and found to be relatively free of lead-based paint both inside and outside) as a standard for comparison. Therefore, in addition to abated houses, dust and soil samples were collected from control houses. The objective in measuring lead levels at control houses was to determine whether lead levels observed at abated houses were in fact greater than those found at houses having very few components covered with lead-based paint and therefore affected by only non-paint sources of lead.

In the FHA portion of the HUD Demonstration, a total of 304 houses of similar age and construction were tested by XRF for lead-based paint, and 172 were abated. The number of components in the remaining unabated houses covered with lead-based paint ranged from zero to above ten. A brief synopsis of these is displayed in Table 2. When performing the XRF tests, HUD took three replicate XRF readings at each sampling location and based their decisions at each location on the average of those three readings. While only a single round of XRF testing was performed at unabated houses, in some cases a second round of XRF and/or AAS testing was performed at abated houses to confirm inconclusive XRF results.

TABLE 2--Number of unabated houses tested by XRF in the HUD Demonstration.

| | Number of LBP Components[1] | | | | |
City	0	1-2	3-9	10 or More	Total
Baltimore	1	6	3	10	20
Birmingham	4	5	...	5	14
Denver	13	10	14	3	40
Indianapolis	5	9	5	...	19
Seattle/Tacoma	10	3	2	5	20
Washington	4	2	4	9	19
Total	37	35	28	32	132

[1]Structural components for which XRF testing identified presence of lead-based paint.

Control houses for the CAP Study were recruited from the set of unabated houses in Denver tested by XRF in the HUD Demonstration. For the purposes of selecting control houses, the detailed XRF results supplied by HUD were used under the assumption that they provided an accurate and current assessment of the paint in these houses. Using a criterion that equally weighted (1) the number of housing components testing positive by XRF for lead-based paint (see Table 2), and (2) the average XRF testing result, the 40 unabated houses in Denver were prioritized for selection as control houses for the CAP Study. Twenty unabated houses were recruited as control houses for the CAP Study, including 19 houses from among the 31 houses with the lowest XRF readings.

During the CAP Study a variety of environmental samples were collected along with questionnaire and field inspection information to help assess the performance of abatement methods used in the HUD Demonstration. The environmental sampling for the study included regular vacuum dust and soil core samples as well as field quality control (QC) samples. The latter included wipe dust samples, blanks, and side-by-side dust and soil duplicate samples. Table 3 presents the number of regular and field quality control samples collected in the study. The role of each sample type in meeting the objectives of the study are presented in Table 4. All samples were chemically analyzed to measure the amount of lead present. A detailed discussion of the sampling and chemical analysis methods used in the study is presented by Dewalt et al. [4].

RESULTS

Figure 1 presents the box and whisker plot of the lead concentrations across all the housing units for all the regular sample types. In the box and whisker plot, the arithmetic mean of the lead concentration is indicated by the diamond while the

TABLE 3--Summary of environmental sampling planned for the CAP Study.

	Number of Samples Planned		
Sample Type	For 17 Control Units	For 22 Abated Units[1]	For 13 Abated Units[2]
Regular Samples			
1. Vacuum dust			
a. Perimeter floor	2	2	3
b. Window channel[3]	2	2	3
c. Window stool[4]	2	2	3
d. Air ducts	2	2	3
e. Int. entryway floor	2	2	2
f. Ext. entryway surface	2	2	2
2. Soil cores			
a. Near foundation	2	2	2
b. Property boundary	2	2	2
c. Entryway	2	2	2
Quality Control Samples			
3. Wipe vs. vacuum			
a. Floor wipe dust	0	2	2
b. Floor vacuum dust	0	2	2
4. Blanks			
a. Vacuum dust field blank	1	1	1
b. Vacuum dust trip blank	1	1	1
c. Soil core field blank	1	1	1
d. Wipe dust field blank	0	1	1
5. Side-by-side samples			
a. Vacuum dust floor	1	1	1
b. Soil cores	1	1	1
Total samples	23	28	32

[1]22 units - sampling conducted in 2 rooms. [2]13 units - sampling conducted in 3 rooms.
[3]Window channel is surface below window sash and inside screen and/or storm window.
[4]Window stool (or sill) is horizontal board inside the window.

(micrograms of lead per unit area sampled, $\mu g/ft^2$). The results for wipe dust samples are presented only on a loading basis, and the results for soil median is indicated by the center horizontal line. The lower and upper quartiles of the lead concentration are represented by the bottom and top of the box, respectively. The distance embodied by the box is termed the interquartile range; the range from the 25th to the 75th percentiles. The ends of the whiskers extending from bottom and top of the box represent the minimum and maximum of the lead concentrations. The median is indicated by the center horizontal line. The extreme data points are classified as either minor (pluses) or extreme (stars) outliers based on their distance from the quartiles relative to the interquartile range. Similarly, the box and whisker plot of the

TABLE 4--Role of environmental samples collected in the CAP Study.

Sample Type	Purpose	Abbreviation
Vacuum dust, Perimeter floor and window stool	Primary measures of performance for interior abatement	FLR/WST
Vacuum dust, Window channel	Provides measure of performance for interior abatement, possible measure of performance for exterior abatement, and possible transport of exterior soil from outside to inside the house	WCH
Vacuum dust, Air duct	Provides measure of source contribution to interior dust lead levels	ARD
Vacuum dust, Interior and exterior entryways	Provides measure of possible transport of exterior soil from outside to inside the house	EWI, EWO
Soil cores (Entryways, foundation, and boundary)	Provides primary measure of performance of exterior abatement, and measure of possible transport of exterior soil lead into the house	EWY, FDN, BDY
Floor wipe dust	Provides consistency check against earlier results from HUD Demonstration and other studies, and makes comparison with vacuum dust samples possible	FLW
Blanks	Provides assessment of potential sample contamination and uncertainty in sample weighing	...
Side-by-side samples	Provides assessment of sampling variability	...

lead loadings for all the dust sample types are presented in Figure 2. Table 5 summarizes the lead concentration, lead loading, and dust loading for all the sample types. The results forvacuum dust samples are presented on both a concentration basis (micrograms of lead per gram of dust, $\mu g/g$) and a loading basiscore samples are presented only on a concentration basis. The following descriptive statistics are included in Table 5: number of samples collected, geometric mean, arithmetic mean, logarithmic standard deviation, minimum, and maximum. The geometric mean and logarithmic standard deviation are natural summary parameters for lognormally distributed data. It is worth noting in the figures that the lead concentrations and lead loadings are closer in form to the lognormal distribution than the normal distribution. The geometric means are often much closer to the medians (compare using Table 5 and both figures) than the arithmetic means, providing evidence that the distributions are more symmetric on a log scale than a linear scale. Reeves et al. have also supported the lognormal distribution for environmental lead measures [7].

The lead levels varied greatly for different media and sampling locations as illustrated in Figures 1 through 2 and Table 5. In dust, geometric mean lead concentrations varied from a low of 150 $\mu g/g$ for floor vacuum dust samples to a high of

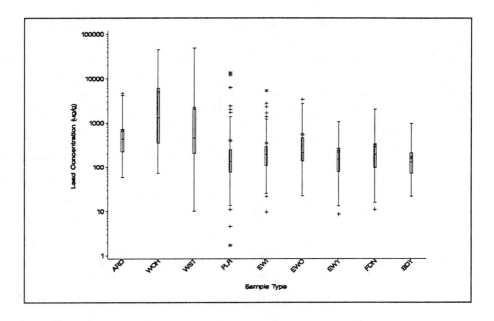

FIG. 1--Lead concentration (μg/g) by sample type.

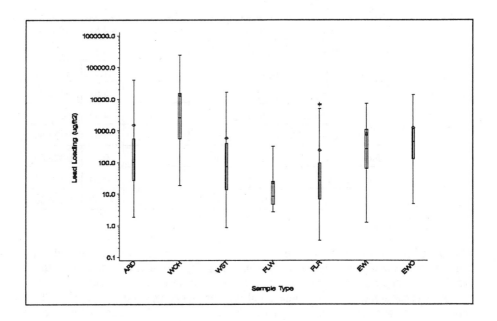

FIG. 2--Lead loading (μg/ft^2) by sample type.

TABLE 5--<u>Descriptive statistics for lead loading, lead concentration, and dust loading by sample type (Note: 1 μg/ft^2 = 10.76 μg/m^2).</u>

Measurement	Sample Type[1]		Geo. Mean	Arth. Mean	Min.	Max.
Lead Loading, (μg/ft^2)	Air Duct	(109)	120.36	1530.60	1.85	40863.60
	Window Channel	(98)	2515.59	13637.20	19.12	244581.21
	Window Stool	(113)	74.43	584.62	0.86	16710.45
	Floor Wipe	(67)	11.24	22.68	2.72	333.56
	Floor Vacuum	(238)	27.15	244.22	0.34	11641.25
	Entryway Int.	(100)	208.00	774.18	1.23	7349.00
	Entryway Ext.	(97)	384.17	1234.56	3.97	14021.00
Lead Concentration, (μg/g)	Air Duct	(109)	427.19	664.07	58.48	5644.54
	Window Channel	(98)	1438.61	4920.84	72.90	45229.26
	Window Stool	(113)	622.94	2168.84	10.15	48271.93
	Floor Vacuum	(238)	150.31	395.92	1.71	13567.76
	Entryway Int.	(100)	186.25	344.97	9.24	5332.00
	Entryway Ext.	(97)	237.48	542.39	8.84	16335.45
	Entryway Soil	(109)	148.77	222.92	4.55	1068.07
	Foundation Soil	(118)	185.75	299.52	8.51	3351.12
	Boundary Soil	(120)	125.46	161.62	21.35	1072.76
Dust Loading, mg/ft^2	Air Duct	(109)	281.75	3554.57	5.01	128646.00
	Window Channel	(98)	1748.63	4386.95	4.80	46328.75
	Window Stool	(113)	119.48	244.15	4.63	2824.00
	Floor	(238)	180.60	572.17	0.43	14426.00
	Entryway Int.	(100)	1116.70	2891.59	8.50	20857.40
	Entryway Ext.	(97)	1617.67	3143.55	40.60	22170.30

[1] Number of samples in parentheses.

1439 μg/g for window channel samples. In soil, the lowest geometric mean lead concentration was observed in boundary samples (125 μg/g) and the highest near the foundation (186 μg/g). The greatest relative variability in lead concentrations was seen in window stool, window channel, and interior entryway samples; the smallest variability was observed in air ducts and in the soil samples. Minimum individual lead concentrations for most sample types were typically on the order of 10 μg/g except in the air ducts and window channels where levels were at least 50 $\mu g/g$. Maximum individual lead concentrations were lowest for boundary and entryway soil samples (1073 and 1068 $\mu g/g$, respectively) and highest for window stool and window channel dust samples (48272 and 45229 $\mu g/g$, respectively).

The lowest geometric mean lead loading was seen for floor wipe dust samples (11 $\mu g/ft^2$ or 121 $\mu g/m^2$) while the highest mean lead loading was observed for window channels (2516 $\mu g/ft^2$ or 27068 $\mu g/m^2$). Both interior and exterior entryway lead loadings were more than ten times higher than those observed for regular floor dust samples. Lead loading relative variability was high for all sample types, except for floor wipe samples. Minimum individual lead loadings for all sample types were typically only a few $\mu g/ft^2$. Maximum individual lead loadings were lowest for floor dust samples (wipe; 334 $\mu g/ft^2$ or 3589 $\mu g/m^2$, and vacuum; 11641 $\mu g/ft^2$ or 125260 $\mu g/m^2$) and highest for window channel dust samples (244581 $\mu g/ft^2$ or 2631694 $\mu g/m^2$). It is worthwhile to note that the geometric mean lead loadings for both floors and window stools were close to their respective HUD interim dust standards of 200 $\mu g/ft^2$ (2152 $\mu g/m^2$) and 500 $\mu g/ft^2$ (5380 $\mu g/m^2$) while the geometric mean window channel lead loadings were well above the standard of 800 $\mu g/ft^2$ (8608 $\mu g/m^2$).

COMPARISON WITH OTHER STUDIES

We will compare the dust-lead loading results from the CAP Study with the corresponding results from four studies: HUD Abatement Demonstration Study [2], HUD National Survey of Lead-Based Paint [5], Traditional versus Modified Practices Study [8], and Experimental Abatement Practices Pilot Study [9].

Though considerable differences exist in the sampling frames, collection procedures, and instrumental analyses used in each study, the respective lead loading results may still provide insight on the range of environmental-lead levels which exist in U.S. housing. The dust lead loading results for these studies were either calculated from available datasets or extracted from reported results in the scientific literature.

Tables 6, 7, and 8 present lead loadings in floor, window stool, and window channel samples for the CAP Study and the other four studies. Along with the geometric mean lead loadings, these tables also present the logarithmic standard deviation, 10th, and 90th percentile lead loadings when they were available.

As can be seen in these tables, CAP Study lead loadings are at or below those in the other studies, with two exceptions. First, the CAP Study window channel lead loadings (approx. 2500 $\mu g/ft^2$ or 26900 $\mu g/m^2$) were significantly higher than those recorded for the HUD Demonstration Study (approx. 500 $\mu g/ft^2$ or 5380 $\mu g/m^2$). This difference might be due to the fact that the CAP Study sampled only in Denver, while the HUD Demonstration Study sampled in Denver and six other metropolitan areas. The difference might also be due to increased sample recovery achieved in the CAP Study using cyclone vacuum sampling as opposed to the HUD Demonstration Study using wipe sampling. The difference is probably not due to a failure of the abatements in Denver since the CAP Study lead levels in Table 8 are equivalent for abated and control houses.

The second case in which CAP Study lead loadings were high is in comparison with HUD National Survey results. For floor, window stool, and window channel

TABLE 6--Descriptive statistics for floor dust lead loadings by abatement efficacy field study (Note: 1 $\mu g/ft^2$ = 10.76 $\mu g/m^2$).

Study		Unit Type	Samples Collected	Log St.Dev.	P10, $\mu g/ft^2$	Geo.Mean, $\mu g/ft^2$	P90, $\mu g/ft^2$
CAP		Control	51	2.12	1.09	21.38	289.23
		Abated	187	2.00	1.69	28.97	408.58
HUD Demo[1][2]		...	1026	1.53	9.31	66.01	467.99
HUD National		High XRF[2]	234	1.82	0.23	2.40	24.90
Survey[5]		Low XRF[3]	304	1.61	0.08	0.64	5.08
Kennedy-	Pre-Abate.	Traditional	280, 82	...	...	250.84	...
Kreiger		Modified	82	...	...	288.00	...
[8]	Post	Traditional	271	...	...	1440.00	...
		Modified	50	...	...	650.32	...
	Post	Traditional	234	...	...	315.87	...
	(6 months)	Modified	57	...	...	315.87	...
Kennedy-	Pre-Abate.	Experimental	70	...	...	520.26	...
Kreiger	Post	Experimental	70	...	...	130.06	...
[9]	Post (6 m)	Experimental	63	...	...	55.74	...

TABLE 7--Descriptive statistics for window stool dust lead loadings by abatement efficacy field study (Note: 1 $\mu g/ft^2$ = 10.76 $\mu g/m^2$).

Study		Unit Type	Samples Collected	Log St.Dev.	P10, $\mu g/ft^2$	Geo.Mean, $\mu g/ft^2$	P90, $\mu g/ft^2$
CAP		Control	35	1.93	3.79	46.90	571.47
		Abated	78	2.18	7.02	91.57	1315.08
HUD Demo[1][2]		...	783	1.79	9.03	89.06	878.56
HUD National		High XRF[2]	123	2.64	0.29	8.40	246.22
Survey[5]		Low XRF[3]	126	2.13	0.10	1.57	24.06
Kennedy-	Pre-Abate.	Traditional	280	...	...	1337.80	...
Kreiger		Modified	82	...	...	1802.32	...
[8]	Post	Traditional	271	...	...	3595.35	...
		Modified	50	...	...	603.87	...
	Post	Traditional	234	...	...	1542.19	...
	(6 months)	Modified	57	...	...	1635.09	...
Kennedy-	Pre	Experimental	70	...	...	4607.99	...
Kreiger	Post	Experimental	70	...	...	325.16	...
[9]	Post (6 m)	Experimental	63	...	...	408.77	...

TABLE 8--Descriptive statistics for window channel dust lead loadings by abatement efficacy field study (Note: 1 μg/ft^2 = 10.76 μg/m^2).

Study		Unit Type	Samples Collected	Log St.Dev.	P10, μg/ft^2	Geo.Mean μg/ft^2	P90, μg/ft^2
CAP		Control	27	2.02	84.16	2330.21	20517.84
		Abated	71	2.33	51.74	2589.90	39308.26
HUD Demo[1][2]		...	756	1.93	42.90	506.21	5973.47
HUD National Survey[5]		High XRF[2]	56	2.28	11.91	220.00	4065.07
		Low XRF[3]	38	2.46	0.73	17.18	402.41
Kennedy-Kreiger [8]	Pre-Abate.	Traditional	280	...	...	15496.22	...
		Modified	82	...	...	18274.03	...
	Post	Traditional	271	...	...	14353.52	...
		Modified	50	...	...	8082.56	...
	Post	Traditional	234	...	...	12467.59	...
	(6 mo)	Modified	57	...	...	24879.43	...
Kennedy-Kreiger [9]	Pre-Abate.	Experimental	70	...	...	29422.39	...
	Post	Experimental	70	...	...	938.32	...
	Post(6 mo)	Experimental	63	...	...	1003.35	...

[1] All metropolitan areas in FHA portion. [2] At least one interior and exterior XRF reading exceeded 10 mg/cm^2. [3] All XRF readings at the residences were below 1.0 mg/cm^2.

samples, the CAP Study lead levels were an order of magnitude higher than for National Survey samples. This difference is probably mostly accounted for by low sample recoveries obtained in the HUD National Survey. Subsequent laboratory testing by Midwest Research Institute [10], as well as vacuum versus wipe field testing by [1][6], indicated that in general the vacuum sampling protocol used in the HUD National Survey recovers only about 20% of the dust present. Although vacuum recovery depends significantly on the substrate being sampled, this difference would account, at least in part, for the difference in lead loadings found between the CAP Study and HUD National Survey.

CONCLUSIONS

The CAP study involved a selection of 52 FHA repossessed houses in Denver. Extensive measures were taken to provide the most optimal design for successful investigation of the study objectives. This included a pilot study performed about one year in advance involving dust and soil sampling of six houses (four abated, two control) from the same pool of residences to assess variability.

Lead levels in the HUD Demonstration houses in Denver two years after abatement were found to vary greatly for different media and sampling locations. In dust, high lead concentrations and high loadings were observed in window channels. The geometric mean window channel lead loadings were well above the HUD interim standard of 800 $\mu g/ft^2$ (8608 $\mu g/m^2$). The dust on floors had low lead concentrations and low lead loadings. Geometric mean lead loadings for floors were not much higher than its standard of 200 $\mu g/ft^2$ (2152 $\mu g/m^2$). Air ducts and window stools had somewhat high lead concentrations but low lead loadings, however, one needs to recognize that air ducts were covered, but not abated, during abatement. Entryways, both interior and exterior, had relatively low lead concentrations. Lead loadings for entryways were at the level of concern for floors. Like floors, the geometric mean lead loadings for window stools were not much higher than its standard of 500 $\mu g/ft^2$ (5380 $\mu g/m^2$). In soil, the lead concentrations near the entryway, the boundary, and the foundation were low (near 115 $\mu g/g$) and did not vary greatly.

The dust-lead loading results from the CAP Study were contrasted with the corresponding results of other abatement efficacy studies. This comparison provided insight on the range of environmental-lead levels which exist in U.S. housing. It was found that CAP Study lead loadings are at or below those in the other studies, with two notable exceptions. First, the CAP Study window channel lead loadings are higher than the levels measured in the HUD Demonstration. Second, the floor and window stool, and window channel lead loading levels measured in the CAP Study were higher than the corresponding values in the HUD National Survey. The difference in lead loadings between the CAP Study and HUD Demonstration is likely due to the increased sample recovery achieved by the sampling method employed in the CAP Study, and that the CAP Study sampled only in Denver while the HUD Demonstration Study sampled in Denver and six other metropolitan areas. Most of the difference in lead loadings found between the CAP Study and HUD National Survey would be accounted for by the difference in the sample recovery achieved by vacuum sampling methods employed in these studies.

It is important to recognize in the interpretation of these results that various important factors were not controlled for in this presentation. For instance, the substrate from which each dust sample was collected was found to be significant. In regard to abatement, the amount and type of abatement performed at each house was important. Age of the house was also a discriminator. Part II of this report [3] presents a discussion of the impact of these and other factors on lead levels.

REFERENCES

[1]   Battelle Memorial Institute and Midwest Research Institute, "Draft Final Report, Comprehensive Abatement Performance Study", report to U.S. EPA Office of Pollution Prevention and Toxics, prepared under contract Nos. 68-D2-0139 and 68-D0-0137, 1993.

[2]   U.S. Department of Housing and Urban Development, "The HUD Lead-Based Paint Abatement Demonstration (FHA)", Office of Policy Development and Research, Washington, DC, 1991.

[3]   Buxton, B.E., Rust, S.W., Kinateder, J.G., Schwemberger, J.G., Lim, B., Constant, P., and Dewalt, G., "Comprehensive Abatement Performance Study Part II: Comparison of Encapsulation/Enclosure and Removal Methods for

Lead-Based Paint Abatement," Lead in Paint, Soil, and Dust: Health Risks, Exposure Studies, Control Measures, Measurement Methods, and Quality Assurance, ASTM STP 1226, Michael E. Beard and S.D. Allen Iske, Eds., American Society for Testing and Materials, Philadelphia, 1994.

[4]   Dewalt, F.G. and Constant, P., Buxton, B.E., Rust, S.W., Lim, B., Schwemberger, J.G. "Sampling and Analysis of Lead in Dust and Soil for the Comprehensive Abatement Performance Study (CAPS)", Lead in Paint, Soil, and Dust: Health Risks, Exposure Studies, Control Measures, Measurement Methods, and Quality Assurance, ASTM STP 1226, Michael E. Beard and S.D. Allen Iske, Eds., American Society for Testing and Materials, Philadelphia, 1994.

[5]   U.S. Department of Housing and Urban Development, Comprehensive and Workable Plan for the Abatement of Lead-Based Paint in Privately Owned Housing, report to Congress, Washington, DC, December 7, 1990.

[6]   Battelle Memorial Institute and Midwest Research Institute, "Draft Final Report Comprehensive Abatement Performance Pilot Study", report to U.S. EPA Office of Pollution Prevention and Toxics, prepared under contract Nos. 68-D0-0126 and 68-D0-0137, 1991.

[7]   Reeves, R., Kjellstrom, T., Dallow, M., Mullins, P., New Zealand Journal of Science, Vol. 25, 1982, pp 221-227.

[8]   Farfel, M.R. and Chisolm, J.J., Jr., "Health and Environmental Outcomes of Traditional ad Modified Practices for Abatement of Residential Lead-Based Paint", American Journal of Public Health, Vol. 80, No. 10, October 1990, pp 1240-1245.

[9]   Farfel, M.R. and Chisolm, J.J., Jr., "An Evaluation of Experimental Practices for Abatement of Residential Lead-Based Paint: Report on a Pilot Project", Environmental Research. Vol. 55, 1991, pp 199-212.

[10]   Midwest Research Institute, "Engineering Study to Explore Improvements in Vacuum Dust Collection", report to U.S. EPA Office of Pollution Prevention and Toxics, prepared under contract No. 68-D0-0137, 1991.

R. Frederick Eberle[1]

THE DESIGN OF THE HUD LEAD-BASED PAINT ABATEMENT DEMONSTRATION IN PUBLIC
HOUSING

REFERENCE: Eberle, R. F., "The Design of the HUD Lead-Based Paint
Abatement Demonstration in Public Housing," Lead in Paint, Soil and Dust:
Health Risks, Exposure Studies, Control Measures, Measurement Methods, and
Quality Assurance, ASTM STP 1226, Michael E. Beard and S. D. Allen Iske,
Eds., American Society for Testing and Materials, Philadelphia, 1995.

ABSTRACT: A component of HUD's Lead-Based Paint Abatement Demonstration
is the lead-based paint (LBP) abatement of 109 units of multi-family
public housing. These units are owned by Public Housing Authorities
(PHAs) and were scheduled for modernization.

The PHA Demonstration allowed HUD to examine the problems, and
opportunities, which arise when LBP abatement and modernization are
carried out together. In particular, the PHA Demonstration provided much
more opportunity to examine the problems associated with removal and
demolition of building components which would be replaced under
modernization . When abatement was complete, final clearance wipes were
taken in accordance with HUD's Interim Guidelines, and when the work area
passed final clearance, construction contractors completed the
modernization work.

Other objectives of the Demonstration included extensive data collection
of air and clearance wipes samples of the different methods of abatement,
an analysis of the extent that lead hazards can be contained within
dwelling units, and the feasibility of lead-based paint abatement of lead
hazards to the 0.06% by weight standard in selected units. The disposal
of waste also became an issue during the PHA Demonstration.

The PHA Demonstration Report should be submitted to HUD during the fall
of 1993.

KEYWORDS: PHA Demonstration, FHA Demonstration, Needlegun, Clearance wipe
tests, 0.06% experiment, Dust migration, TCLP testing, HUD Guidelines

---

BACKGROUND

The Lead-Based Paint Abatement Demonstration was designed by the
Department of Housing and Urban Development (HUD) to have two components.
The first component, the Federal Housing Administration Demonstration (FHA
Demonstration) was a lead-based paint abatement demonstration in 172
vacant single-family housing units owned by the FHA as a result of
foreclosure action. Findings from this component of the demonstration
were published in August 1991 [1].

The FHA Demonstration utilized six methods of Lead-Based Paint
Abatement: (1) Encapsulation, (2) Enclosure, (3) Abrasive Removal, (4)

---

[1]Associate, Environmental Services, Dewberry & Davis, Fairfax, VA
22031

Hand-Scraping with a Heat Gun, (5) Chemical Removal, and (6) Removal and Replacement. This FHA Demonstration was designed to achieve three major objectives [2] with regard to Lead-Based Paint Abatement:

- To estimate the comparative costs of alternative methods of abatement
- To assess the efficacy of alternative methods of abatement
- To confirm the adequacy of worker protection safeguards during abatement

The findings [3] of the FHA Demonstration as they relate to the objectives were that encapsulation (sealing surfaces with durable coatings) was the least expensive method of Lead-Based Paint Abatement and generated the lowest levels of airborne lead dust during abatement. Enclosure (covering surfaces with durable materials, e.g. gypsum board) was also found to be a low lead-dust generation method, although it is more costly than encapsulation, and cannot be used as extensively. The report does caution that more study is necessary because it is not known how effective these methods will remain over time.

Hand-scraping with a heat gun generated more airborne lead dust than the other abatement methods involving removal. Chemical removal was typically more costly than other methods, required more worker protection than other methods and generated more hazardous wastes than other methods. However, depending on worker skills, chemical removal can be used on a wide variety of substrates.

Replacement (removal of lead containing substrate, e.g. baseboard) was found to be the most promising of the removal methods in almost all circumstances. This method generated relatively little airborne lead dust, although it did produce bulk hazardous waste.

The nature of the FHA Demonstration did not create many opportunities for abrasive (blasting, grinding, or sanding methods) removal. This was due to the random selection of the abatement method and the fact that many building substrates containing lead-based paint were not compatible to this type of removal.

PHA DEMONSTRATION

The second component of the LBP Abatement Demonstration is the Public Housing Authority demonstration (PHA Demonstration) of lead-based paint abatement in 109 units of multi-family public housing. These units are owned by PHAs in Albany, NY, Cambridge, MA, and Omaha, NE. In each case, the units are scheduled for modernization under the Comprehensive Improvement Assistance Program (CIAP) and they will all have been vacated prior to abatement. The CIAP is a funding mechanism by which HUD grants PHAs money to upgrade existing public housing. Each of the three PHAs entered into a contract to: (1) perform field testing for lead hazards; (2) develop an abatement plan which is consistent with modernization requirements, but research oriented, (3) assist in contractor solicitation and training; (4) monitor and collect data during construction and (5) report on the findings of the research on each site.

The FHA Demonstration examined strictly the abatement activities mentioned above. No effort or work, except to secure a structure, was made to repair or upgrade a structure beyond abating lead-based paint. In contrast, the PHA demonstration allowed us to examine the problems, and opportunities, which arise when LBP abatement and modernization are carried out together. In particular, the PHA demonstration provided much more opportunity to examine the problems associated with removal and demolition of building components which would be replaced under modernization. On each site, the PHA's elected to separate the work into

2 phases -- one protected and one unprotected. The protected phase was the actual abatement conducted by workers trained in Lead-Based Paint hazards using full worker protection, while the unprotected phase was the construction that followed. When abatement was complete, final clearance wipes were taken in accordance with HUD's Interim Guidelines for Hazard Identification and Abatement in Public and Indian Housing [4]. When the work area passed final clearance, construction contractors completed the modernization work (unprotected phase).

Final clearance wipes were collected from floors, window sills, and window wells of an abated area.   These wipe samples are sent to a laboratory for analysis of lead content. Wipe samples must be taken in a known area, and results are reported in micrograms (of lead) per square foot. The Guidelines recommend that an area has passed final clearance if the wipe results are less than or equal to 200 micrograms per square foot for floors, 500 micrograms per square foot for window sills and 800 micrograms per square foot for window wells [5]. It should be understood that this clearance procedure only documents how clean an area is or has been made after abatement; it has no direct relationship to the quality of the abatement work or any remaining intact Lead-Based Paint.   A thorough visual examination is required to assure compliance with these factors.

Housing Authorities often are required to reconfigure interior partition walls during modernization. Removal of lead-based paint on walls must be performed during the protected phase to allow demolition of any remaining walls during the unprotected phase.   Otherwise, all demolition must be performed with worker protection in place. The primary method used to remove this paint during the PHA Demonstration was to chisel paint from plaster walls. Generally, a layer of the plaster came off with the paint. Wet methods were always used and air monitoring indicated lead dust was below the action level. Air monitoring in the breathing zone of workers and in adjacent work areas was performed during the PHA Demonstration. Air monitoring involves drawing a known volume of ambient air through a filter. The filter is then analyzed for lead content by a laboratory and a result reported in micrograms per cubic meter.

HUD has adopted the Occupational Safety and Health Administrations (OSHA) regulations for occupational exposure to lead [6].   These regulations cite an action level of 30 micrograms of lead per cubic meter of air and a permissible exposure limit (PEL) of 50 micrograms of lead per cubic meter of air, both averaged over an 8-hour period. The action level is that level where employees must be enrolled in a medical surveillance program (Blood Lead Testing). The PEL is that level where engineering controls must be practiced. If engineering controls cannot reduce levels below the PEL, then they must be supplemented by the use of respiratory protection.   It should be noted that by specification the PHA Demonstration required the use of full worker protection at all times including respirators and engineering controls without regard to air monitoring data.

Toxic Characteristic Leaching Procedure (TCLP) [7] testing was performed on the resultant plaster debris.   The TCLP test always determined that this debris was below the hazardous waste threshold of 5 parts per million (ppm). Therefore the debris was disposed of in a construction debris approved landfill. (The TCLP test will be discussed later in this paper.)

Many PHA units have metal door frames that were fitted into openings during wall construction. This type of construction makes it nearly impossible to remove the frames without cutting through the wall. Although other methods were available, the Demonstration in Cambridge used the needlegun to remove paint from door frames in a building. The FHA demonstration did not present many opportunities to test the needlegun, due to limitations of the substrates (as the needlegun seems to work best on metal surfaces). These metal door frames presented an excellent opportunity to use this method in the Demonstration.

A needlegun looks similar to a machine gun. It is pneumatically operated at approximately 110 psi encasing about 30-3mm rods to hammer the surface. A High Efficiency Particulate Air (HEPA) vacuum is attached to the needlegun to collect lead dust. Worker Protection for noise, eye and respiratory protection is critical. Powered Air Purifying Respirators were used for respiratory protection, and are recommended. Benefits of this system include a reduced waste stream (only paint chips or dust) and a surface that is slightly roughened and ready for painting. The significance of a reduced waste stream is that the resultant paint chip and dust debris must almost always be disposed of as hazardous waste. Less volume or weight equates to lower disposal cost.

The PHA Demonstration also examined the integration of lead-based paint abatement with planned renovation activity under CIAP. This involved the phased sequencing of various construction activities. One housing authority utilized in-house labor (force account) and the others used abatement contractors. The use of force account labor allowed the abatement activity or method to change without the need for change orders. This allowed the opportunity for the PHA to adjust a sequencing for abatement based on field conditions at minimal cost and delay. The PHA did have to accept more liability and purchase abatement equipment; however, the work force was easy to train and quickly became skilled at LBP abatement.

The "Force Account" work force employed by the Housing Authority was obtained from local construction trade unions. This work force was under the direct supervision of full-time housing authority staff. These workers were trained in lead hazard awareness per the Guidelines [8] and received Lead-Based Paint Abatement training in the field. The commitment of resources by the Housing Authority and quality work performed by the work force were key to the undertaking and success of this project.

Deleading contractors possessed different advantages/disadvantages. They were for the most part already trained, owned the appropriate equipment, and carried their own liability insurance. Changes in the work process or sequence had to be more carefully analyzed, however, in light of change order costs. This is significant with respect to the recommended Pilot Abatement Project [9] as stated in the Guidelines and the fact that data observed during the pilot abatement can be used to change the scope of the project.

Other elements of the Demonstration include the extensive collection and analysis of air and clearance dust wipe samples, an examination of the extent to which lead hazards can be contained within dwelling units, and an assessment of the feasibility of lead-based paint abatement to the 0.06% by weight standard (or 600 ppm) level in selected units. The 0.06% by weight standard was established by the Consumer Product Safety Commission (CPSC) as the allowable maximum lead level in new paint. The Stewart B. McKinney Homeless Amendments Act of 1989 (PL100-628, November 7, 1988) required HUD to determine whether testing and abatement to such a standard is scientifically and practically feasible [10].

The guidelines require abatement of Lead-Based Paint hazards at a level of 1.0 milligram per square centimeter (mg/cm^2) and prescribe abatement at 0.5% by weight (5000 ppm) [11]. X-Ray Fluorescence (XRF) instruments measure levels of lead in paint. Paint chip analysis performed in a laboratory by Atomic Absorption Spectroscopy (AAS) can be reported in either mg/cm^2 (with area of paint chip) or percent by weight. It is important to understand that mg/cm^2 and percent by weight (ppm) are not directly comparable. Therefore, the XRF cannot be used for the 0.06% feasibility study, nor can the 1.0 mg/cm^2 abatement threshold be directly compared to the 0.06% by weight CPSC standard or the 0.5% by weight abatement threshold. This work must be performed by laboratory analysis with results reported in percent by weight.

Personal air samples were obtained on all workers throughout the abatement process in all three cities. These data, for the most part, reflect full shift worker exposures. Data on worker tasks were collected hourly, to permit examination of the relationship between worker exposure and worker tasks. The results and data analysis are on-going and will be provided in the final report to Congress.

Another objective of the Demonstration was to examine the relationships between abatement methods, as compared to pass/fail rates of clearance wipe tests. Preliminary data analysis indicates that wipe cleanup on the floors was more difficult to achieve where caustic paint removal was performed than where other types of abatement methods were performed.

Another major component of the Demonstration was an initial experiment in all three cities to determine if migration of dust to adjacent units occurs as a result of abatement activity in a single unit. This was performed by abating a single unit per building or floor and performing air and wipe testing in adjacent units. While preliminary indications are that dust spread was minimal, further analysis of the data obtained from this experiment is necessary to draw definitive conclusions.

The Demonstration scope also required a study of the feasibility of abatement of lead hazards to the 0.06% by weight standard. From the above discussion, this value is a low abatement threshold especially when compared to the prescribed 0.5% by weight abatement threshold. This experiment is still progressing, and involves the retesting of abated substrates in already abated units to determine if they are below 0.06% by weight standard. This experiment will be performed by core drilling abated substrates and analyzing the cuttings. In addition, previously tested lead-free paint will be applied to surfaces, and after a "curing period", this paint will be sampled by AAS to determine if lead is present above 0.06% by weight standard. These data will then be analyzed to determine if abatement to this standard is feasible and practical.

The Demonstration also looked at two additional topics: the application of the Guidelines in testing and abatement and in the hazardous waste process. In all three cities, the Guidelines were followed. The final report will comment on the application of the Guidelines to actual testing and abatement.

The waste disposal issue became an interesting component of the PHA Demonstration. The Toxic Characteristic Leaching Procedure (TCLP) [12] test for hazardous waste determination was used for the PHA Demonstration. Results of this test were in striking contrast to results of the Extraction Procedure toxicity test (EP toxicity) [13] that was used during the FHA Demonstration, since many more of the TCLP analyses were positive for lead. Due to contractual issues, two different laboratories were employed to perform TCLP test analysis of removed substrates. One laboratory routinely reported the substrate to be below the hazardous threshold while the other reported results to be far above the hazardous waste threshold. Upon investigation, it was determined each laboratory interpreted the TCLP procedure differently. Consultation with EPA's Office of Solid Waste indicated that the samples needed to fit through a 9.5mm sieve and they recommended dicing the sample into cubes or dowels as part of the sample preparation protocol. When both laboratories did this, the results were above the hazardous waste threshold, but considerably less than the extreme high results of the first test.

The TCLP test is designed to simulate the leaching of lead from a substrate in a landfill. The EP Toxicity Test was an earlier test to simulate this same leaching process. While there are several differences between the two analytical methods, a significant difference is that the EP Toxicity Test included a "structural integrity procedure". This procedure can be performed on a solid component such as a piece of door frame, baseboard or other such component. If the component "passed" this procedure, the solid "chunk" would be analyzed by the EP Toxicity method, instead of cutting it to fit through a 9.5mm sieve as required by the TCLP test.

The critical issue with the TCLP test is the preparation of the sample for testing; in particular a solid waste such as a Lead-Based Paint containing door, window, or other such component. The HUD guidelines require that all removed components be wrapped in 6-mil polyethylene, in manageable lengths [14]. It is not clear, however, that this waste disposed in a landfill breaks into 9.5mm cubes or is released from the 6-mil polyethylene. The laboratory that initially reported the waste to be below the hazardous threshold followed all parts of the TCLP test except for cutting the sample into 9.5mm cubes. Instead, they used a solid piece of component to simulate what would actually be disposed of in the landfill.

No one associated with the PHA Demonstration wants to be a party to contaminating our earth. However, it is not evident that the preparation of the sample for TCLP analysis is simulating what occurs to components in a landfill. More research is needed on testing methods and sample preparation for determining disposed criteria of lead-based paint containing components.

RESULTS

The PHA Demonstration field activities are currently in progress. Reports will be issued to HUD on a city by city basis as the data are collected and analyzed. At least one city report has been submitted to Congress for review. The other two city reports and an overall project report are expected to be released through 1994.

CONCLUSION

The PHA Demonstration report should be submitted to HUD by the end of 1994. Individual city reports will be submitted to HUD during this time period as well. Conclusions would be inappropriate at present and inconclusive as data are still under analysis and the reports must be submitted to HUD. These reports, when released for public distribution can be obtained by placing an order through HUD USER at (301) 251-5154.

REFERENCES

[1]   U.S. Department of Housing and Urban Development, *The HUD Lead-Based Paint Abatement Demonstration (FHA)*, HUD-1316(1)-PDR, U.S. Government Printing Office, Washington, D.C., 1991.

[2]   U.S. Department of Housing and Urban Development, *The HUD Lead-Based Paint Abatement Demonstration (FHA)*, Page ii.

[3]   U.S. Department of Housing and Urban Development, *The HUD Lead-Based Paint Abatement Demonstration (FHA)*, Pages 1x-1 - 1x-10.

[4]   U.S. Department of Housing and Urban Development, *Lead-Based Paint: Interim Guidelines for Hazard Identification and Abatement in Public and Indian Housing*, 281-930/44406, U.S. Government Printing Office, Washington, D.C., September 1990, Revised May 1991.

[5]   U.S. Department of Housing and Urban Development, *Lead-Based Paint: Interim Guidelines for Hazard Identification and Abatement in Public and Indian Housing*, Sections 10.4.2 - 10.4.3, pages 122 - 125.

[6]   Occupational Safety and Health Administration Regulation, *29 Code of Federal Regulation 1910.1025*, Office of the Federal Register National Archives and Records Administration, Washington, D.C., 1988, Chapter XVII.

[7]   U.S. Environmental Protection Agency, *40 Code of Federal Regulation*, Part 261 Appendix II, Office of the Federal Register National Archives and Records Administration, Washington, D.C., 1991, Chapter 1.

[8]   U.S. Department of Housing and Urban Development, *Lead-Based Paint: Interim Guidelines for Hazard Identification and Abatement in Public and Indian Housing,* Section 8.8, Page 91.

[9]   U.S. Department of housing and Urban Development, *Lead-Based Paint: Interim Guidelines for Hazard Abatement in Public and Indian Housing*, Chapter 6, Section 6.3.2, Page 61.

[10]   U.S. Department of Housing and Urban Development, *Lead-Based Paint: Interim Guidelines for Hazard Identification and Abatement in Public and Indian Housing,* Chapter 1, Page 2.

[11]   U.S. Department of Housing and Urban Development, *Lead-Based Paint: Interim Guidelines for Hazard Abatement in Public and Indian Housing*, Chapter 4, Page 25.

[12]   U.S. Environmental Protection Agency, *Part 261 Appendix II, Office of the Federal Register National Archives and Records Administration*, Washington, D.C., 1991, Chapter 1.

[13]   U.S. Environmental Protection Agency, *Test Methods for Evaluating Solid Waste*, SW-846, 3rd edition, Office of Waste and Emergency Response, 1986.

[14]   U.S. Department of Housing and Urban Development, *Lead-Based Paint: Interim Guidelines for Hazard Abatement in Public and Indian Housing,* Section 10.2.2.1, Page 117.

Michael B. Rabinowitz[1]

IMPUTING LEAD SOURCES FROM BLOOD LEAD ISOTOPE RATIOS

REFERENCE: Rabinowitz, M.B., **"Imputing Lead Sources from Blood Lead Isotope Ratios,"** Lead in Paint, Soil and Dust: Health Risks, Exposure Studies, Control Measures, Measurement Methods, and Quality Assurance, ASTM STP 1226, Michael E. Beard and S.D. Allen Iske, Eds., American Society for Testing and Materials, Philadelphia, 1995.

ABSTRACT: Of all of the metals, only lead, displays natural variations among mining districts in the relative abundances of its stable (non-radioactive) isotopes. The abundances of the four stable isotopes are commonly expressed as 206/204, 206/207, and 206/208 atomic ratios, is usually determined by mass spectrometry. Precisions of 0.5% for 206/204 and even better for the other pairs are obtainable.

The three ratios covary strongly and depend on when the ore was formed. Older, Precambrian ores such as from Coer d'Alene, Idaho have 206/204 near 16. More recent ores, such as in Missouri, have ratios above 20. These variations provide a tracer for following a particular batch of lead.

A major limitations to this method is that it is useful to only those problems where the potential sources are few in number and isotopically distinct. Several examples are offered where this method has been successfully employed in the fields of archeology, environmental pollution, childhood lead poisoning, and biokinetic modeling of bone lead.

KEYWORDS: Lead, stable isotopes, mass spectrometry, isotope tracer, isotopic composition, ore, paint, mass fractionation

---

The purpose of this paper is to describe the limited ability of stable isotope techniques to match lead in the blood with lead from one or more suspected sources. The geochemical and historical reasons for the observed variability among industrial leads will be reviewed. Examples using this technique will be presented.

---

1 Associate Scientist, Marine Biological Laboratory, Woods Hole, MA 02543.

The student of stable isotope techniques is forced to turn to the geological sciences for guidance, even if environmental or biological issues are to be investigated. This is because the literature on stable isotopes of lead is predominantly found among planetary science journals. A citation survey of published articles is shown in Table 1. Three different published literature bases were searched:Medline for medicine and health, GeoRef for the earth sciences, and Life Sciences for biology. Although all three sets have thousands of articles with "lead" as a key word and much fewer have "stable isotope", almost all the articles with both topics are in the earth sciences. Using "isotopic composition" or "isotope ratio" showed the same pattern.

TABLE 1 -- Literature citations of stable isotopes of lead.

Literature Data Base	Years Covered	Number of "Lead" #1	Articles with Key Words "Stable Isotope" #2	Both #1 and #2
Medline	1989-1992	15,554	96	3
GeoRef	1785-1992	24,032	2,637	1,642
Life Sciences	1986-1991	11,400	1,724	4

MEASURING STABLE ISOTOPE ABUNDANCE RATIOS

Advantages of using stable isotopes include safety, in that radio-isotopes are not used and, also, the ability to measure slow or long term phenomena since the tracer does not decay. Natural radio-isotopes of lead have half-lives that are too short (lead-212, 11 hours and lead-210, 22 years) to allow the specific activity of lead to be useful for source discrimination.

Perhaps the greatest advantage is the ability to measure the isotope abundance ratios of even microgram amounts of lead to great precision with modern mass spectrometers. Attempts have been made to measure isotopic composition by activation analysis or specialized atomic absorption spectro-photometers for several elements. For lead, mass spectrometry, involving ion generation, separation of the ions according to their mass-to-charge ratio, and ion detection has proven the only viable method. Current routine techniques with a solid source ionizer, magnetic sector mass analyzer, and rapid mass scanning cycles or multiple collectors yield precisions of the 206/204 ratio of 0.5%. As an example of the current state of the art, McCulloch and Woodhead [1] report repeated analysis of standard reference material with a variability, two standard deviations divided by the mean, of the 206/204 ratio of 0.2%. By using double-spiking corrections [2], they reduced the variability by a factor of 3 to 5. External reproducabilities, the difference between the observed and

known ratios, which was independent of the operator,
approximate 0.03%.

The sources of residual error include sample
contamination and mass fractionation. The potential for
contamination is especially severe since usually only very
small quantities of lead are present in the sample. Sample
collection, transport, storage and chemical extraction must
each be monitored for their contribution to contamination.
Mass fractionation, which is the tendency for lighter
isotopes to be preferentially evaporated from the filament
in the spectrometer, is a source of analytical noise
requiring assessment. This variability is the result of
inconsistent mass fractionation which depends on sample
loading, matrix effects, filament condition, and non-
linearities in the ion path or electronics. Mass
fractionation causes not only random noise, but also
systematic errors. These have been seen with both filament
and plasma ionization machines. Lead reference standards of
known isotopic composition, such as SRM 981 and 982
(National Institute of Standards and Technology,
Gaithersburg, MD 20899) are available to guide the analyst.

GEOCHEMICAL BASIS FOR DIFFERENCES IN RATIOS AMONG LEAD ORES

Geologists measure the four stable isotopes of lead
because it yields information about the ages of ore minerals
and their source region (upper crust, lower crust, mantle)
for an ore [3]. Also, it has be applied to other rocks, such
as volcanic basalt, which contain lead in trace amounts [4].
Aston first used a mass spectrometer to measure the isotopes
of lead [5]. In 1938 Nier published the orderly pattern of
variations from a world-wide sampling of lead ores, which we
recognize today [6].

The reason that different ore bodies have different
isotopic compositions is that they were formed at different
times in the Earth's history [7]. Some lead was present
when the Earth was formed, but most lead has accumulated
from the radioactive decay of thorium and uranium with half
lives of billions of years. These radioactive parent
elements reside dispersed within the earth until some
geochemical event, such as the cooling and fractional
crystallization of an intrusive magma, causes mobilization
of that lead and separation from the uranium and thorium
parents. This fluid lead was then concentrated into ore
bodies, some distance away, most usually as the sulphide
mineral, galena. Thus, ore formed 2 billion years ago had
more original lead and only some decay products. Ores formed
only 50 million years ago, will also include lead formed in
the intervening billion years. The earlier lead has somewhat
less Pb-207 than recent lead, but recent lead ores have more
Pb-206 and Pb-208 because they are produced by a slower
decay rate. Pb-204 has no significant radiogenic source, and
what is present now is primordial.

All three pairs of ratios are collected and should be published. Often only 206/204 ratios are shown because of the wider range in 206/204 ratios than 206/207 and the generally very strong correlation among the three ratio pairs [8]. Which ratio has the greatest discriminating power in a particular application may be different according to the resolution of the mass spectrometer used, the range of lead considered, and the thorium to uranium ratio of the source material. For example, in Tokyo Bay the 206/207 was found to be the most diagnostic [9].

APPLICATIONS OF LEAD ISOTOPES TO ARCHEOLOGY

Several basic concepts about utilizing lead isotopes to understand sources can be illustrated from examples in the field of archeology. Because lead is present in copper ores, it has been possible to identify the source ore bodies of Bronze Age artifacts recovered in the Eastern Mediterranean. Isotope ratios of ores from Laurion, Greece are different from those from Cyprus [10]. When plotted, the ranges or fields of values from these two mining sites did not overlap. Bronze figurines from the Late Minnoan from Crete, for example, have values within the range of Greek ores [11]. Similar work had been done with Chinese, Korean, and Japanese metal artifacts. From this the earliest importation of Korean bronzes into Japan has been established [12].

It should be emphasized that a major limitations to this method is that it is useful to only those problems where the potential sources are few in number and have been analyzed and found to be isotopically distinct. So, in these successful applications, although a range of values was seen for each source, the ranges did not overlap. Assigning a source to a sample is then possible. Similarly this methodology has been successfully applied to the question of the origin of lead in contaminated soils in South Australia where mining activity or automobile exhaust could be sources [13].

HISTORICAL BASIS FOR DIFFERENCES IN ISOTOPE RATIOS AMONG PAINTS

Various ore bodies have been mined and converted to paint during our history. Therefore, paint made at different periods in different locals may be expected to have different isotope ratios [14]. The years of maximum use of lead for the manufacture of lead paint were from 1910 to 1950.

The history of lead mining in America began at least 300 years earlier. The first recorded smelting of lead was 1621 in Fall Creek, Virginia Colony. Bullets in the War for Independence were produced in every state, but only Virginia (the Austinville mine, opened 1750)   and   New York

(Dutchess, 1740) maintained steady production for the next century [15]. There were many small, mixed ore deposits in New England [16]. However the combined lead production of all the Eastern and Southern states seldom exceed 5,000 tons/year. Galena, Illinois, was the major producer from 1830-1845, peaking at 24,000 tons/year, nearly 80 % of US production at the time [17].

The large deposits of Missouri, Utah, and Idaho provided the bulk of lead ores from the late 1800's to the present time. The discoveries in Joplin, Bonne Terre, and Doe Run eventually brought Missouri production to 100,000 tons/year by 1900 and double that again by 1929. In the late 1960's the development of the New Lead Belt brought production to over 400,000 tons/year. Oklahoma production peaked in 1925 at 80,000 tons/year; Kansas rarely produced more than 20,000 tons/year [18].

The Utah deposits at Cottonwood (1850), Brigham Canyon, Frisco, and Tintic have been steady producers for nearly 100 years. When railroads arrived in 1869 production was 25,000 tons/year and steadily grew to 155,000 in 1927. It declined to 71,000 in 1942 and 38,000 in 1962. Nearby Leadville, Colorado, was a major producer by 1880 but it peaked in 1900 at 82,000 tons/year. Minor deposits in Montana, Arizona, Nevada, California, and New Mexico each produced less than 1% of domestic production [19].

The immense Idaho find in 1885 was producing 85,000 tons/year by 1900, making Idaho the number one lead mining state, a position it shared with Missouri for the rest of this century. There have been major recent finds in Alaska, but these would not have been available to paint manufacturers. The United States mined and smelted one third of the world's lead by 1900 and nearly one half by 1910, making the United States the world's leading producer of lead for most of this century.

Imported ore or metal was a very small contributor from 1800 through the 1950s. For example, in 1931 it was 43,000 versus 567,000 tons of domestic production. Mexico was by far the largest source. Canadian production began in 1880 in Ontario and was minor until the 1920s when the Sullivan Mine with a smelter in Trail expanded. Peru and Chile have been suppliers since the 1920s.

In the case of pigments, the balance of trade has been even more one-sided. For example, in 1932 imported lead pigments were valued at $12,000 compared with exports of $562,000. In 1938 the values were $22,000 versus $605,000. Imported lead from Mexico, Peru, Australia, and Canada have played a significant and varying role in the production of tetra-ethyl lead.

The increased use of recycled lead metal has been a factor more significant than imports. The recovery of lead from finished products, especially batteries and cable covers was only 8 % of domestic production in 1907. By 1931 41% of domestic lead production came from recovered metals and 63 % by 1967. The fraction of lead pigment made from

Table 2-- <u>Lead isotope ratios for some mining districts.</u>

Mining District	Pb-206/Pb-204 Abundance Ratio	
Mississippi Valley		
SE Missouri	20.5 - 21.5	****
Wisconsin-Illinois	21.0 - 24.4	
Tri-State Ks,Ok,Mo	21.3 - 22.6	*
Montana	16.6	
Colorado	17.7	*
Utah	17.6 - 20.0	**
Idaho -Coeur d'Alene	16.3	***
Washington	18.7	
California, Shasta	17.9	
Kernville	19.5	
British Columbia, Sullivan	16.6	
New York		
Balmat-Edwards	17.0	
Rossie	18.0 - 21.0	
Quebec, Eastern Township	17.8	
Alaska, Red Dog	18.4	
Mexico, Zacatecas	18.8	
Peru	18.6 -18.8	
Australia, Broken Hill	16.1	*

* major economic importance for American lead paint

refined scrap lead and the sources of that scrap will tend to average the observed ratios. Most scrap is derived from batteries and recycled back into the production of new batteries, which have a life time of about 4 years. Another trend in lead production has been the consolidation of smelting into fewer, larger operations. In 1947 there were prmary lead smelters in 11 states: California, Colorado, Idaho, Illinois, Indiana, Kansas, Missouri, Montana, New Jersey, Utah and Texas. By 1979, there were only 5 states with primary smelters or refiners: Missouri, Idaho, Montana, Texas, and Nebraska.

The isotopic composition of lead ores from each of these mining districts have been thoroughly analyzed, and a useful compendium has been published [20]. A data base has been created of published values [21]. Often the analyses over-represent mines with particularly interesting geological features rather than the economically significant mines. The general pattern among several mining districts is shown in Table 2. Some have small ranges, but others, such as the Mississippi Valley ores, having much wider ranges [22], [23], and [24]. Utah ores are uniform within a mine, but among mining districts there are systematic trends, with varying amounts of crustal lead mixing with the main

Tertiary intrusive deposit [25]. The largest ore bodies are closest to the intrusive body, and tend to be less radiogenic and more isotopically uniform with values between 18.0 and 18.7. This feature has made lead isotopes very useful for exploratory geochemistry and site evaluation [26]. Table 2 shows the 206/204 ratios among some mining districts.

A paint sample will retain the distinct isotopic composition of an ore body only if it is not mixed with batches of lead from other regions as it was made into metal, pigment, paint, and then one of several layers on a surface. In the past smelters were supplied with ore from just one mining district. That was more generally the rule in the earlier part of this century, but by the 1970's Idaho lead ore was being smelted in Glover, Missouri. The smelter in Selby, California processed ores from many foreign mines [27]. Most of the lead in paints came from long term agreements between lead refiners in a district and paint manufacturers, who often had shared financial interests [28]. So, a container of paint which was applied in the 1920s or 1930s perhaps likely contained lead from only one ore district. Buildings are repainted, often with different brands, and samples which include several layers of lead paint would in these cases contain these mixtures from different ores.

OBSERVED DIFFERENCES AMONG PAINT SAMPLES

Despite these reasons to expect that the distinctions seen among ores will be averaged and blurred in looking at paint samples, observations of paint samples in Boston [29], and California [30] show considerable intersample variability, In Boston, 13 samples of lead paint from five homes were measured. The mean 206/204 ratio was 18.0 with a wide range from 16.9 to 19.8. The error in each determination is less than .01 units. This range is considerably greater than aerosol samples that year (18.6 to 18.9, n=9) , or gasoline (18.2 to 19.9, n=13). Three samples of lead paint from different locations within three homes showed considerable clustering of values within each home. The mean (standard deviation) 206/204 ratio were 17.6 (.07) , 18.5 (0.4), and 18.1 (.2). The differences among homes can far exceed the difference within a home, but that may not always be the case. Large differences may also be found within a home.

MATCHING BLOOD AND PAINT LEAD ISOTOPICALLY

Isotopic analysis of lead from the blood of three lead poisoned children from these homes is shown along with paint samples in Table 3 [29]. In two case the blood matched very closely at least one of the paint samples, but not another samples of paint from the home. The term "matches" here implies that the observed ratios are very close. The possibility still exists that an unsampled source or a combination of several other sources "matches" the observed ratios.

Table 3-- Lead isotope ratios in 3 cases of poisoning.

Sample 206/207	Lead content	206/204	
Home 1			
blood	1.2 ug/g	17.53	1.140
feces	77 ug/g	17.81	1.141
paint A interior	35 %	17.57	1.129
paint B exterior	10 %	17.45	1.129
paint C interior	2 %	17.70	1.140
Home 2			
blood	0.8 ug/g	18.81	1.204 #
feces	4 ug/g	18.85	1.204 #
paint wall	10 %	18.72	1.197
paint sill	10 %	18.79	1.205 #
paint kitchen	5 %	18.04	1.151
Home 3			
blood	0.7 ug/g	18.33	1.163 #
paint exterior	2 %	18.17	1.159
paint classroom	2 %	17.77	1.133
paint bedroom	1 %	18.32	1.163 #
Ambient airborne lead		19.3	1.207
Urban soil	500 - 2000 ug/g	18.5	1.187

# indicates "matches", adapted from reference [29]

The degree to which a blood sample resembles the paint, even when that paint was the major source of lead, also depends on the time since exposure. Lead in blood is exchanging with lead in deeper body pools as well as other inputs such as diet, air and water. If blood lead levels are still elevated, it is reasonable to assume that the lead sampled would isotopically resemble the source. That may not be the case later when blood lead levels have fallen.
   The closeness of matching 206/204 values from blood with a paint depends on the extent to which that source dominates the exposure. Since we are all exposed to background levels of lead only a factor of 5 to 10 below those which can cause poisoning, and that background lead has a range of isotopic ratios, then the value seen in blood

would be displaced from that of the paint alone.   In
addition to the lead from the paint, the blood is still
receiving lead from the air and diet as well as lead
mobilized from deeper body stores. Unfortunately, we do not
know for children, normal or lead poisoned, the exchange
rates for lead into or out of blood or bone.   In isotopic
tracer studies with adults even after months of chronic
exposure, the lead in blood never comes to fully resemble a
dietary tracer, even after accounting for airborne inputs,
because of unlabelled lead coming out of bone [31]. However,
children have not had the years of opportunity to accumulate
lead in the their bones.

Even if the child had no lead coming into their blood
from their bones, the background exposure would deflect
their blood lead value away from the pure paint value. For
example, if background lead 206/204 ratio were 19 and a
paint ratio were 17.5, and if blood lead rose from 10 to 50
ug/dL (0.1 to 0.5 ug/g) by the exposure to that paint, then
the blood value would be about 17.8. That difference of 0.3
between the paint and blood ratios depends on how completely
the paint overwhelms the other sources combined. It could be
0.1 or 0.5. So, if two suspect paints samples are only 0.3
different, even though they can be resolved analytically, it
may not be possible to state which paint matches the blood.

For these reasons, the imperfect reflection of the
paint ratio in a blood sample and the generally happen-
stance nature of the ratios observed from paint samples,
this methodology can not always be expected to be useful for
source identification. This is true even if every source of
lead were sampled and analyzed perfectly. Different paints
from different manufacturers may happen to have the same
ratios, making it indistinguishable, or the ratio of a paint
may be within the range seen in background samples, also
making it indistinct.

To trace backwards the lead that poisoned a child not
only to what painted surface, but furthermore, to what
geological district, the paint value, rather than the blood
value could be used for matching. Also, the paint pigment
may have been made from lead metal including recycled scrap
lead. This could result in a paint made from mixing two ores
that happen to match a third ore.

Instead of relying on only one isotope ratio, a second
or even the third measured pair may allow some additional
resolution. The difference between two samples would be a
distance in a two or three dimensional space. This has
proven useful in differentiating Korean from Japanese ores
because they came from source materials with different
uranium-thorium ratios. However, in most case, because ores
fall very close to an average line, and the three ratios
covary so strongly, a third ratio gives very little
additional information.

SOME FUTURE APPLICATIONS FOR STABLE ISOTOPE TRACERS

Since it is possible to compare lead in blood with lead in paint, a particular paint sample could be ruled out as a source of the lead. However, matching of isotope ratios does not assure that the source of the child's lead was indeed that paint. It could be another surface or batch with the same ratio. Paints may not be unique. As experience accumulates it may be seen whether it is the paint surface that is most deteriorated that proves to be the source most often, or if even apparently intact paint can be the source.

Another possible future application of this technique could be in the recontamination of a home after abatement. Some time after abatement the dust may become recontaminated with lead from perhaps incomplete local deleading, residential lead paint remaining nearby or the ambient urban windblown, contamination. Clearly it would be necessary to sample and characterize any other sources of lead in the area such as industrial activity. Isotope ratios could prove some guidance here too.

Several recent examples illustrate this ability of stable isotope methods to consider the importance of a purported source against a background exposure from mixed sources. For example, in Saudi Arabia some traditional folk remedies and cosmetics, along with gasoline, soil and dust contain high concentrations of lead. The isotopic analysis of the blood of children with elevated lead levels was performed by inductively-coupled plasma mass spectrometry. It was concluded that cosmetics and remedies, rather than the gasoline, matched the blood [32].

As a final example, it may be possible to resolve the impact of remobilized bone stores of lead, back into the blood during times of metabolic stress, such as pregnancy. Since the bones contain more than 100 times as much lead as the blood compartment, it has ben speculated that a small metabolic shift could mobilize the stored lead and have a major impact on blood lead levels. In order to quantify that flux of lead, efforts are currently underway using stable isotope tracers. In Canada, animal isotope feeding studies have demonstrated the uptake of lead into the bones, and plans call for monitoring blood levels during pregnancy [33]. Meanwhile, in Australia women who lived in one area, but moved to another and are expected to become pregnant are being monitored. The idea is to see if their blood lead isotopes, which have come to resemble their new surroundings, are deflected towards their earlier levels by the release of bone stores into the blood. In the future we can expect to know how important that bone source can be.

CONCLUSION

Stable isotope ratios in environmental samples can show considerable variation. This can provide useful clues about the origins and transport of lead pollution. However, unlike fingerprinting, a one to one match between lead in blood and lead in a suspected paint is not always possible. A major limitations to this method is that it is useful to only those problems where the potential sources are few in number and have been analyzed and found to be isotopically distinct. We can only attempt to refute the hypothesis that lead from a given paint is the source. Strictly speaking, the most we can do is exclude a paint as the sole source if the ratios do not match.

REFERENCES

[1]. McCulloch, M. and Woodhead, J., "Lead Isotopic Evidence for Deep Crustal-Scale Fluid Transport during Granite Petrogenesis," Geochemica et Cosmochemica Acta, Vol. 57, No. 3, March 1993, pp 659-674.

[2]. Gale, N.,"A Solution in Closed Form for Lead Isotopic Analysis using a Double Spike," Chemical Geology, Vol.6,No.4, April 1970, pp 306-310.

[3]. Faure, G. Principles of Isotope Geology 2nd Edition, J Wiley, New York, 1986.

[4]. Hart, S. "Hetrogeneous Mantle Domains," Earth and Planetary Science Letters, Vol 90, No. 3-18, November 1988, pp 273- 296.

[5]. Aston, F., "The Constitution of Ordinary Lead," Nature Vol. 120, No. 3015, August 1927, pp 224-227.

[6]. Nier, A., "Variations in the Relative Abundances of the isotopes of Common Lead from Various Sources," Journal of the American Chemical Society, Vol. 60, No. 7, July 1938, pp 1571-1576.

[7]. Cannon, R., Pierce, A., Antweiler, J. and Buck, K., "Data of Lead Isotope Geology Related to Problems of Ore Genesis," Economic Geology, Vol. 56, No. 1, January 1961, pp 1-38.

[8]. Doe,B. and Stacey, J., "The Application of Lead Isotopes to the Problems of Ore Genesis and Ore Prospect Evaluation," Economic Geology Vol. 69, No. 6, June 1974, pp 757-776.

[9]. Hirao Y., "Lead Isotope Ratios in Tokyo Bay Sediments and Their Implications in the Lead Consumption of Japanese Industries", Geochemical Journal, Vol. 20,

No. 1, 1986, pp 1-15.

[10]. Gale, N. and Stos-Gale, Z., "Bronze Age Copper Sources
in the Mediterranean". Science, Vol. 216, No. 4541,
April 2, 1982, pp 11-19.

[11]. Gale, N. and Stos-Gale, Z., "Lead and Silver in the
Ancient Aegean," Scientific American Vol. 244, No. 6,
June 1981, pp 176-192.

[12]. Mabuchi, H., Hirao, Y., and Nishida, H., "Lead Isotope
Approach to the Understanding of Early Japanese Bronze
Culture," Archaeometry, Vol. 27, No. 2, 1985 pp 131-
159.

[13]. Gulson, B., Tiller, K., Mizon, K. and Merry, R., "The
use of Lead Isotopes in Soils to Identify the Sources
of Lead Contamination near Adelaide, South Australia,"
June 1981, pp 691-6.

[14]. Rabinowitz, M., "Stable Isotope Ratios of Lead
Contaminated Soil," Environmental Geochemistry
and Health, Vol 9, Supplement, 1989, pp 131-141.

[15]. McCord, C., "Lead and Lead Poisoning in Early
America," Industrial Medicine and Surgery, Vol. 22,
No. 5, 1953, pp 534-539.

[16]. Secord, T. and Brown, P., "Geology and Geochemistry of
Ore Hill Zn-Pb-Cu Massiver Sulfide Deposit, Warren,
New Hampshire," Economic Geology, Vol. 81, No. 2,
March/April 1986, pp 371-397.

[17]. Libby, O. "An Economic and Social Study of the Lead
Region of Wisconsin, Illinois and Iowa," Transactions
of the Wisconsin Academy of Science, Vol 13, 1900, pp
188-281.

[18]. United States Bureau of Mines, "Summarized Data of
Lead Production," Economic Paper No. 5, 1929.

[19]. United States Bureau of Mines. Chapters "Lead" and
"Lead and Zinc Pigments", Mineral Yearbooks, 1932,
1937, 1942, 1947, 1952, 1957, 1962, 1972, and 1980.

[20]. Doe, B., Lead Isotopes, Springer, Heidelberg,1970.

[21]. Doe, B. and Rohrbough, R., "Lead Isotope Data Bank:
3,458 Samples and Analyses Cited," Open File 79-661,
United States Geological Survey, Reston, 1977.

[22]. Zartman, R., "Lead Isotopic Provinces in the
Cordillera of the Western United States and Their
Geological Significance," Economic Geology, Vol. 69,

No. 6, 1974, pp 792-805.

[23]. Hagni, R. "Tri-State Ore Deposits", Handbook of Strata Bound and Stratiform Ore Deposits, Wolf, K., Editor, Chapter 10, Vol 6, pp 457-494, Elsevier, Amsterdam, 1976.

[24]. Heyl, A., Landis,G., and Zartman, R. "Isotopic Evidence for the Origins of Mississippi Valley-Type Mineral Deposits," Economic Geology, Vol. 69, No. 6, pp 992-1006.

[25]. Stacey, J., Zartman,R., and Nkomo, I. "Lead Isotope Study of Galena and Selected Feldspars from Mining Districts in Utah," Economic Geology, Vol. 63, No. 7, 1968, pp 796-814.

[26]. Gulson, B. "Lead Isotopes in Mineral Exploration". Elseiver. Amsterdam, 1986.

[27]. Rabinowitz, M. and Wetherill, G. "Identifying Sources of Lead Contamination by Stable Isotope Techniques," Environmental Science and Technology, Vol.6, No.8, August 1972, pp 705-709, and Vol. 7, No. 6, June 1973, pp 555-557.

[28]. United States Bureau of Mines. "Sources of Lead for Pigment Manufacturers," Annual Mineral Resources of the United States, part II, 1931.

[29]. Rabinowitz, M., "Stable Isotope Mass Spectrometry in Childhood Lead Poisoning," Biological Trace Element Research, Vol. 12, pp 223 - 229, 1987.

[30]. Yaffee, Y. et al "Identification of Lead Sources in California Children Using the Stable Isotope Ratio Technique," Archives of Environmental Health, Vol. 38, No. 4, July/August 1983, pp 238-245.

[31]. Rabinowitz, M., Wetherill, G., and Kopple, J., "Kinetic Analysis of Lead Metabolism in Healthy Humans," Journal of Clinical Investigations, Vol. 58, No. 2, August 1976,pp 260 - 270.

[32]. Al-Saleh, I.A., Fellows, C., Delves, T., and Taylor, A.,"Identification of Sources of Lead Exposure among Children in Arar, Saudi Arabia," Annals of Clinical Biochemistry, Vol.30, 1993, pp 142-145.

[33]. Inskip,M.,Franklin, C.,Subramanian,K.,BlenkinsopJ.,and Wandelmaier,F., "Sampling of Cortical and Trabelular Bone for Lead Analysis" Neurotoxicology, vol.13, 1992, pp825-834.

David A. Burgoon,[1] Samuel F. Brown,[2] and Ronald G. Menton[1]

LITERATURE REVIEW OF SOURCES OF ELEVATED SOIL-LEAD CONCENTRATIONS

REFERENCE: Burgoon, D. A., Brown, S. F., and Menton, R. G., "Literature Review of Sources of Elevated Soil-Lead Concentrations," Lead in Paint, Soil, and Dust: Health Risks, Exposure Studies, Control Measures, Measurement Methods, and Quality Assurance, ASTM STP 1226, Michael E. Beard and S. D. Allen Iske, Eds., American Society for Testing and Materials, Philadelphia, 1995.

ABSTRACT: There is widespread evidence that elevated levels of lead in children's blood may result from exposure to house dust and soil containing lead. The U.S. Environmental Protection Agency conducted a comprehensive review of the scientific literature investigating the sources of the lead contamination of soil. This review focused on the evidence, cited in the literature, that a given source of lead was responsible for elevated soil-lead concentrations. Three primary sources of elevated soil lead were reported: 1) lead-based paint, 2) leaded gasoline emissions, and 3) lead point-source emitters. A range of analytical approaches were utilized to support the assertion that a particular source of lead contributed to surrounding elevated soil-lead levels. The interaction among the three sources, especially in urban environments, makes it difficult to ascertain which source might be the primary culprit in a particular environment. The highest soil-lead concentrations, however, are generally the result of peeling lead-based paint.

KEYWORDS: review, lead, soil, source identification, lead-based paint, leaded gasoline emissions

[1]Research Scientist and Senior Research Scientist, respectively, Statistics and Data Analysis Systems, Battelle, 505 King Avenue, Columbus, OH 43201.

[2]Mathematical Statistician, Office of Pollution Prevention and Toxics, U. S. Environmental Protection Agency, 401 M Street, SW, Washington, DC 20460

INTRODUCTION

Significant adverse health effects have been shown to result from elevated blood-lead levels in children. Ten µg of lead (Pb) per 100 mL of blood is the level of concern adopted for lead poisoning by both the Centers for Disease Control (CDC) and the U.S. Environmental Protection Agency (EPA). Hand to mouth activity is usually cited as the dominant mechanism of childhood lead exposure. The existing reservoir of lead in the surrounding soil and dust represents, therefore, a source of lead exposure in young children. Dust and soil abatement studies are underway to assess the impact of such intervention on the blood-lead levels of affected children. Companion questions are the extent of this existing reservoir and its varied sources.

The EPA conducted a review of the scientific literature investigating lead levels found in soil. The review emphasized the sources of elevated soil-lead concentrations and the evidence cited to support the assertion that the identified source was responsible for the elevated levels. The literature search examined documented studies of soil-lead levels in the United States, published in journal articles and government reports between 1980 and 1993. Despite these constraints, a computerized literature search identified over 700 prospective documents. Sixty-three directly relevant documents were selected by evaluating their associated abstracts. These 63 documents formed the basis of the review reported in this manuscript.

GEOGRAPHIC VARIATION

Studies assessing soil-lead concentration (PbS) and its sources have been conducted in a wide variety of communities. They range from large urban centers such as Boston, MA, smaller cities like Butte, MT, to small towns such as Telluride, CO. Studies have been conducted all over the United States, including: Portland, ME; New Orleans, LA; Dallas, TX; Seattle, WA; and Minneapolis, MN. The sites where studies were conducted to assess soil-lead levels are indicated in (Figure 1). Darkened circles on the map represent communities where PbS has been examined and documented within the literature. In some studies, the samples were collected to characterize soil-lead levels on a community-wide basis. Other studies sought PbS levels at particular residences or neighborhoods within the community.

Unfortunately, it is difficult to compare the results of the individual studies. Different studies have distinct objectives, sampling locations and sampling techniques. A study in Portland, ME assessed PbS at the foundation of buildings with peeling lead-based paint. Core samples were collected at the foundation, entryway, and boundary of formerly abated residences in Denver, CO. For a period of six years in Beltsville, MD, samples were collected 8, 25, and 50 m from a freeway. Another study examined patterns of exposure as a function of distance from two smelters in Dallas, TX. In Baltimore MD, core soil samples were collected from gardens throughout the city. A study in Aspen, CO also collected garden soil samples, but in the vicinity of mining waste. How are the measured soil-lead levels from these individual studies to be compared? If differences are identified, to what source might

FIG. 1—Sites for Studies Assessing Lead Concentrations in Soil.

they be attributed? Since each study has its own objectives, it is extremely difficult to acquire, strictly from the literature, comparable assessments of soil lead contamination. Regional differences are confounded with differences in study design and study objectives.

The 63 documents identified in the review cited results from 37 field studies of elevated soil-lead concentrations and the sources potentially responsible (Table 1). For each site, a reference for the study, the year the study was conducted, the total number of soil samples collected, the range in measured soil-lead concentrations, the hypothesized source of the lead, and the type of evidence cited in identifying the source are presented. Only the range is reported since consistent measures of central tendency were unavailable. Few documents reported mean soil-lead concentrations across the studied community. Instead, the measures of central tendency reported were consistent with the study's design and objectives. One study reports arithmetic mean soil-lead concentration by type of housing, while another documents geometric mean soil-lead concentration by volume of traffic on nearby roadways. If such diverse results were incorporated, the resulting table would be incomprehensible. For the purposes of this geographic examination, the table is sorted into four time-zone regions: Eastern, Central, Mountain, and Pacific.

TABLE 1—Studies identified in the literature, by region.

Study Location	Ref. #	Year	# of Samples	Range (ppm)	Source *	Evidence **
Beltsville, MD	16	1977	na	na	3	5,7
Baltimore, MD	22	1982	422	1-10900	1,3	8
Baltimore, MD	28	1989	27	159-3621	1	2
Boston, MA	29	1981	195	7-13240	1,3	5,6
Charleston, SC	19	1974	164	9-7890	1,3	2,4,5,7,8
Cincinnati, OH	9	1980	80	76-54519	1,3	1,2,3,4
Indianapolis, IN	28	1989	105	47-4743	1	2
New Haven, CT	6	1977	487	30-7000	1,3	1,2,3,4,6
Portland, ME	8	1988	100	50-10900	1	2,3,4
Washington, DC	28	1989	27	99-2678	1	2
Aspen, CO	30	1983	65	135-21700	2	5
Birmingham, AL	28	1989	92	89-9711	1	2
Chicago, IL	20	1985	306	na	1,3	5,6,7,8
Corpus Christi, TX	21	1984	485	8-2969	1,3	5,6,7
Dallas, TX	12	1982	2795	na	2	5,8
Duluth, MN	3	1986	32	12-11110	1,3	1,2,3,4,5,7,8
El Paso, TX	14	1971	54	560-11450	1,2,3	1,3,4,5,6
Minneapolis, MN	3	1986	199	35-20136	1,3	1,2,3,4,5,7,8
Mt. Pleasant, MI	7	1990	189	100-16839	1,2,3	3,4,5,6,7,8
New Orleans, LA	24	1991	na	na	1,3	1,3,8
Omaha, NB	18	1977	176	16-4792	1,2,3	1,6,8
Rochester, MN	3	1986	19	2-1930	1,3	1,2,3,4,5,7,8
St. Cloud, MN	3	1986	13	9-1952	1,3	1,2,3,4,5,7,8
St. Paul, MN	3	1986	127	3-7994	1,3	1,2,3,4,5,7,8
Butte, MT	4	1990	650	20-2460	1,2	2,3,4,5
Denver, CO	28	1989	131	49-1331	1	2
Denver, CO	31	1992	347	5-3351	1	1,2,3,4
East Helena, MT	32	1983	731	3-7964	1,2	1,2,5,6

TABLE 1—Studies identified in the literature, by region.

Study Location	Ref. #	Year	# of Samples	Range (ppm)	Source *	Evidence **
Leadville, CO	33	1987	371	0.5-424	1,2	2,3,5
Midvale, UT	11	1989	288	1-6665	1,2	2,3,4,5
Telluride, CO	5	1986	45	16-1895	1,2	2,5
Honolulu, HI	17	1987	18	na	3	5,7
Kellogg, ID	13	1975	781	50-24600	1,2	2,4,5,6
Kellogg, ID	10	1983	597	37-41200	1,2	2,4,5,6
Seattle, WA	34	1990	51	150-74000	1,3	2,3,5,7
Seattle/Tacoma,WA	28	1989	99	40-7382	1	2
National Pb Survey	2	1990	762	1-22974	1	2,3,4

* Source: lead-based paint, 1; point-source emitter, 2; leaded gasoline emissions, 3.

** Evidence: residential areal pattern, 1; paint-lead loading, 2; age of residence, 3; type and condition of housing, 4; distance from source, 5; ambient air-lead levels, 6; traffic volume, 7; community areal pattern, 8.

na: Range was not reported in the available literature.

The literature contains a preponderance of urban and smelter community studies. This emphasis is likely the result of attempts to target the populations most at risk and examine communities with extensive environmental lead exposure. As will be discussed later, the heavily populated urban environment is commonly contaminated with lead from both leaded gasoline emissions and lead-based paint. Smelter communities often have widespread lead contamination of their environmental media. Rural community studies, on the other hand, are rare. In fact, rural soil-lead concentrations are usually only used as a measure of background lead when examining the PbS results from urban environments.

SOURCES

Lead is present naturally in soil, though usually at relatively low levels. The U.S. Geological Survey has estimated the concentration of naturally occurring lead in soil to have a national geometric mean of 16 ppm [1]. The literature ascribes the elevated lead levels found in soil to a variety of activities including: peeling, chalking, or active removal of lead-based paint; demolition of buildings containing considerable amounts of lead; fallout from airborne emissions of metal smelter operations; migration of tailings (or dross) from mining operations; use of pesticides containing lead; fallout from the discharge of community waste incinerators; dumping or burning of lead batteries and their casings; and emission fallout from vehicles fueled with leaded gasoline. The sources of the lead deposited into the soil by these activities fall into three major categories: 1) lead-based paint, 2) point-source emitters (e.g. smelters, batteries, mine tailings), and 3) leaded gasoline emissions.

Lead-Based Paint as a Source

Lead-based paint is the source of elevated soil lead most commonly cited in the literature. Weathering of exterior lead-based paint may cause it to crumble, peel, or chalk. The resulting paint chips and particles then contaminate the surrounding soil. Abatement of the paint using scraping or sandblasting techniques, as well as demolition or renovation activities may also result in lead contamination of the local soil. There is extensive evidence for these mechanisms of exposure. The literature reports four general types of evidence used to demonstrate that lead-based paint is a source of lead in soil: 1) residential areal pattern, 2) relationship to paint-lead loading, 3) association with age of residence, and 4) association with type and condition of residence.

Some studies identify an areal pattern to lead contamination of soil at a residence. Samples collected near the foundation of residences have higher lead concentrations than samples collected at more remote locations. The geometric mean PbS for samples collected at the drip line of dwelling units examined in the National Lead Survey was 72 ppm (logarithmic standard deviation: 1.68), compared to 47 ppm (log SD: 1.42) for samples collected at remote locations [2]. Schmitt et al. [3] considered soil samples collected from a number of locations surrounding residences. The geometric mean PbS was highest for foundation samples in all of the five Minnesota communities examined. Of the residences examined in this survey, 213 had wood exteriors, 88 were brick. The wood exterior residences had a geometric mean PbS of 522 ppm (geometric SD: 6.4), compared to 158 ppm (GSD: 4.3) for the brick residences. Furthermore, "virtually every sample exceeding 2000 [ppm] and 140 of 160 samples exceeding 1000 [ppm] were collected near house foundations." Deteriorating lead-based paint may primarily supply soils immediately adjacent to the weathered surface.

Other studies cited a relationship between x-ray fluorescence (XRF) measured lead loadings on exterior surfaces and PbS. The Butte-Silver Bow study [4] noted the following categories of exterior paint-lead loading and associated geometric mean PbS: 0.00-0.99 mg/cm^2, 200 ppm; 1.00-2.99 mg/cm^2, 300 ppm; 3.00-11.99 mg/cm^2, 650 ppm; and ≥ 12 mg/cm^2, 1100 ppm. Bornschein et al. noted a 0.49 correlation coefficient between maximum exterior XRF loading for a residence and the adjacent PbS in Telluride, CO [5]. In New Haven, CT, Stark et al. [6] reported a correlation coefficient of 0.43 between maximum exterior XRF loading and nearby PbS. One hundred and two housing units in the National Lead Survey with at least one surface measured at or above 1.0 mg/cm^2 had a geometric mean PbS of 140.24 ppm, compared to 27.46 ppm for eighty units without any such surfaces. These studies suggest that higher paint-lead loadings on exterior surfaces are associated with increased lead concentration in the surrounding soil.

Age of residence is sometimes used as an indicator for the presence of lead-based paint. The use of lead in interior and exterior house paint has markedly declined since the 1940s. In the 1970s, it was virtually banned from use in residential paints. Homes built before this period, therefore, are more likely to possess lead-based paint. A reanalysis of the soil samples collected in the National Lead Survey [2] found dwelling unit age to be among "the strongest predictors of soil lead." Francek [7] found the following relationship in Mt. Pleasant, MI between age of home and median PbS at the home's foundation: < 20 years, 200 ppm; 20-100 years, 960 ppm; > 100 years, 1040 ppm. He also notes a significant correlation, 0.59, between home age and PbS. In Portland, ME, Krueger et al. [8] reported that the average PbS collected from the foundations of painted frame buildings at least 30 years old was 1275 ppm (range: 50-10900 ppm), compared to 205 ppm (range: 50-700 ppm) for those collected from other areas ("everything else such as playgrounds and parks").

The type and condition of the residence have also been used in analyses as representative measures of the degree of paint-lead loading at the residence. Bornschein et al. [9] reported the following relationship in Cincinnati, OH between housing condition and the geometric mean lead concentration for the collected soil samples: public, 248 ppm; rehabilitated, 1654 ppm; 19th century in satisfactory condition, 7362 ppm. An XRF measure, XRF-hazard, which incorporated the condition of the surface sampled was also developed. A significant correlation coefficient between log(PbS) and log(XRF-hazard) of 0.41 is noted. A study in Mt. Pleasant, MI also documented the effect on PbS from lead-based paint as the condition of the building deteriorates [7]. Francek found the following inverse relationship between median foundation soil-lead concentrations and condition of the home: homes in excellent condition, 200 ppm; good, 200 ppm; fair, 940 ppm; poor, 1140 ppm.

Point-Source Emitter as Source

A point-source emitter is a fixed site from which lead emanates. Examples include operating metal smelters and refuse incinerators, areas containing mine tailings, and dump sites for lead-acid batteries. Whereas vehicles and their leaded gasoline emissions existed nationwide, point-source emissions are particular to an area. There is only a fixed (though potentially quite wide) range over which contamination from the emitter may spread. Not surprisingly, the mechanisms by which surrounding soil may be supplied with lead are varied. Mine dross, for example, may spread via erosion and airborne transmittal. A significant portion of the literature on lead contamination has focused on point-source emitters, especially formerly operating smelters. Two general types of evidence are commonly employed in identifying point-source emitters as the source of elevated soil-lead levels: 1) distance from the source, and 2) association with ambient air-lead concentration.

Lead pollution caused by emitters is usually assessed by collecting environmental and body burden measures from individuals residing varying distances from the point-source. In the Kellogg-Revisited Lead Survey [10] the community was partitioned into three concentric rings emanating from the smelter site. The foundation

PbS for residences sampled within one mile (0.8 km) of the site had a geometric mean of 5163 ppm; 1.0-2.5 miles (0.8-2 km), 2512 ppm; and 2.5-6.0 miles (2-4.8 km), 541 ppm. For Midvale, UT, Bornschein et al. [11] reported a -0.68 correlation coefficient between maximum PbS at the residence and the distance to the mill building. Brown et al. [12] used geostatistical methods to generate isopleths of constant PbS in the vicinity of two Dallas, TX smelters. The authors conclude that the smelters are the primary sources of lead contamination in the area based on the observed increase in soil-lead concentrations with decreasing distance from the emitter.

In those instances where the emitter consistently produces airborne lead emissions, relationships may sometimes be drawn between ambient air-lead levels and PbS. A smelter study in the Silver Valley area of northern Idaho, for example, found a 0.52 correlation coefficient between composite PbS from the residence and ambient air-lead levels [13]. Other studies have noted that soil-lead concentrations may follow geographical distributions similar to those determined for ambient air-lead levels [14]. If the emitter is the primary active source of lead into the environment, it should not be surprising to find associations between ambient air-lead levels and PbS.

Leaded Gasoline Emissions as Source

Lead's use in the United States as a performance additive to gasoline was gradually phased-out during the 1970's and 1980's. Between 1971 and 1984 the percentage of lead used as a gasoline additive declined from 18.5% to 6.5% (at its peak it represented 25-30% of total use) [15]. Unfortunately, most of that lead (approximately 75%) was discharged in the resulting vehicle exhaust. The emitted lead particles have spread well beyond the confines of the roadway. After decades of leaded gasoline usage, the environment now includes a tremendous reservoir of lead. This reservoir is retained in the surrounding soil and dust. Studies of this source of contamination have included assessments of soil lead contamination near highways, and the implications of leaded gasoline emissions in the urban environment. Four general types of evidence have been used within the literature in identifying leaded gasoline as a source of lead in soil: 1) distance from the roadway, 2) association with ambient air-lead levels, 3) association with traffic volume, and 4) community areal pattern.

Forty percent of the lead emitted as vehicular exhaust is in sufficiently large particles (>10 μm mass median aerodynamic diameter (mmad)) to be deposited near the roadway [15]. It seems reasonable, therefore, that PbS would decrease with increasing distance from the roadway. This, in fact, is borne out in the literature. A longitudinal study of PbS adjacent to a newly constructed roadway [16] noted that, "soil Pb levels decreased with distance from the roadway [8, 25, 50 m] and with depth [0-5, 5-10, 10-15 cm] in the soil profile." In Honolulu, HI, Fu et al. [17] noted that PbS from a boulevard median strip adjacent to a park was 1650 ppm, and that, "elsewhere through the park, soil [-lead levels] fell with distance from the boulevard but rose again as the beach road was reached." In the more rural community of Mt. Pleasant, Francek [7] measured median PbS in roadside soils of 280 ppm (range: 100-840 ppm), compared to 200 ppm (range: 100-220 ppm) in background soils.

Some studies have found associations between ambient air-lead levels and the concentration of lead in the surrounding soil. In the absence of a significant point-source emitter, such an association may suggest leaded gasoline as a source only if the study was conducted while leaded gasoline was still commonly utilized. A 1977 study in Omaha, NB reported a 0.37 correlation coefficient between ambient air-lead levels and composite residence PbS [18]. Similarly, a Boston, MA study in the early 1980s estimated a 0.18 correlation coefficient [9]. Both studies were conducted while leaded gasoline additives were prevalent. With the phase-out of leaded fuels such associations are unlikely (except, of course, in the vicinity of point-source emitters of airborne lead contaminants), but other approaches have shown associations between leaded gasoline emissions and PbS.

Soil-lead concentrations were also analyzed as a function of traffic volume on nearby roadways. As the number of vehicles emitting lead exhaust increases, one would expect the lead concentration in surrounding soil to elevate. In Charleston, SC, Galke et al. [19] noted that for residences with PbS < 585 ppm, the median traffic volume (cars/day) within 250 feet (76.2 m) was 1100. In contrast, residences with PbS ≥ 585 ppm had a median traffic volume of 3200. LaBelle et al. [20] reported the following arithmetic means for PbS, by total traffic volume on the adjacent roadway in Illinois: less than 5000 cars/day, 90 ppm; 5000-9999, 141 ppm; 10000-19999, 187 ppm; 20000-49999, 265 ppm; ≥50000, 236 ppm. Some authors have hypothesized that traffic volume alone is insufficient to explain the nearby soil-lead levels. Harrison, for example, suggests that the velocity of the traffic is also important [21]. He hypothesizes that heavily congested roadways with gridlocked, idling traffic may produce higher soil-lead levels than more rapidly moving traffic. There is some evidence to support this conclusion [15, 21].

Researchers have found that soil-lead concentration areal patterns in communities often follow the highway infrastructure. This is particularly true in urban environments. Most inner-cities have tightly clustered, congested roadways. These roadways spread out as they emanate from the city's center. Leaded gasoline emissions appear to have often polluted the surrounding soil accordingly. Mielke et al. have reported that the highest lead concentrations in soil in both Baltimore, MD, [22] and Minneapolis-St. Paul, MN, [23] were clustered toward the center of the city. Preliminary results in the city of New Orleans, LA, [24] suggest a similar pattern. In the case of Baltimore, the clustering could have occurred by chance with a probability of less than 10^{-23}. Furthermore, "the most consistently high garden soil Pb levels were found in the area of the city that was predominantly unpainted brick buildings [25]." In Corpus Christi, TX, PbS was reported to be concentrated in and around its roadways [21]. Angle and McIntire examined three communities in Omaha, NB [18]: a suburban neighborhood (S), an urban-commercial area (C), and an urban area contiguous to downtown (M). The geometric mean PbS in area S was 81 ppm (range: 16-341 ppm), compared to 262 ppm (range: 53-1615 ppm) for area C and 339 ppm (range: 20-4792 ppm) for area M.

Interaction Among Sources of Lead in Soil

The mechanism of lead contamination by vehicular emissions produces an interaction among two source categories of lead in soil, leaded gasoline emissions and lead-based paint. Whereas approximately 40% of the discharged lead from leaded gasoline was in large particles (>10 mmad), 35% or so was in the form of fine particles (<0.25 mmad) able to disperse over large distances from the roadway [15]. In a typical urban environment these small particles may have spread lead over most of the city. The extent of resulting lead exposure may be a function of wind direction and weather pattern. Chaney and Mielke [25], among others, relate how the particles, "waft through the city and adhere to surfaces they come in contact with." These particulates may be washed down into the surrounding soil. Larger surface areas may then collect more of these small particles. This suggests that elevated PbS at an urban residence's foundation may not derive solely from lead-based paint. It may also stem from leaded gasoline emissions and the large surface area presented by the external walls and roof of the residence. For residences with large yards, this suggests a pattern of soil lead exposure high near the roadway, gradually decreasing toward the center of the yard, only to elevate again near the residence's foundation. The foundation soil could be further elevated, obviously, by lead-based paint on the exterior surfaces.

There is some evidence to support this hypothesized pattern of contamination. Lead concentrations in soil samples collected next to the roadways in the Minneapolis-St. Paul were found to be closely related to soil-lead concentrations measured at the foundations of adjacent residences [26]. A significant correlation coefficient of 0.72 is reported. Linton et al. [27] employ scanning electron microscopy associated with energy dispersive x-ray analysis to inspect a foundation soil sample collected next to a brick building with lead-based paint covering the window trim. Despite the building being more than 50 feet (15.2 m) removed from a major roadway (2000 cars/day), "it is estimated that 80-90% of lead present in this building line sample is derived from paint chips with the remaining 10-20% being of automobile origin." In addition, a few studies have found elevated foundation PbS near unpainted buildings. There does not appear to be, however, a definitive assessment of the relative contributions of lead-based paint versus leaded gasoline emissions in urban environments. It seems likely that their relative contributions would vary considerably from one residence to another, in addition to differences among communities.

The interaction among potential source categories of elevated soil-lead concentrations is enhanced by the fact that many cities in the United States grew outward from a central core. Older homes, more likely to have been coated with lead-based paint, are located in the center of the city. Residences with lead-based paint already polluting their surrounding soil were also exposed to higher leaded gasoline emissions. If the industrial district originated downtown, soil lead from point-source emitters is also a potential factor. In these areas, therefore, it is extremely difficult to differentiate among the three prospective sources.

CONCLUSIONS

Three general source categories of elevated lead levels in soil have been identified. In many communities, the elevated soil-lead levels are due to a combination of these sources. Lead contamination of soil is additive; additional sources simply increase the degree of the contamination.

It is often difficult to determine whether the elevated soil-lead levels are a function of a point-source emitter, lead-based paint, or leaded gasoline emissions. Rural environments with old, painted structures or urban communities with brick buildings may be easily classified. Urban communities with painted structures, however, are more difficult. Even more complex to classify are those cities with smelter or waste incinerator sites. The dispersal mechanism of vehicular emissions, the growth pattern of many cities, urban renewal, soil erosion, and landscaping confound the issue.

Any attempt to apportion the sources of elevated soil-lead levels may well require complex physicochemical or statistical analyses. Multi-element statistical analyses, lead isotope ratio analyses, and analyses such as those employed by Linton et al. [27] are potentially viable approaches to source apportionment, but require considerable environmental sampling and resources. Moreover, these analyses may only be relevant to the particular residence examined. In most communities, it is likely that determining which source is the primary culprit of the elevated soil-lead concentrations is a non-trivial undertaking.

It does appear that lead-based paint is generally responsible for higher concentrations of lead in the surrounding soil. Within the literature, the highest PbS levels are frequently at the foundation of a building with flaking lead-based paint. For instance, consider the results from the soil survey of five Minnesota communities [3]. Geometric mean soil lead concentrations adjacent to wood-sided residences were more than three times higher than those adjacent to brick residences (522 ppm/158 ppm). Whereas leaded gasoline emissions spread their lead exposure over a wide area, contamination from lead-based paint is localized about the residence. The remarkably high concentrations of lead found in the soils adjacent to residences may reflect the large quantity of lead present on the exterior surfaces of a house painted with lead-based paint.

REFERENCES

[1]   Shacklette, H. T., and Boerngen, J. G., "Element Concentrations in Soils and Other Surficial Materials of the Conterminous United States," U.S. Geological Survey Professional Paper 1270. U.S. Government Printing Office, Washington D.C., 1984.

[2]   U.S. Environmental Protection Agency, "Data Analysis of Lead in Soil and Dust," Office of Pollution Prevention and Toxics, EPA 747-R-93-011, September 1993.

[3]   Schmitt, M. D. C., Trippler, D. J., Wachtler, J. N., and Lund, G. V., "Soil Lead Concentrations in Residential Minnesota as Measured by ICP-AES." Water, Air, and Soil Pollution. Vol. 39, 1988, pp. 157-168.

[4]   Butte-Silver Bow Department of Health; Department of Environmental Health, University of Cincinnati., "The Butte-Silver Bow Environmental Health Lead Study," Draft Final Report, June 1991.

[5]   Bornschein, R. L., Clark, S., Grote, J., Peace, B., Roda, S., and Succop, P., "Soil Lead-Blood Lead Relationship in a Former Lead Mining Town." In: Lead in Soil: Issues and Guidelines, Supplement to Volume 9 of Environmental Geochemistry and Health. Edited by Davis, B.E. and Wixson, B.G., 1988.

[6]   Stark, A. D., Quah R. F., Meigs, J. W., and DeLouise, E. R., "The Relationship of Environmental Lead to Blood-Lead Levels in Children," Environmental Research, Vol. 27, 1982, pp. 372-383.

[7]   Francek, M. A., "Soil Lead Levels in a Small Town Environment: A Case Study from Mt. Pleasant, Michigan," Environmental Pollution, Vol. 76, 1992, pp. 251-257.

[8]   Krueger, J. A., and Duguay, K. M., "Comparative Analysis of Lead in Maine Urban Soils," Bulletin of Environmental Contamination and Toxicology, Vol. 42, 1989, pp.574-581.

[9]   Bornschein, R. L., Succop, P. A., Krafft, K. M., Clark, C. S., Peace, B., and Hammond, P. B., "Exterior Surface Dust Lead, Interior House Dust Lead and Childhood Lead Exposure in an Urban Environment," Trace Metals in Environmental Health, II, Columbia, MO, Edited by Hemphill, D. D., 1986.

[10]   Panhandle District Health Department, Idaho Department of Health and Welfare, Centers for Disease Control, and U.S. Environmental Protection Agency., "Kellogg Revisited–1983: Childhood Blood Lead and Environmental Status Report," Final Report of the U.S. Public Health Service, July 1986.

[11]   Bornschein, R. L., Clark, S., Pan, W., and Succop, P., "Midvale Community Lead Study," Final Report of the University of Cincinnati, July 1990.

[12]   Brown, K. W., Mullins, J. W., Richitt, E. P. Jr., Flatman, G. T., Black, S. C., and Simon S. J., "Assessing Soil Lead Contamination in Dallas, Texas," Environmental Monitoring and Assessment. Vol. 5, 1985, pp. 137-154.

[13]   Yankel, A. J., von Lindern, I. H., and Walter, S. D., "The Silver Valley Lead Study: The Relationship Between Childhood Blood Lead Levels and Environmental Exposure," Journal of the Air Pollution Control Association. Vol. 27, No. 8, 1977, pp. 763-767.

[14]   Landrigan, P., Gehlbach, S., Rosenblum, B., Shoults, J., Candelaria, R., Barthel, W., Liddle, J., Smrek, A., Staehling, N., and Sanders, J., "Epidemic Lead Absorption Near an Ore Smelter: The Role of Particulate Lead," New England Journal of Medicine. Vol. 292, No. 3, 1975, pp. 123-129.

[15]   U.S. Environmental Protection Agency, "Air Quality Criteria for Lead, Volumes I-IV." EPA Report No. EPA-600/8-83-028CF. Environmental Criteria and Assessment Office, Office of Research and Development, Research Triangle Park, NC. 1986.

[16]   Milberg, R. P., Lagerwerff, J. V., Brower, D. L., and Biersdorf, G. T., "Soil Lead Accumulation Alongside a Newly Constructed Roadway." Journal of Environmental Quality. Vol. 9, 1980, pp. 6-8.

[17]   Fu, S., Hashimoto, H., Siegel, B. Z., and Siegel, S. M., "Variations in Plant and Soil Lead and Mercury Content in a Major Honolulu Park, 1972 to 1987, a Period of Significant Source Reduction," Water, Air, and Soil Pollution. Vol. 43, 1989, pp. 109-118.

[18]   Angle, C. R., and McIntire, M. S., "Environmental Lead and Children: the Omaha Study," Journal of Toxicological and Environmental Health. Vol. 5, 1979, pp. 855-870.

[19]   Galke, W. A., Hammer, D. I., Keil, J. E., and Lawrence, S. W., "Environmental Determinants of Lead Burdens in Children," In: T. C. Hutchinson, S. Epstein, A. I. Page, J. VanLoon and T. Davey (eds.), International Conference on Heavy Metals in the Environment: Symposium Proceedings, Institute for Environmental Studies, Toronto, ON, Canada. Vol. 3, 1975, pp. 53-74.

[20]   LaBelle, S. J., Lindahl, P. C., Hinchman, R. R., Ruskamp, J., and McHugh, K., "Pilot Study of the Relationship of Regional Road Traffic to Surface-Soil Lead Levels in Illinois," Published Report of the Argonne National Laboratory. ANL/ES-154, 1987.

[21]   Harrison, G., "A Survey of the Lead Distribution in the Soil of Corpus Christi, Texas," Texas Journal of Science. Vol. 39, No. 1, 1987, pp. 15-22.

[22]   Mielke, H. W., Anderson, J. C., Berry, K. J., Mielke, P. W., Chaney, R. L, and Leech, M., "Lead Concentrations in Inner-City Soils as a Factor in the Child Lead Problem," American Journal of Public Health. Vol. 73, No. 12, 1983, pp. 1366-1369.

[23]   Mielke, H. W., Blake, B., Burroughs, S., and Hassinger, N., "Urban Lead Levels in Minneapolis: The Case of the Hmong Children," Environmental Research. Vol. 34, 1984, pp. 64-76.

[24]   Mielke, H. W., "Lead in Residential Soils: Background and Preliminary Results of New Orleans," Water, Air, and Soil Pollution. Vol. 57-58, 1991, pp. 111-119.

[25]   Chaney, R. L., and Mielke, H. W., "Standards for Soil Lead Limitations in the United States," Trace Substances in Environmental Health. Vol. 20, 1986, pp. 357-377.

[26]   Mielke, H. W., and Adams, J. L., "Environmental Lead Risk in the Twin Cities," Report of the Center for Urban and Regional Affairs. CURA-89-4, 1989.

[27]   Linton, R. W., Natusch, D. F. S., Solomon, R. L., and Evans, C. A., Jr., "Physicochemical Characterization of Lead in Urban Dusts. A Microanalytical Approach to Lead Tracing," Environmental Science and Technology. Vol. 14, No. 2,1980, pp. 159-164.

[28]   U.S. Department of Housing and Urban Development, "The HUD Lead-Based Paint Abatement Demonstration (FHA)," Office of Policy Development and Research, Washington, D.C., 1991.

[29]   Rabinowitz, M. B., and Bellinger, D. C., "Soil Lead - Blood Lead Relationship Among Boston Children," Bulletin of Environmental Contamination and Toxicology. Vol. 41, 1988, pp. 791-797.

[30]   Boon, D. Y., and Soltanpour, P. N., "Lead, Cadmium, and Zinc Contamination of Aspen Garden Soils and Vegetation," Journal of Environmental Quality. Vol. 21, 1992, pp. 82-86.

[31]   Buxton, B. E., Rust, S. W., Kinateder, J. G., Schwemberger, J. E., Lim, B., Constant, P., Dewalt, G., "Post-Abatement Performance of Encapsulation and Removal Methods for Lead-Based Paint Abatement," Lead in Paint, Soil, and Dust. Health Risks, Exposure Studies, Control Measures, Measurement Methods, and Quality Assurance, ASTM STP 1226, Michael E. Beard and S. D. Allen Iske, Eds., American Society for Testing and Materials, Philadelphia, 1994.

[32]   Centers for Disease Control, "East Helena, Montana Child Lead Study," Report by the CDC, Public Health Services, U. S. Department of Public Health and Human Services. Atlanta, GA, 1983.

[33]   Colorado Department of Health, University of Colorado at Denver, and U.S. Department of Health and Human Services, "Leadville Metals Exposure Study," Final Report, April, 1990.

[34]   Roberts, J. W., Camann, D. E., and Spittler, T. M., "Reducing Lead Exposure from Remodeling and Soil Track-In in Older Homes," Air and Waste Management Association, 84th Annual Meeting. Vancouver, British Columbia. June 16-21, 1991.

BIBLIOGRAPHY

Duggan, M. J., and Inskip, M. J., "Childhood Exposure to Lead in Surface Dust and Soil: A Community Health Problem," Public Health Reviews. Vol. 13, No. 1-2, 1985, pp. 1-54.

Madhavan, S., Rosenman, K.D., and Shehata, T., "Lead in Soil: Recommended Maximum Permissible Levels," Environmental Research. Vol. 49, No. 1, 1989, pp. 136-142.

Mielke, H. W., Adams, J. L., Reagan, P. L., and Mielke, P. W., Jr., "Soil-Dust Lead and Childhood Lead Exposure as a Function of City Size and Community Traffic Flow: The Case for Lead Abatement in Minnesota," In: Lead in Soil: Issues and Guidelines, Supplement to Volume 9 of Environmental Geochemistry and Health. Edited by Davis, B. E. and Wixson, B. G., 1989.

Minnesota Pollution Control Agency and Minnesota Department of Health, "Soil Lead Report to the Minnesota State Legislature," 1987.

Pierce, F., Dowdy, R., and Grigal, D., "Concentrations of Six Trace Metals in Some Major Minnesota Soil Series," Journal of Environmental Quality. Vol. 11, No. 3, 1982, pp. 416-422.

Rabinowitz, M., Leviton, A., Needleman, H., Bellinger, D., and Waternaux, C., "Environmental Correlates of Infant Blood Lead Levels in Boston," Environmental Research. Vol. 38, 1985, pp. 96-107.

Reagan, P. L., and Silbergeld, E. K., "Establishing a Health Based Standard for Lead in Residential Soils," Trace Substances in Environmental Health. Vol. 23, 1990, pp. 199-238.

Schilling, R. J., and Bain, R. P., "Prediction of Children's Blood Lead Levels on the Basis of Household-Specific Soil Lead Levels," American Journal of Epidemiology. Vol. 3, 1988, pp. 197-205.

Trippler, D. J., Schmitt, M. D. C., and Lund, G. V., "Soil Lead in Minnesota," In: Lead in Soil: Issues and Guidelines, Supplement to Volume 9 of Environmental Geochemistry and Health. Edited by Davis, B.E., Wixson, B.G., 1989, pp 273-280.

U.S. Department of Housing and Urban Development, "Comprehensive and Workable Plan for the Abatement of Lead-Based Paint in Privately Owned Housing: A Report to Congress," Washington, DC. December 7, 1990.

Ronald G. Menton[1], David A. Burgoon[1], and Allan H. Marcus[2]

PATHWAYS OF LEAD CONTAMINATION FOR THE BRIGHAM AND WOMEN'S HOSPITAL LONGITUDINAL LEAD STUDY

REFERENCE: Menton, R. G., Burgoon, D. A., Marcus, A. H., "Pathways of Lead Contamination for the Brigham and Women's Hospital Longitudinal Lead Study", Lead in Paint, Soil and Dust: Health Risks, Exposure Studies, Control Measures, Measurement Methods, and Quality Assurance, ASTM STP 1226, Michael E. Beard and S.D. Allen Iske, Eds., American Society for Testing and Materials, Philadelphia, 1995.

ABSTRACT: Pathways of lead contamination in households include lead-based paint, lead contaminated dust, and lead contaminated soil. The Brigham and Women's Hospital longitudinal lead study investigated the relationship between infant blood levels from late pregnancy to two years of age and lead levels in environmental media. Environmental media sampled and analyzed for lead included dust from floors, furniture surfaces, and window sills, soil, tap water, and interior air.

Multiple regression models were fitted to the data to determine the relationship between exterior and interior levels of lead, and childhood blood-lead levels. Soil and other environmental lead sources may directly affect blood-lead levels by ingestion or inhalation pathways, and indirectly through their contribution to house dust or other environmental media. Bornschein and his co-workers have proposed the use of structural equation models for determining both the direct and indirect effects of lead levels in the environment on blood-lead levels. Structural equation models fitted to the data suggested a pathway of lead from soil to the dust on the window sill to the dust on the floor to childhood blood.

KEYWORDS: blood-lead, environmental-lead, dust-lead, environmental pathways, multiple regression, log-additive model, structural equation models.

INTRODUCTION

Environmental lead is known to come from multiple sources: drinking water, food, lead-based paint, emissions from mobile sources, and emissions from industrial sources. Federal and state regulatory actions have resulted in substantial progress in reducing lead levels in air, food and paint products. While reductions in air and food have reduced exposures, elevated blood-lead levels in children continue to be a problem due to contamination of the existing environment [1]. In fact, the Agency for Toxic Substances and Disease Registry [2] stated in 1988 that lead in paint, dust and soil will continue to be hazardous sources of childhood lead poisoning in the future.

---

[1]Senior Research Scientist and Research Scientist, respectively, Statistics and Data Analysis Systems, Battelle Memorial Institute, 505 King Avenue, Columbus, OH 43201.

[2]United States Environmental Protection Agency, Research Triangle Park, NC 27711.

Current efforts to reduce the lead hazard in households are focused on lead-paint abatement [3]. An extensive lead-paint abatement program might possibly overlook an important source of lead, and hence, fail to halt childhood lead poisoning cases. Therefore, the Environmental Protection Agency (EPA) has undertaken a number of research programs to assess the sources of lead in residences. These programs have included: (1) conduct of literature searches, (2) re-analysis of existing data from environmental-lead field studies, and (3) conduct of environmental-lead field studies. This paper summarizes a statistical analysis of the relationships between lead in environmental media and blood-lead using the data from the Brigham and Women's Hospital Longitudinal Lead Study (BWHLLS) [4-7]. The objective of the statistical analysis was to assess the environmental pathways of lead exposure.

PATHWAYS OF LEAD CONTAMINATION

Lead has been found in environmental media such as soil, interior household dust, exterior dust, water, and air. Potential sources for this lead contamination include deteriorating lead-based paint, emissions from mobile sources and industrial sources, and the long-term accumulation of lead in soil from dustfall of airborne lead. Environmental pathways of lead exposure include air, water, food, household dust, soil, and lead-based paint [3,8].

Lead-based paint may act both as a direct and indirect pathway to childhood lead exposure. Young children with strong propensities to consume nonfood items (Pica) are exposed to the direct pathway through the consumption of paint chips. Severe cases of lead poisoning may often result from this direct pathway [8,9]. Lead-based paint may also indirectly contribute to lead exposure though its disintegration and contamination of dust and soil. With growing awareness that a young child's mouthing behavior [6,8-14] is an important environmental pathway for lead exposures, several studies have focused on the sources most relevant to the hand-to-mouth pathway of dust- and soil- lead. Blood-lead levels have been found to peak in young children at about two to three years of age [15], a period when children are most prone to hand to mouth activity . Duggan [11] suggested that the hand-mouth pathway of dust- and soil-lead may be responsible for this trend. Airborne lead may directly contribute to human exposures through inhalation, and indirectly by fallout of airborne lead to surface dust and soil. While the phaseout of leaded gasoline has most certainly reduced the role of airborne lead in lead exposures to most people, disturbance of interior dust, possibly by means of remodeling or renovation activities, may generate higher levels of lead in the indoor air. Direct ingestion of even small amounts of lead in drinking water is of concern due to the higher rate of absorption of lead in water compared to other substances.

Bornschein and coworkers [12-14] have investigated both the direct and indirect effects of lead levels in lead-based paint, soil, dust, and hand-lead on blood-lead levels. An analysis of these pathways using structural equation models (SEM) fitted to the data from the Cincinnati Lead Study [13] suggested the following environmental pathways of lead exposures, where PbS, PbD, PbH and PbB denote lead in soil, dust, hand wipes and blood, respectively, and LBP is an ordinal measure of lead-level paint that combined X-Ray fluorescence (XRF) scores with visual observations of paint condition.

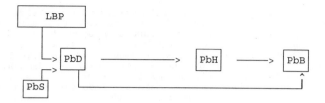

Figure 1.   Environmental Pathways from the Cincinnati Lead Study [13].

Analogous analyses conducted on the data from Telluride, Colorado, yielded qualitatively similar results [14].
    The presence of statistically significant correlations were utilized in [4] to establish environmental pathways for the BWHLLS. Rabinowitz concluded that lead levels in soil, air, and dust were highly correlated and that blood-lead levels were significantly associated with levels of lead in soil, paint, and dust, but not in air or water. This paper presents the results of statistical models fitted to the data from BWHLLS for investigating environmental pathways of lead exposure. Several statistical models were utilized, including: linear regression, multivariate regression, nonlinear regression, and structural equation models.

DESCRIPTION OF THE DATA

    Details of the blood-lead and environmental-lead sampling and analysis are described in [4], and are briefly reviewed herein. Umbilical cord blood-lead samples were collected for 11,837 births at the Brigham and Women's Hospital from April 1979 to April 1981. Of these, 249 children were selected for an on-going follow-up study involving environmental, behavioral, and developmental measurements. The hospital's base population and study selection criteria resulted in a sample quite different from those studied in most other environmental-lead field studies: mothers were typically well educated, white, married, and middle class.

TABLE 1--<u>Number of observations for each sampled media.</u>

Media	Age of Child (months)					
	0	1	6	12	18	24
Blood	249		220	208	213	202
Air			217		193	125
Floor Dust		247	228		205	191
Furniture Dust		247	231		204	190
Window Sill Dust		240	231		203	189
Water		245	230		17	17
Soil					152	148

    Environmental- and/or blood- lead samples were collected at 1, 6, 12, 18, and 24 months of age. The number of measurements sampled for each media at each sampling timepoint are displayed (Table 1).

Capillary blood-lead samples were analyzed using anodic stripping
voltammetry. Environmental media sampled and analyzed for lead included
dust from floors, furniture surfaces, and window sills, soil, tap water,
and interior air. Wipe dust samples were collected from the living room
floors and furniture surfaces using a 1 ft^2 plastic template, and from
window sills using a 0.5 ft^2 plastic template. Dust samples were
analyzed for lead using flameless atomic absorption. Soil samples were
collected from the top centimeter of the turf at random places at least
three meters from a street or structure. Soil samples were analyzed for
lead using flame atomic absorption. Tap water samples were collected by
a four-liter flush of the cold water tap in the kitchen. Water samples
were analyzed for lead using anodic stripping voltammetry. Interior air
samples were collected over 12 hr in the room most frequented by the
child using a Dupont Personal Air Sampler. The total particulate lead
in the sample membrane was analyzed by graphite furnace atomic
absorption. Lead loadings in paint, measured by X-ray fluorescence,
were available only for a small number of homes, and therefore, were not
considered in the statistical analysis discussed herein.

Data Analyzed

    Extensive sets of environmental- and blood-lead measurements were
taken at 6, 18, and 24 months (Table 1). Preliminary analyses examined
the correlations between blood-lead and environmental-lead at both 18
and 24 months. Results presented herein are based on the dust-, air-,
and blood- lead measurements collected at 24 months. Many soil lead
samples were missing due to frozen ground, or for some other reasons.
To increase the number of nonmissing soil-lead measurements, available
soil-lead samples were averaged for each home to yield a single soil-
lead sample. Similarly, available water-lead samples were averaged for
each home to yield a single water-lead sample.

    Responses utilized in the statistical analysis are:

    PbB24=   concentration of lead in blood (μg/dl) at 24 months,
    FLPb24=   amount of lead (μg) in floor dust wipe at 24 months,
    FRPb24=   amount of lead (μg) in furniture dust wipe at 24 months,
    WDPb24=   amount of lead (μg) in window sill dust wipe at 24
                months,
    AIR24=   amount of particulate lead (μg/m^3) in air sampled at 24
                months,
    PbW=   average concentration of lead (μg/L) in water,
    PbS=   average concentration of lead (μg/g) in soil, and
    Refin24=   an indication of the presence of any refinishing or
                remodeling activity within the preceding 6 months.

INVESTIGATION OF PATHWAYS VIA REGRESSION MODELS

    Blood-lead levels at 24 months ranged from 0 to 64 μg/dl. Blood-
and environmental-lead measures were highly skewed, and therefore were
transformed using the natural logarithm (ln) function. The geometric
mean of blood-lead at 24 months was 4.1 μg/dl with a geometric standard
deviation of 4.01. Descriptive statistics for the environmental-lead
measures are presented (Table 2). Correlations between log-transformed
blood- and environmental-lead are displayed in the last row of the
table: blood-lead levels were more strongly correlated with the dust
and soil measures compared to the other variables.

TABLE 2--<u>Descriptive statistics of lead in floor dust, furniture dust, window sill dust, and air at 24 months, and average levels of water and soil.</u>

	FLPb24 (μg)	FRPb24 (μg)	WDPb24 (μg)	AIR24 (μg/m^3)	PbW (μg/L)	PbS (μg/g)
Sample Size	191	190	189	125	250	195
Geometric Mean	3.44	2.44	11.03	0.06	3.36	360.83
Geometric Standard Deviation	3.12	2.74	4.37	2.84	2.26	3.32*
Minimum	0	0	0	0	0	7.00
Maximum	380.00	170.00	1536.00	0.52	52.50	13236.49
Correlation[1]	0.31	0.20	0.26	-0.00	0.06	0.29

[1] Correlation coefficient between ln(PbB24) and ln(PbE) where PbE = FLPb24, FRPb24, WDPb24, AIR24, PbW or PbS.

* Correlation with ln(PbB24) was statistically significant at the five percent significance level.

Multiple Regression Models

The data suggest that a number of factors affect blood-lead levels. A multiple regression model was fitted to the data to assess the combined contribution of the ln(environmental-lead) factors on ln(blood-lead). The estimated equation for the multiple regression model is

ln(PbB24) =   0.527 + 0.234ln(FLPb24) - 0.018ln(FRPb24) + 0.123ln(WDPb24) + 0.090ln(PbS) - 0.004ln(AIR24) - 0.033ln(PBW)

Not one of the environmental-lead measures was determined to be significantly related to increases in blood-lead levels (Table 3). The apparent contradiction between the results from the correlations and multiple regression models is a consequence of the inter-correlations among the measures of environmental-lead. For instance, the correlation between ln(FLPb24) and ln(WDPb24) was observed to be 0.42. A portion of the variability in ln(PbB24) explained by ln(FLPb24), is also accounted for by ln(WDPb24), thereby attenuating the significance of ln(FLPb24). The nonsensical negative parameter estimates for FRPb24, AIR24, and PbW are also outcomes of the inter-correlations.

TABLE 3--Parameter estimates for multiple regression model of
ln (blood-lead) on ln (environmental-lead).

Env. Variable	Parameter Estimate	SE	t-stat	p-value
INTERCEP	0.527	0.654	0.806	0.422
FLPb24	0.234	0.129	1.819	0.072
FRPb24	-0.018	0.131	-0.136	0.892
WDPb24	0.123	0.093	1.323	0.189
PbS	0.090	0.092	0.974	0.332
AIR24	-0.004	0.103	-0.041	0.968
PbW	-0.033	0.130	-0.251	0.803

SE   =   standard error of parameter estimate.
t-stat   =   t-statistic for testing whether or not the parameter
              estimate is equal to zero.
p-value   =   observed significance for t-statistic.

A simultaneous hypothesis test was conducted to determine if the
parameter estimates of all three dust variables (FLPb24, FRPb24, and
WDPb24) were jointly equal to zero. The null hypothesis that all three
parameter estimates are equal to zero was rejected at the five percent
significance level, indicating that some combination of the three dust
variables is significantly related to blood-lead. As a first step, we
assumed that the lead in the floor dust is the best predictor of blood-
lead and fitted a regression model containing only one of the three dust
variables. To assess the combined contribution of ln(FLPb24) and
ln(PbS) on ln(PbB24), the following multiple regression model was fitted
to the data

$$\ln(PbB24) = \beta_o + \beta_1 \ln(FLPb24) + \beta_2 \ln(PbS) + \varepsilon.$$

For this dataset, neither PbW nor Air24 were found to be significantly
related to PbB24 and are not included in the above model. The absence
of a statistically significant relationship between PbW and PbB24 may be
due to the relatively low levels of PbW in this study. An examination
of the residuals revealed two outliers. The above model was refitted to
the data after removing the outliers. The results for these multiple
regression models are summarized (Table 4). Estimated slope
coefficients for PbS and FLPb24 may be attenuated due to the sampling
and analytical variability in these measurements. Based on the results
(Table 4), both soil- and dust-lead are significantly related to
increases in blood-lead levels.

TABLE 4--Summary of regression models of ln(PbB24) on
ln(FLPb24) and ln(PbS).

	With Outliers			Without Outliers		
	Est.	SE	p-value	Est.	SE	p-value
FLPb24	0.29	.11	(.008)	0.22	0.075	(.004)
PbS	0.11	.089	(.20)	0.16	.06	(0.16)

Log-additive Regression Models

The concentration of lead in media such as blood, dust, or soil is
often assumed to follow a lognormal distribution, suggesting the use of

analyses based on log transformed variables. The standard linear
regression on log-transformed data (log-linear regression), however, may
be inappropriate for environmental lead pathway analysis. Such models
produce estimated blood-lead concentrations of zero $\mu g/dl$ if any one of
the predictor variables are measured as approximately zero. This would
be the case regardless of the magnitude of the other predictor
variables. Were a child to be exposed to highly elevated levels of lead
in soil and dust, yet spared exposure to lead in the air, it is unlikely
the concentration of lead in the child's blood would be near zero.

An alternative model has been previously proposed [16-18] the log-
additive model. Both sides of a linear additive model are log-
transformed and the random, unmeasured error is assumed to be
multiplicative rather than additive. This results in a variance-
stabilizing model, that preserves the additive nature of lead intake
from environmental media. The following log-additive regression model
was fitted to the blood-lead data using Proc Nlin in SAS (ver. 6.08):

$$\ln(PbB24) = \ln(\beta_0 + \beta_1 FLPb24 + \beta_2 FRPb24 + \beta_3 WDPb24 + \beta_4 PbS + \beta_5 AIR24 + \beta_6 PbW) + \varepsilon.$$

The estimated parameters, their standard deviations and observed
significance levels for the fitted model are displayed (Table 5). Based
on the results of this log-additive regression model, only lead in floor
dust was determined to be significantly related to increases in blood-
lead levels. The lack of statistical significance for many of the
measures of environmental-lead may be due to the inter-correlations. To
assess the combined contribution of FLPb24 and PbS on PbB24, a second
log-additive regression model was fitted to the data

$$\ln(PbB24) = \ln(\beta_0 + \beta_1 FLPb24 + \beta_2 PbS) + \varepsilon.$$

Estimated parameters for both floor dust-lead and soil-lead (β_1=0.173
and β_2= 0.00196) were statistically significant.

TABLE 5--Parameter estimates for log-additive multiple regression model
of blood-lead on environmental-lead.

Env. Variable	Parameter Estimate	SE	t-stat	p-value
INTERCEPT	3.04	0.830	3.66	<0.001
FLPb24	0.277	0.131	2.12	0.036
FRPb24	-0.020	0.036	-0.56	0.577
WDPb24	0.000278	0.00629	0.04	0.965
PbS	0.000572	0.000652	0.88	0.382
AIR24	1.145	5.41	0.21	0.833
PbW	0.0147	0.065	0.23	0.822

SE	=	approximate standard error of parameter estimate.
t-stat	=	approximate t-statistic for testing whether or not the parameter estimate is equal to zero.
p-value	=	approximate observed significance for t-statistic.

Comparison of Regression Models

Both the multiple regression models fitted to log-transformed data
(log-linear models) and the log-additive model indicated that blood-lead
levels are significantly related to dust-lead on floors and soil-lead.
These models were utilized to predict blood-lead levels for dust-lead
ranging from 0 to 400 μg, while holding soil-lead constant at its
geometric mean of 361 $\mu g/g$. The predicted relationships between blood-
lead and dust-lead in floors for the log-linear and log-additive models
are presented (Fig. 2). Although predicted blood-lead levels are
comparable for dust-lead in the range of 0 to 50 μg, they are

considerably different for dust-lead greater than 50 μg. The
distribution of lead levels on the floors at 24 months ranged from 0 to
380 μg, and was highly skewed with 90 percent of observations less than
18 μg. In fact 98 percent of the dust-lead observations were less than
50 μg. Therefore, the two models appear to be in close agreement except
when extrapolating outside the range of the majority of the data.

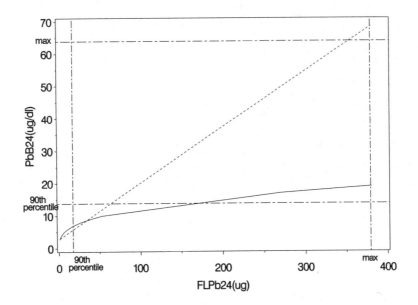

FIG.2--Predicted relationships between blood-lead and dust-lead on
    floors at average soil-lead levels based on log linear
    (———) and log additive models (-----).

INVESTIGATION OF PATHWAYS VIA STRUCTURAL EQUATION MODELS

As discussed above, environmental-lead variables can contribute
directly and indirectly to lead exposures. The indirect effects result
when the lead in one environmental media contaminates the surrounding
media. Inter-correlations among the environmental variables are
manifestations of the indirect pathways. For instance, lead in soil
tracked into the house increases the lead loading in interior dust,
producing a correlation between lead levels in floor dust and soil.
Multiple regression methods are unable to separate the indirect
effects of an environmental-lead measure from its direct effects. When
both dust-lead and soil-lead are used in a regression model to predict
blood-lead, the model attempts to jointly estimate the direct effect of
both environmental-lead measures on blood-lead. If the two variables
are highly correlated, the results can be confusing, with possibly
misleading significance levels or negative parameter estimates. One
option is to perform two regressions: (1) regress dust-lead on soil-lead
to estimate the effect of soil-lead on dust-lead, and (2) regress blood-
lead on dust-lead and the portion of soil-lead not related to dust-lead
levels. This system of coupled regressions may be expressed as follows:

$$\ln(FLPb24) = \beta_o + \beta_1 \ln(PbS)$$

$$\ln(\text{PbB24}) = \beta_2 + \beta_3\ln(\text{FLPb24}) + \beta_4\ln(\text{PbS}).$$

Treating the above equations as two independent regression equations fails to acknowledge the interdependencies of the two equations, and will yield estimates for the blood-lead equation identical to those displayed (Table 4). Structural equation models (SEM) [19,20,21] permit an assessment of both the direct and indirect effects of each environmental variable. Most computer implementations of SEM use maximum likelihood procedures or generalized least squares to simultaneously estimate the parameters in the system of equations. Estimated parameters maximize the concordance between the observed variances and covariances of the environmental- and blood- lead measures with those predicted from the fitted pathway model.

Log-linear SEM

Model 1. Two pathway models were fitted to the data using the structural equation program, Proc Calis, in SAS (ver. 6.08). Model 1 models blood-lead as a function of lead in floor dust, soil, and water, and incidence of refinishing or remodeling activities within the previous six months. Dust-lead on floors is modeled as a function of soil-lead and the incidence of refinishing. Refinishing activity was included in the model because it was previously found to be associated with blood-lead levels [5]. Pathways examined in Model 1 are displayed graphically (Fig. 3).

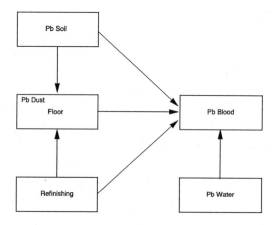

FIG. 3--Pathway Diagram for Model 1.

The SEM results for Model 1 are summarized (Table 6), statistically significant pathways are highlighted (Fig. 4). Parameter estimates for ln(FLPb24) and ln(PbS) in the blood-lead equation are comparable to those shown (Table 4) based on the multiple regression model. The statistically significant pathways (Fig. 4) imply that blood-lead levels are directly related to dust-lead, soil-lead, and the incidence of refinishing, and that soil-lead indirectly effects blood-lead through its contribution to dust-lead. Surprisingly, the incidence of refinishing was not related to levels of lead in dust on the living room floors. This may be an outcome of using a questionnaire to retrospectively determine the incidence of any refinishing activity within the last six months. Furthermore, the question solicited on the incidence of refinishing did not assess the surfaces or rooms in which the activity took place [5].

TABLE 6--Summary of log-linear SEM results for Model One.

Equation	Env. Variable	Parameter Estimate	SE	t-stat	p-value
blood-lead	FLPb24	0.304	0.086	3.522	<0.001
	PbS	0.176	0.082	2.136	0.033
	PbW	0.000	0.117	0.000	1.000
	Refin24	0.470	0.213	2.201	0.028
floor dust	PbS	0.267	0.068	3.905	<0.01
	Refin24	0.277	0.182	1.519	0.129

$$\ln(PbB24) = \beta_0 \ln(FLPb24) + \beta_1 \ln(PbS) + \beta_2 \ln(PbW) + \beta_3 (Refin24)$$
$$\ln(FLPb24) = \beta_4 \ln(PbS) + \beta_5 (Refin24)$$

SE = approximate standard error of parameter estimate.
t-stat = approximate t-statistic for testing whether or not the parameter estimate is equal to zero.
p-value = approximate observed significance for t-statistic.

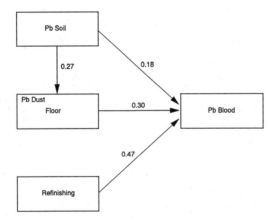

FIG. 4--Significant Pathways found for Model 1.

Model 2. Model 2 is a more complex pathway model that attempts to explain lead in blood as a function of lead in dust on floors and window sills, soil, interior air, and the incidence of refinishing. Lead in floor dust is modeled as a function of lead in dust on the window sill, soil, interior air, and incidence of refinishing or remodeling activities. Pathways are also constructed from soil-lead to the lead in the interior air, and dust on the window sill (Fig. 5).

The SEM results for Model 2 are summarized (Table 7), statistically significant pathways are highlighted (Fig. 6). The parameter estimate for ln(FLPb24) in the blood-lead equation is comparable to those shown (Tables 4 and 6). Statistically significant pathways presented (Fig. 6) imply a pathway of lead from soil to the dust on the window sill to the dust on the floor to childhood blood. Once again, the incidence of refinishing was estimated to directly effect blood-lead levels but not dust-lead on the floor. Pathways between lead in the interior air and other environmental-lead and blood-lead were not significant.

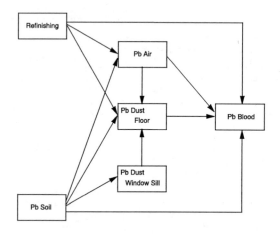

FIG. 5--Pathway Diagram for Model 2.

TABLE 7--Summary of log-linear SEM results for Model Two.

Equation	Env. Variable	Parameter Estimate	SE	t-stat	p-value
blood	FLPb24	0.267	0.102	2.629	0.009
	PbS	0.100	0.085	1.174	0.240
	AIR24	0.000	0.097	0.000	1.000
	Refin24	0.527	0.249	2.121	0.034
floor dust	PbS	0.114	0.071	1.608	0.108
	Refin24	0.055	0.205	0.266	0.790
	WDPb24	0.312	0.065	4.796	<0.001
	Air24	0.054	0.080	0.669	0.504
air	PbS	0.038	0.078	0.487	0.626
	Refin24	0.113	0.235	0.481	0.631
window sill	PbS	0.299	0.096	3.114	0.002

$$\ln(PbB24) = \beta_0 \cdot \ln(FLPb24) + \beta_1 \cdot \ln(PbS) + \beta_2 \cdot \ln(Air24) + \beta_3 \cdot (Refin24)$$
$$\ln(FLPb24) = \beta_4 \cdot \ln(PbS) + \beta_5 \cdot (Refin24) + \beta_6 \cdot \ln(WDPb24) + \beta_7 \cdot \ln(Air24)$$
$$\ln(AIR24) = \beta_8 \cdot \ln(PbS) + \beta_9 \cdot (Refin24)$$
$$\ln(WDPb24) = \beta_{10} \cdot \ln(PbS)$$

SE	=	approximate standard error of parameter estimate.
t-stat	=	approximate t-statistic for testing whether or not the parameter estimate is equal to zero.
p-value	=	approximate observed significance for t-statistic.

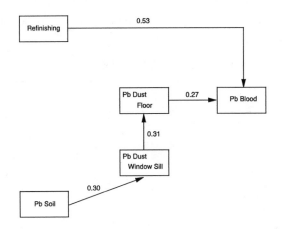

FIG. 6--Significant Pathways found for Model 2.

Log-additive SEM

Pathway models exhibited (Figs. 3 and 5) were fitted to the data utilizing systems of log-additive equations rather than systems of linear equations of log-transformed data. The log-additive SEMs were fitted to the data using Proc Model in SAS (ver. 6.08). Results for Model 1, based on fitting the log-additive system of equations, are summarized (Table 8). The log-additive structural equation model directs attention to the same pathways as produced by the log-linear structural equation model: blood-lead levels are directly related to dust-lead, soil-lead, and the incidence of refinishing, and soil-lead indirectly effects blood-lead through its contribution to dust-lead.

TABLE 8--Summary of log-additive SEM results for Model One.

Equation	Env. Variable	Parameter Estimate	SE	t-stat	p-value
blood-lead	FLPb24	0.164	0.075	2.20	0.029
	PbS	0.00141	0.000740	1.91	0.058
	PbW	0.000649	0.465	0.01	0.989
	Refin24	0.258	1.20	2.15	0.033
floor dust	PbS	0.00151	0.000591	2.6	0.01
	Refin24	1.16	0.753	1.54	0.126

$$\ln(PbB24) = \ln(\beta_0 + \beta_1 FLPb24 + \beta_2 PbS + \beta_3 PbW + \beta_4 Refin24) + \varepsilon_1$$
$$\ln(FLPb24) = \ln(\beta_5 + \beta_6 PbS + \beta_7 Refin24) + \varepsilon_2$$

SE   =   approximate standard error of parameter estimate.
t-stat =   approximate t-statistic for testing whether or not the parameter estimate is equal to zero.
p-value =   approximate observed significance for t-statistic.

The results of fitting the log-additive system of equations for Model 2 are summarized (Table 9). There are some notable differences between the pathways determined to be statistically significant based on the log-additive and log-linear SEM. Most conspicuous, is the absence of any significant relationships between soil-lead and dust-lead on floors and window sills, and on blood-lead. The log-additive structural equation model implicates a pathway from dust-lead on window sills to dust-lead on floors to blood-lead, and refinishing as the primary exposure pathways.

TABLE 9--Summary of log-additive SEM results for Model Two.

Equation	Env. Variable	Parameter Estimate	SE	t-stat	p-value
blood	FLPb24	0.244	0.113	2.15	0.0333
	PbS	0.000439	0.000559	0.79	0.434
	AIR24	-0.539	5.04	-0.11	0.915
	Refin24	3.08	1.72	1.78	0.077
floor dust	PbS	0.000339	0.000329	1.03	0.306
	Refin24	0.137	0.650	0.21	0.833
	WDPb24	0.0614	0.0185	3.32	0.0012
	AIR24	2.58	2.99	0.86	0.390
air	PbS	0.00	0.00	0.92	0.361
	Refin24	0.00680	0.0143	0.47	0.636
window sill	PbS	0.00337	0.00231	1.46	0.146

$$\ln(PbB24) = \ln(\beta_0 + \beta_1 \cdot FLPb24 + \beta_2 \cdot PbS + \beta_3 \cdot Air24 + \beta_4 \cdot Refin24) + \varepsilon_1$$
$$\ln(FLPb24) = \ln(\beta_5 + \beta_6 \cdot PbS + \beta_7 \cdot Refin24 + \beta_8 \cdot WDPb24 + \beta_9 \cdot Air24) + \varepsilon_2$$
$$\ln(Air24) = \ln(\beta_{10} + \beta_{11} \cdot PbS + \beta_{12} \cdot Refin24) + \varepsilon_3$$
$$\ln(WDPb24) = \ln(\beta_{13} + \beta_{14} \cdot PbS) + \varepsilon_4$$

SE   =   approximate standard error of parameter estimate.
t-stat   =   approximate t-statistic for testing whether or not the parameter estimate is equal to zero.
p-value =   approximate observed significance for t-statistic.

CONCLUSIONS

Log-linear and log-additive multiple regression and structural equation models were fitted to the data from the BWHLLS to assess the relationships between environmental-lead and blood-lead. In general, results obtained from the various statistical models are relatively consistent: blood-lead levels are significantly related to dust-lead and soil-lead, and the incidence of refinishing activities. Structural equation models fitted to the log-transformed data suggested a pathway from lead in soil to lead in dust on the window sill to lead in dust on the floor to childhood blood. Neither lead in indoor air or drinking water were significantly related to lead in soil, dust, or blood. Variability in measured data may have obscured the ability to detect these and other pathways as statistically significant. Unfortunately, only limited amount of data were available for lead-based paint, and pathways from lead-based paint to soil, dust, and blood were not considered in this analysis.

The analysis presented herein considered only the environmental- and blood-lead data collected at 24 months of age. Buncher and Succop [19] have studied the use of SEM to investigate longitudinal data collected on environmental- and blood- lead. One of the co-authors of this paper is presently re-analyzing the BWHLLS data using longitudinal models implemented through SEM. Those results, while preliminary, gave rise to the same general conclusions expressed in this paper and others [4,7].

REFERENCES

[1]   Angle, C. R., and M. S. McIntire, "Environmental Lead and
      Children: The Omaha Study," _Journal of Toxicological and
      Environmental Health_, Vol. 5, 1979, pp. 855-870.

[2]   ATSDR, _The Nature and Extent of Lead Poisoning in Children in the
      United States; A Report to Congress_, U.S. Department of Health and
      Human Services Public Health Services, Atlanta, GA., 1988.

[3]   U.S. Department of Health and Human Services, _Strategic Plan for
      the Elimination of Childhood Lead Poisoning_, U.S. Department of
      Health and Human Services, Atlanta, GA., February, 1991.

[4]   Rabinowitz, M., A. Leviton, H. Needleman, D. Bellinger, and C.
      Waternaux, "Environmental Correlates of Infant Blood Lead Levels
      in Boston," _Environmental Research_. Vol. 38, 1985, pp. 96-107.

[5]   Rabinowitz, M., A. Leviton, and D. Bellinger, "Home Refinishing,
      Lead Paint, and Infant Blood Lead Levels," _American Journal of
      Public Health_, Vol. 75, No. 4, 1985, pp. 403-404.

[6]   Rabinowitz, M. and Bellinger, D., _Bulletin of Environmental
      Contamination Toxicology_, 1988.

[7]   Bellinger, D., Leviton, A., Rabinowitz, M., et al., "Correlates of
      Low-Level Lead Exposure in Urban Children at 2 Years of Age,"
      Pediatrics. Vol. 77, No. 6, 1986, pp. 826-833.

[8]   U.S. Department of Housing and Urban Development, _Comprehensive
      and Workable Plan for the Abatement of Lead-Based Paint in
      Privately Owned Housing: A Report to Congress_, U.S. Department of
      Housing and Urban Development, Washington, DC., December 7, 1990.

[9]   Charney, E., J. Sayre, and M. Coulter. "Increased Lead Absorption
      in Inner City Children: Where Does Lead Come From?," _Pediatrics_,
      Vol. 65, No. 2, 1980, pp. 226-231.

[10] Charney, E., B. Kessler, M. Farfel, and D. Jackson, "Childhood
      Lead Poisoning: A Controlled Trial of the Effect of Dust Control
      Measures on Blood Lead Levels," _New England Journal of Medicine_,
      Vol. 309, 1983, pp. 1089-1093.

[11] Duggan, M. J., and M. J. Inskip, "Childhood Exposure to Lead in
      Surface Dust and Soil: A Community Health Problem," _Public Health
      Reviews_, Vol. 13, No. 1-2, 1985, pp. 1-54.

[12] Bornschein, R.L., Succop, P.A., Dietrich, R.N., Clark, C.S., Que
      Hee, S., Hammond, P.B. (1985), The Influence of Social and
      Environmental Factors on Dust Lead, Hand Lead, and Blood Lead
      Levels in Young Children. _Environmental Research_. Vol. 38, pp.
      108-118.

[13] Bornschein, R. L., P. A. Succop, K. M. Krafft, C. S. Clark, B.
      Peace, and P. B. Hammond, _Exterior Surface Dust Lead, Interior
      House Dust Lead and Childhood Lead Exposure in an Urban
      Environment_, Conference in Trace Metals in Environmental Health,
      Columbia, MO, 1986.

[14] Bornschein, R. L., C. S. Clark, J. Grote, B. Peace, S. Roda, and
      P. Succop, _Soil Lead-Blood Lead Relationship in a Former Lead
      Mining Town; in Lead in Soil: Issues and Guidelines_. Edited by
      Davis, B.E. and Wixson, B.G, 1989.

[15] Mahaffey, K.R., J.L. Annest, H.E. Barbano, and R.S. Murphy,
      "Preliminary Analysis of Blood-Lead Concentrations for Children
      and Adults; NHANES II, 1976-1978", in <u>Trace Substances in
      Environmental Health</u>. Edited by Hemphill, D.B., University of
      Missouri, 1979, pp. 37-51.

[16] Angle, C.R., Marcus, A.H., Cheng, E.H., McIntire, M.S., Omaha
      Childhood Blood Lead and Environmental Lead: A Linear Total
      Exposure Model. <u>Environmental Research</u>. Vol. 35, 1984, pp. 160-
      170.

[17] Marcus, A.H., and J. Cohen, "Modeling the Blood Lead - Soil Lead
      Relationship," <u>In Lead In Soil: Issues and Guidelines, Supplement
      to Volume 9 of Environmental Geochemistry and Health</u>, Edited by
      Davis, B.E., Wixson, B.G. pp. 161-174.

[18] U.S. EPA, <u>Air Quality Criteria for Lead Volume I - IV</u>, EPA
      Report No. EPA-600/8-83-028CF, Environmental Criteria and
      Assessment Office, Office of Research and Development, Research
      Triangle Park, NC., 1986.

[19] Buncher, R.C., P.A. Succop, and K.N. Dietrich, "Structural
      Equation Modeling in Environmental Risk Assessment," <u>Environmental
      Health Perspectives</u>, Vol. 90, 1991, pp. 209-213.

[20] Bentler, P.M., <u>EQS Structural Equations Program Manual</u>, BMDP
      Statistical Software, Los Angeles, CA, 1989.

[21] Duncan, O.D., <u>Introduction to Structural Equation Models</u>, Academic
      Press, New York, 1975.

Mark R. Farfel[1] and Benjamin S. Lim[2]

THE LEAD PAINT ABATEMENT AND REPAIR & MAINTENANCE STUDY IN BALTIMORE

REFERENCE: Farfel, M. R., and Lim, B. S., **"The Lead Paint Abatement and Repair & Maintenance Study in Baltimore,"** Lead in Paint, Soil, and Dust: Health Risks, Exposure Studies, Control Measures, Measurement Methods, and Quality Assurance, ASTM STP 1226, Michael E. Beard and S.D. Allen Iske, Eds, American Society for Testing and Materials, Philadelphia, 1995.

ABSTRACT: This study is to characterize and compare the short and long-term efficacy of full lead-paint abatement and less costly Repair and Maintenance (R&M) interventions for reducing lead in settled house dust (PbD) and children's blood. This research is important because dusts and residential paints are major sources of exposure in U.S. children, particularly those living in houses with deteriorating paint and elevated PbD levels. The R&M approach may provide a practical and cost-effective means of reducing exposure for future generations of children who will continue to occupy lead-painted housing. In this study, three levels of R&M interventions are being tested in 75 older dwellings, with 15 modern and 15 previously abated dwellings serving as controls. EPA funding is anticipated to measure lead in dust, soil, water, and children's blood over a 2-year period of followup. This paper describes the design and status of this ongoing study as of March, 1994.

KEYWORDS: lead abatement, lead exposure, abatement alternatives, lead-based paint, lead-containing settled dust

---

[1] Project Director, Kennedy Krieger Institute, 707 N. Broadway, Baltimore, MD 21205 and Assistant Professor, Dept. of Health Policy and Management, Johns Hopkins University School of Hygiene and Public Health

[2] EPA Work Assignment Manager, Chemical Management Branch, Office of Pollution Prevention and Toxics, U.S. EPA.

BACKGROUND AND PURPOSE

The purpose of this study is to characterize and compare the short and long-term efficacy of comprehensive lead-paint abatement and less costly Repair and Maintenance interventions for reducing lead in settled house dust which in turn should reduce lead in children's blood. The key to evaluating housing interventions is to measure their long-term costs and effectiveness for maintaining lead in children's bodies and in interior house dust at low levels. This research is important because lead in settled house dust and residential paints have been identified as major pathways and sources of lead into U.S. children via the hand-to-mouth route of ingestion [1]. The most recently published estimate is that 57 million privately owned and occupied U.S. housing units contain some lead-based paint (≥ 1 mg Pb/cm^2). Families with children under the age of seven years occupy an estimated 10 million of these dwellings. At highest risk are children in the nearly 4 million houses with deteriorating paint and elevated dust-lead levels [2].

Given the extent and potential costs of the problem in U.S. housing, it is imperative that low-cost and practical Repair and Maintenance (R&M) approaches are investigated in addition to more comprehensive forms of lead paint abatement. The preventive R&M approach may provide a practical means of reducing lead exposure for future generations of children. Children will continue to occupy millions of older lead-painted dwellings which cannot be fully abated or rehabilitated without substantial subsidy.

Systematic studies of the R&M approach have not been done. The frequency and costs of follow-up repairs to sustain any benefits of the initial R&M intervention are not known. Our goal is to provide information relevant to defining a standard of care for older lead-painted dwellings. Data collection for this multi-year study began in January of 1993. This paper describes the study objectives and design and the status of field activities.

Objectives

The study objectives are to:

1. Measure short and long-term changes of lead in settled house dust (PbD) and children's blood (PbB) associated with 3 levels of R&M interventions and full abatement.

2. Evaluate dust sampling methodologies, specifically wipe and cyclone/vacuum-based methods.

3. Characterize the relationship between lead in children's blood and settled house dust.

STUDY DESIGN

This prospective study has two main components and a total of five groups of study houses (Table 1). The first component is designed to obtain serial measurements of lead in venous blood (PbB) of children 6 months through 4 years of age, settled house dust, soil, and drinking water in three groups of 25 dwellings (total of 75 dwellings), each receiving one of three levels of R&M interventions. PbB measurements in children in all R&M study dwellings are planned at the following campaigns: pre-R&M and 2, 6, 12, 18, 24 months post-R&M. PbB measurements are obtained at 2-months and not at immediate post-intervention in order to allow time for the children's blood lead levels to equilibrate to their new post-intervention environments.

PbD measurements in R&M dwellings are planned at pre- and immediate post-R&M and at 2, 6, 12, 18, 24 months post-intervention. Measurements of lead in exterior soil and drinking water are planned at pre-R&M, immediately post-intervention (soil only), and 6 and 18 months post-intervention. The study questionnaire, designed to obtain information on demographics, and covariates which could influence lead exposure in the home (e.g., hobbies, child behavior, diet and occupation) will be done at six month intervals starting at enrollment.

TABLE 1--<u>Five study groups.</u>

Study group	No. of dwellings
R&M Level I	25
R&M Level II	25
R&M Level III	25
Previously Abated	15
Modern Urban	15
Total	105

Occupied dwellings are randomly assigned to receive either R&M Level I or R&M Level II interventions. Dwellings vacant at the time of intervention are randomly assigned to receive R&M Level II or Level III interventions. Since R&M Level II interventions are suitable for both occupied and vacant units the randomization scheme will ensure that equal numbers of dwellings (n=25) are assigned to each R&M treatment level.

The second component of the study design is to obtain serial measurements of lead in venous blood of children 6 months through 4 years of age, house dust, soil and drinking water in a sample of 15 dwellings which received full lead-

paint abatement performed by pilot abatement projects in
Baltimore between May of 1988 and February of 1991.
Measurements of lead in blood and settled dust are planned
at the following times: enrollment and 6, 12, 18, and 24
months post-enrollment. Measurements of lead in exterior
soil and drinking water are planned at enrollment and at 6
and 18 months post-enrollment. The study questionnaire will
be administered at six month intervals starting at
enrollment. The two years of planned follow-up will provide
an opportunity to measure the efficacy of full abatement at
4 to 6 years post-abatement.   Pre-abatement and post-
abatement dust lead data are available as baseline data for
this study group.

        The 15 modern urban dwellings free of lead-based paint
constitute the fifth study group, a negative control group.
The types of measurements and the frequency of collection
campaigns are the same as those for the previously abated
dwellings.

        Table 2 provides a summary of data collection campaigns
by study group. More frequent sampling campaigns are
planned for R&M dwellings during the first year to allow for
the estimation of the rate of reaccumulation of PbD and an
assessment of the need for further cleanups/repairs over
time.

Selection Criteria

The following are selection criteria for dwellings and
households:

1.   Dwelling of size 75-110 m^2 in structurally sound
      condition that is not excessively furnished.
2.   Household includes at least one eligible child 6 months
      through 48 months of age who spends most of his/her
      time at the dwelling.
3.   R&M dwellings documented to contain lead-based paint
      and elevated PbD levels prior to intervention.
4.   Previously abated dwellings have pre- and immediately
      post-abatemen⁺ PbD measurements available from previous
      studies.

TABLE 2--Summary of data collection.[a]

Sampling Campaign	R&M units occupied at intervention	R&M units vacant at intervention	Previously abated units	Modern control units
Enrollment/ Pre-R&M	D, S, W, B, Q	D, S	D, S, W, B, Q,	D, S, W, B, Q
Immediate Post-R&M	D, S	D, S	Not Applicable	Not Applicable
At time of reoccupancy	Not Applicable	W, Q, B	Not Applicable	Not Applicable
2 months	D, B	D, B	---	---
6 months	D, S, W, B, Q	D, S, W, B, Q	D, S, W, B, Q	D, S, W, B, Q
12 months	D, B, Q	D, B, Q	D, B, Q	D, B, Q
18 months	D, S, W, B, Q	D, S, W, B, Q	D, S, W, B, Q	D, S, W, B, Q
24 months	D, B, Q	D, B, Q	D, B, Q	D, B, Q

[a]B=Child blood (venous sample); D=Settled dust; W=Drinking water; S=Soil core; Q=Questionnaire.

Repair & Maintenance Interventions

Three levels of R&M interventions are planned for study in older lead-painted housing that is moderately well maintained. Initial R&M treatment costs are capped as follows: Level I: $1,650; Level II: $3,500; Level III: $6,000. R&M Level I includes wet scraping of peeling and flaking lead-paint on interior surfaces, limited repainting of scraped surfaces, wet cleaning with high phosphate detergent and vacuuming with a high efficiency particle accumulator (HEPA) vacuum to the extent possible in an occupied unit, an entryway mat, education of occupants and owners, and stabilization of exterior surfaces to the extent possible given the budget cap. Two key elements added in R&M Level II are floor treatments to make them smooth and cleanable and in-place window and door treatments to reduce lead dust generated by friction. R&M Level III adds window replacement; floor, doorway and stairway treatments; and encapsulation of certain wall and trim surfaces.

These R&M interventions have been designed in conjunction with experts in lead-paint abatement and the management and maintenance of low-income housing. Decision trees have been developed to help ensure the homogeneity of R&M treatments across dwellings and contractors. All R&M work is being performed by workers trained in lead paint abatement work according to Maryland regulations.

DATA COLLECTION

Field Sampling

Trained field teams collect all environmental samples in the study dwellings. Table 3 lists the types of field and quality control (QC) samples included in the study sampling plan.

Venous blood is collected from children at the Kennedy Krieger Institute Lead Clinic by a pediatric phlebotomist. Settled house dust is collected using a modified high volume cyclone sampler (HVS3) originally developed for EPA for the evaluation of pesticide residues in house dust [3,4]. The modified device, referred to as the R&M cyclone, is described in detail and characterized elsewhere [5]. The standard HVS3 device consists of a cast aluminum cyclone incorporated into an upright floor vacuum. To increase portability, a smaller hand held vacuum was substituted as the air mover for the system. A new sampling arm made from Tygon tubing is used to collect dust from floor and window surfaces. The bottom fitting of the R&M cyclone was changed to accept a 100 mL Teflon® microwave digestion liner as the sample collection container in order to minimize the opportunity for sample loss prior to digestion.

TABLE 3--<u>Types of field samples.</u>

<u>Sample type</u>

<u>Settled-dust (R&M cyclone)</u>
  Perimeter floor composite
  Window sill composite
  Window well composite
  Air duct/upholstery
  Interior entryway
  Exterior entryway

<u>Settled dust (wipe method)</u>
<u>(clearance testing only)</u>:

  Floors
  Window sills
  Window wells

<u>Soil core</u>
  Drip line
  Property boundary

<u>Drinking water</u>
Kitchen faucet

<u>Field QC</u>
  Blanks and duplicates
  for all sample types.

The sampling plan for settled dust is to collect three composite floor samples per dwelling - one across rooms with windows on the first floor, one across rooms with windows on the second floor and one from first and second floor rooms without windows. Two randomly selected 929 cm^2 perimeter floor locations are sampled in each room included in a composite sample. Composite window sill and window well samples are collected separately from all 1st and 2nd floor windows available for sampling, respectively. Settled dust is collected from air ducts and interior and exterior entryways as individual samples.

Soil core samples are collected as separate composites of the top 1.3 cm of soil from 3 randomly selected locations at the drip line and the property boundary respectively. Cores are collected using a 15.2 cm stainless steel recovery probe. Drinking water samples are collected as 2-hour fixed-time stagnation samples from the kitchen faucet. The procedure is to run the cold water for at least 2 minutes to flush the pipes and then to collect the first flush of water after a 2-hour interval. Information on the study children and their households is collected using a structured questionnaire in order to assess other influences on lead exposure in the home such as occupation, food preparation practices, child activities, degree of hand-to-mouth activity, diet, and hobbies.

Laboratory Measurement Processes

Settled dust, exterior soil, water and venous blood are analyzed at the Kennedy Krieger Institute's Trace Metal Laboratory using established analytical methods. Microwave digestion is used for dust, soil and water samples. Analysis of dust and soil digestates is performed using inductively coupled plasma-atomic emission spectrometry (ICP) and graphite furnace atomic absorption spectrometry (GFAA). Analysis of drinking water is by GFAA. The GFAA option using nitric acid (no hydrochloric acid (HCl)) is used for all samples regardless of the analytical technique being used. Blood samples are analyzed by GFAA and anodic stripping voltammetry (ASV). Wipe dust samples are extracted using 0.15 M HCl and analyzed by flame-atomic absorption spectrometry using procedures employed in past KKI studies [6-8].

RECRUITMENT AND ENROLLMENT

The enrollment process has entailed a three step process of pre-enrollment, formal enrollment, and ongoing pre-enrollment activity as described below.

STEP 1:   Pre-Enrollment

Extensive home visiting activity (1100 home visits to over 650 modern, previously abated and older occupied dwellings) was performed by field staff as part of pre-enrollment field activities during the spring and summer of 1992. Over 90% of eligible households identified indicated an interest in participating in the study. This early pre-enrollment activity yielded 100 interested and eligible households for formal enrollment.

STEP 2:   Formal Enrollment

Formal enrollment refers to the obtaining of signed informed consent statements for study participation from parents or legal guardians for both environmental and biological sampling. If a dwelling had multiple children eligible for the study, separate consent statements were obtained for each child enrolled in the study. Informed consent was obtained using forms approved by the review committee of the Johns Hopkins Medical Institutions.

A total of 94 of the pre-enrolled families with eligible children were enrolled between the end of August and December of 1992. By that time, enrollment milestones had been reached for each applicable study group (Table 4). Families not enrolled included those that had moved between the time of pre-enrollment and formal enrollment, declined formal enrollment or were subsequently found to be ineligible. One family was rejected for enrollment due to limited access to rooms in their dwelling.

TABLE 4--Enrollment by group as of December 31, 1992.[a]

Dwelling category	Number families enrolled	Study target number
Modern Urban	28	15[b]
Previously Abated	26	15[b]
Occupied R&M	40	37
Total	94	87

[a] Families moving into vacant R&M dwellings were enrolled later as R&M Level II and III work was completed.
[b] The study consent forms alerted enrollees that all enrolled households in the study may not be included due to limited study resources.

STEP 3: Ongoing Enrollment Activity

     Between the time of formal enrollment and the first data collection campaign (initiated in January, 1993) some enrolled households were lost to the study, primarily due to the aging of the children and the moving of families to other dwellings. In some cases, the losses necessitated ongoing pre-enrollment activity to identify an increased pool of potential study participants.
     As of March, 1994, the status of enrollment of families was as follows: modern urban dwellings (n=15, 100%), previously abated dwellings (n=15, 100%), occupied older dwellings which get R&M Level I and II interventions (n=37, n=100%). Additionally, enrolled families have been identified and moved into 31 of 38 (79%) vacant dwellings treated using R&M Level II and III interventions.

METHODOLOGICAL STUDIES

     Prior to the R&M Study, four studies of dust collection methodologies were conducted. These studies were needed since no standard methods have been established for the collection and analysis of settled house dust. The main findings of these studies are summarized below.

Pilot Study of the Feasibility of Compositing Dust Samples

     Pilot study data from 16 rooms in four houses suggest that floor dust composites can serve as a practical means of determining floor dust-lead levels in a room. Compositing can reduce the number of samples needed per house without sacrificing information on total lead loading [9].

Study of Two Cyclone Devices for Collection of Settled Dust

The performances of two portable cyclone devices were compared via replicate samplings of three types of dusts over the range of particle sizes expected in house dust (0.9-2000 μm). The R&M cyclone device had significantly higher dust recoveries, more consistent recoveries across particle sizes and dust loadings as well as higher precision across replicate samplings. Given the lack of information on the particle size and loading distributions of house dusts and lead-containing dusts, the R&M cyclone was selected as the preferred dust collection device for use in the R&M study [5].

Field Study of Side-by-Side Wipe and Vacuum Dust Samples

This study characterized the relationship between a wipe dust collection method and a vacuum-based in-line filter method used to collect dust in a survey of lead in paint and dust in U.S. housing. Seventy-one (71) pairs of side-by-side wipe and vacuum dust samples were collected from hard floors, window sills and window wells in 6 houses. Geometric mean (GM) wipe lead loadings estimates (PbD, mg/m²) exceeded those for vacuum samples by factors of 3.9 and 5.7 for floors and window sills, respectively. The GM vacuum PbD estimate for window wells based on the use of an alternative vacuum nozzle exceeded that for wipes by a factor of 3.4. Higher estimates of the prevalence of U.S. homes with elevated dust lead loadings may have resulted had wipe sampling been used in lieu of the vacuum sampling method in the national survey [10].

Field Study of Side-by-Side Wipe and Cyclone Dust Samples

This work compared estimates of lead loadings (PbD, mg/m²) based on a wipe dust collection method to those based on the R&M cyclone device. Pairs of side-by-side dust samples (n=71) were collected in seven houses from uncarpeted floors and window surfaces. The R&M cyclone device was observed to collect dust in cracks on rough surfaces. Geometric mean (GM) cyclone PbD estimates were higher than GM wipe PbD estimates by factors ranging from 2.5 to 10.4, for floors, window sills, and window wells respectively [11].

CURRENT STATUS AND FUTURE WORK

The expected completion data of the R&M Study is October of 1997. As of March, 1994 the initial and 6 month sampling campaigns have been completed in the modern urban and previously abated houses and the 12-month campaign is in process. Pre- and immediately post-R&M sampling has been completed for 61 of the 75 (81%) R&M houses. The 2-month and 6-month campaigns in these R&M houses are in process.

Overall, families have been cooperating well with the clinic visits for the collection of venous blood from study children. Through March, 1994, 268 blood-lead measurements have been made across all study groups and campaigns. The final 24-month campaign is anticipated to be completed by late spring of 1996.

A series of preliminary reports are planned as the data become available from the different campaigns. These reports will include analyses of short-term and longer-term changes in dust-lead and blood-lead levels over time within and across study groups.

Currently, information on the short and long-term effectiveness of practical interventions to reduce children's exposure to lead in residential paints and dusts is limited. By documenting the longer-term effectiveness of three repair and maintenance strategies, the R&M Study can help resolve the current confusion over what the standard of care should be in lead-painted residences. It is anticipated that the study findings will be useful to public agencies and private organizations in addressing the problem of lead poisoning in children.

REFERENCES

[1]   U.S. Agency for Toxic Substances and Disease Registry, "The Nature and Extent of Lead Poisoning in United States Children: A Report to Congress," Washington, DC, 1988.

[2]   U.S. Department of Housing and Urban Development, "Comprehensive and Workable Plan for the Abatement of Lead-Based Paint in Privately Owned Housing: A Report to Congress," Washington, DC, 1990.

[3]   Roberts, J.W., Budd, W.T., Ruby, M.G., et. al., "A Small High Volume Surface Sampler, (HVS3) for Pesticides, and Other Toxic Substances in House Dust," Paper No. 91-150.2 In: Proceeding of the 84th Annual Meeting & Exhibition of the Air & Waste Management Association, Vancouver, British Columbia, June 1991.

[4]   Research Triangle Institute and Engineering Plus, "Development of a High Volume Small Surface Sampler for Pesticides and Toxics in House Dust - Final Report," Submitted to US EPA Exposure Assessment Research Division. Research Triangle Park, NC, June 29, 1990.

[5]   Farfel, M. R., Lees, P. S. J., Lim, B., Rohde, C. A., "Comparison of Two Cyclone-Based Devices for the Evaluation of Lead-Containing Residential Dusts," Applied Occupational and Environmental Hygiene, Vol. 9, No. 3, March 1994, pp 212-217.

[6] Farfel, M.R. and Chisolm, J.J. Jr., "Health and
     Environmental Outcomes of Traditional and Modified
     Practices for Abatement of Residential Lead-Based
     Paint," American Journal of Public Health, Vol. 80,
     No.10, October 1990,   pp 1240-1245.

[7] Farfel, M.R. and Chisolm, J.J. Jr., "An Evaluation of
     Experimental Practices for Abatement of Residential
     Lead-Based Paint: Report on a Pilot Project,"
     Environmental Research Vol. 55, 1991, pp 199-212.

[8] Farfel, M. R., Chisolm, J. J. Jr., Rohde, C. A., "The
     Longer-Term Effectiveness of Residential Lead Paint
     Abatement," Environmental Research, in press.

[9] Farfel, M.R., Rohde, C.A., "Determination of
     Environmental Lead Using Compositing of House Dust
     Samples" In: Proceedings of the American Chemical
     Society's Symposium on Lead Poisoning in Children:
     Exposure, Abatement and Program Issues, sponsored by
     the ACS Division of Environmental Chemistry, August 24-
     25, 1992.

[10] Farfel, M. R., Lees, P. S. J., Rohde, C., et. al.,
     "Comparison of a Wipe and a Vacuum Collection Method
     for the Determination of Lead in Residential Dusts,"
     Environmental Research, in press.

[11] Farfel, M. R., Lees, P. S. J., Rohde C., "Draft Report
     on the Study of Side-by-Side Wipe and Cyclone Dust
     Samples," Submitted by the Kennedy Krieger Institute to
     U.S. EPA Office of Pollution Prevention and Toxics,
     Washington, DC, June 16, 1993.

David A. Burgoon,[1] Steven W. Rust[1], and Bradley D. Schultz[2]

A SUMMARY OF STUDIES ADDRESSING THE EFFICACY OF LEAD ABATEMENT

REFERENCE: Burgoon, D. A., Rust, S. W., Schultz, B. D., "A Summary of Studies Addressing the Efficacy of Lead Abatement," Lead in Paint, Soil, and Dust: Health Risks, Exposure Studies, Control Measures, Measurement Methods, and Quality Assurance, ASTM STP 1226, Michael E. Beard and S. D. Allen Iske, Eds., American Society for Testing and Materials, Philadelphia, 1995.

ABSTRACT: It is expected that lead hazard interventions will both prevent further childhood lead exposure and produce positive health outcomes among children benefitting from the interventions. The extent to which the scientific literature supports this expectation is characterized. Currently available scientific information was compiled on the effectiveness of lead hazard intervention in reducing childhood lead exposure. The studies identified address the efficacy of intervention strategies employed to reduce childhood exposure to lead-based paint, and to elevated soil-lead and dust-lead levels. Results and conclusions from these studies are summarized and their implications are discussed.

KEYWORDS: review, lead, soil, dust, lead-based paint, blood, lead abatement, intervention, effectiveness

INTRODUCTION

Recent years have seen a substantial effort focused on the development and demonstration of methods for reducing childhood lead exposure through the intervention of environmental lead hazards. In this manuscript, a lead hazard intervention is defined as any non-medical activity that seeks to prevent a child from

[1]Research Scientist and Research Leader, respectively, Statistics and Data Analysis Systems, Battelle, 505 King Avenue, Columbus, OH 43201.

[2]Senior Statistician, Office of Pollution Prevention and Toxics, U.S. Environmental Protection Agency, Washington, DC 20460 and Department of Preventive Medicine, University of Wisconsin, Madison, WI 53705.

being exposed to lead in his or her surrounding environment. The Department of Housing and Urban Development (HUD) conducted the Lead-Based Paint Abatement Demonstration (HUD Demo) Study to identify cost-effective methods for lead-based paint hazard abatement. The U.S. Environmental Protection Agency (EPA) subsequently conducted the Comprehensive Abatement Performance (CAP) Study to characterize the long-term efficacy of the paint abatement methods used in the HUD Demonstration. The U.S. EPA is currently concluding the Three City Urban Soil Lead Abatement Demonstration (3-City) Project to investigate whether the removal of lead-contaminated soil and dust from residential environments decreases the blood-lead concentrations of children living in those residences.

The abatement methods examined in the HUD Demonstration, CAP Study, and 3-City Project were comprehensive in nature. The methods generally involved either encapsulation, enclosure, or removal of lead-contaminated paint, dust, or soil. In this manuscript, these methods are categorized as "source isolation or removal" intervention methods. Even if proven efficacious, the application of these methods to our nation's entire stock of lead-contaminated housing could prove to be prohibitively expensive. For this reason, studies have been conducted, or are now underway, to examine the efficacy of "in-place management" intervention methods. In contrast to the encapsulation, enclosure, or removal of lead-contaminated media, these methods generally repair the lead hazard and usually include subsequent maintenance steps.

It is expected that lead hazard interventions will both prevent further exposure and produce positive health outcomes. This manuscript examines the extent to which the scientific literature supports this expectation and discusses the magnitude of the resulting changes identified to date.

REVIEW OF SCIENTIFIC EVIDENCE

A number of studies have examined the effectiveness resulting from the intervention of environmental lead hazards such as lead-based paint, elevated dust-lead levels, and elevated soil-lead concentrations. These studies focus on hand-to-mouth activity as the primary pathway of childhood lead exposure. They seek to assess whether a particular intervention strategy effectively lowers an affected child's blood-lead level or the levels of lead in his or her environment. The intervention considered sometimes depends upon the mechanism by which the child's environment becomes contaminated. One practice may attempt to halt soil track-in, while another continually reduces the elevated dust-lead levels within the home.

Fourteen studies were identified (Table 1). There are nine studies of lead-based paint abatement, three studies of dust abatement, and one study of soil abatement. One additional study utilized a range of intervention practices to alleviate lead exposure in the vicinity of an operating smelter. In total, these studies spanned twenty years, from 1974 to 1993. A timeline locating the period during which the interventions examined in each study were conducted is presented (Figure 1).

A detailed discussion of each of the 14 studies follows in chronological order. These studies are presented chronologically to emphasize the evolutionary nature of some intervention practices.

TABLE 1—Summary table for identified lead intervention studies.

Primary Form of Abatement Studied	Study Title	Method of Intervention Employed				Abatement Included Extensive Clean-Up	Lead Hazard Sources Abated			Blood-Lead Measures Collected
		Source Isolation or Removal			In-Place Management					
		Encaps/ Enclose	Cmplt Rmvl	Partial Rmvl			Soil	Dust	Paint	
Paint	1982 St. Louis Retrospective	●		●					●	●
	Baltimore Traditional/ Modified	●		●					●	●
	Boston Retrospective	●	●			●			●	●
	Baltimore Experimental	●	●			●			●	
	HUD Demo Study	●	●			●			●	
	CAP Study	●	●			●			●	
	1990 St. Louis Retrospective	●		●					●	●
	New York Chelation			●					●	●
	Milwaukee Retrospective	●		●					●	●
Dust	Baltimore Dust Control	●	●		●			●	●	●
	Seattle Track-In				●			●		
	Granite City Blood Lead				●			●		●
Soil	Boston 3-City	●	●	●	●	●	●	●	●	●
General	Silver Valley	●	●				●			●

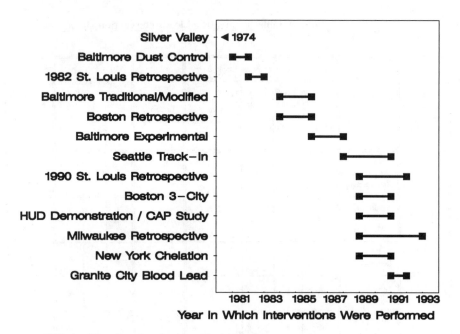

FIG. 1—Timeline for the identified intervention studies.

Silver Valley Lead Study

The 1974 study [1] examined the change in blood-lead levels that may have resulted from remediations undertaken in response to elevated lead levels in the inhabitants and environment surrounding a lead smelter in northern Idaho. The emphasis was on children residing near the primary lead smelter. Emergency measures were initiated in response to an earlier survey finding 99% of the one to nine year old children living within one mile of smelter had blood-lead levels greater than 40 μg/dL. The intervention measures included: chelation therapy for children with levels greater than 80 μg/dL, purchase and destruction of as many residences as possible within 1 mile (0.8 km) of the smelter, delivery of uncontaminated soil and gravel to cover areas of extremely elevated lead levels, hygiene programs within schools, and the reduction of smelter emissions. The original survey examined 1149 children, the follow-up one year later considered 781. The follow-up survey found reduced blood-lead, ambient air-lead, and surface soil-lead concentrations throughout the area, even 6-15 miles (9.7-24.1 km) from the smelter.

Baltimore Dust Control Study

This study [2] in 1981 sought to assess whether periodic dust-control measures in addition to lead-based paint abatement would be more effective in reducing blood-lead concentrations than lead-based paint abatement alone. Forty-nine children aged

15 to 72 months with at least two confirmed blood-lead concentrations between 30 and 49 µg/dL formed the study population. Their residences had all undergone lead-based paint abatement entailing the removal of all peeling lead-containing interior and exterior paint from the residence. No extensive clean-up procedures were required following the abatement. The periodic dust-control procedures involved twice monthly visits by a dust-control team which wet-mopped all rooms in the residence.

Venous blood samples were collected during regular visits to the clinic, approximately every three months during the course of the study. There was a significant reduction of 5.3 µg/dL in mean blood-lead concentration among the 14 children in the experimental group (wet-mopping and abatement) after six months, and a further decrease of 1.3 µg/dL after one year (Figure 2). In contrast, the mean value for the control group (abatement only) did not change significantly over the 12 months. To assess the cleaning's success, dust-lead loading was measured at all areas within the residence where the child spent time, before and after the dust-control teams completed their work. The samples were collected with alcohol-treated wipes within a 1 ft^2 (929 cm^2) area of floor or from the entire window sill. At experimental residences, the bimonthly dust-control efforts reduced the dust-lead loading on measured surfaces (Figure 3). No dust measures were collected in the control group residences so as to avoid attracting attention to dust as a source of lead exposure.

The results suggested that dust-lead loadings may be reduced by regular and focused dust-control efforts within the residence, and that the blood-lead levels in children residing in those homes can be significantly lowered. The children examined in this study had highly elevated blood-lead levels, averaging 39 µg/dL, so it is unclear how efficacious such procedures would be with children exhibiting lower blood-lead concentrations.

1982 St. Louis Retrospective Paint Abatement Study

This 1982 study [3] sought to demonstrate a significant difference between the children living in abated environments after lead hazard intervention compared to children still exposed to lead hazards. The comparison was made among children measured to have a blood-lead concentration greater than 25 µg/dL. The intervention entailed the abatement of the lead-based paint hazard, identified using X-ray fluorescence (XRF), within the residence. Surfaces with peeling or broken lead-based paint were enclosed, replaced or had their lead-based paint removed. No extensive clean-up procedures accompanied the abatement. Blood-lead concentration measurements were collected during routine venipuncture screening.

A retrospective study compared those blood measurements which identified the child as lead poisoned to follow-up samples collected six to twelve months following the initial identification. A total of 102 children had sufficient samples collected to allow this comparison. Follow-up blood-lead concentrations in children whose lead hazards had been abated were found to be an average of 11.29 µg/dL lower than their initial levels (Figure 4). Blood-lead levels decreased on average only 1.24 µg/dL for children whose hazards had not yet been abated. The difference in these mean decreases was statistically significant (p<0.001).

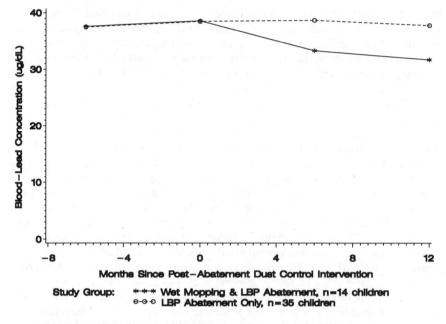

FIG. 2—Arithmetic mean blood-lead concentration (μg/dL) since abatement by study group, Baltimore Dust Control Study.

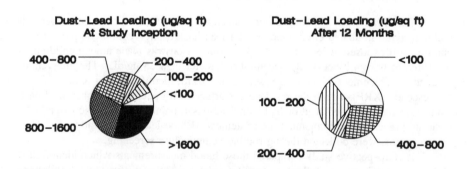

FIG. 3—Percentage of experimental homes with maximum dust-lead loadings (μg/ft^2) in the defined range, Baltimore Dust Control Study.

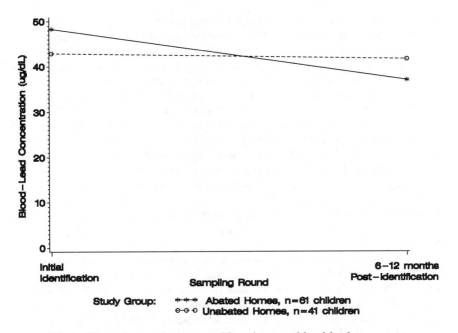

FIG. 4—Pre and post-abatement arithmetic mean blood-lead concentration (µg/dL) by status of residence abatement, 1982 St. Louis Retrospective Paint Abatement Study.

The results indicated that abatement of lead-based paint hazards did significantly reduce the lead burden being borne by children with elevated blood-lead levels. The differences between initial and follow-up samples were confounded, however, with individual differences in the amount of time that passed between the sample collections and their timing relative to the abatement.

Baltimore Traditional/Modified Paint Abatement Study

The goal of this study [4] in 1984-1985 was to evaluate the health and environmental impact of traditional and modified Baltimore practices for the abatement of lead-based paint. The study examined children residing in 71 residences abated in urban Baltimore (53 traditional abatements, 18 modified abatements). Prior to abatement all the residences had multiple interior surfaces coated with lead-based paint and housed at least one child with a blood-lead concentration greater than 30 µg/dL. Traditional Baltimore abatement practices called for addressing deteriorated paint on surfaces up to 4 ft (1.22 m) from the floor, and all hazardous paint on accessible surfaces which may be chewed on. Paint with a lead content greater than 0.7 mg/cm^2 by XRF or 0.5% by weight by wet chemical analysis was determined hazardous. In contrast to the traditional abatements, modified abatement included the repainting of abated surfaces and excluded the use of open-flame burning and sanding techniques.

In addition, modified procedures called for more through clean-up efforts (high-efficiency particulate accumulator (HEPA) vacuuming) and disposal of debris off-site. Clean-up following traditional abatement procedures typically entailed at most dry sweeping. Dust samples were obtained using a alcohol-treated wipe within a defined 1 ft^2 (929 cm^2) area template. Blood samples were collected via venipuncture.

Serial measurements of lead in interior house dust (lead loading), and children's blood-lead concentration were collected. Average increases of 1200 μg/ft^2 (12917 μg/m^2) in floor dust-lead loadings were measured immediately following traditional abatements (usually within two days) on or in close proximity to abated surfaces (Figure 6). Dust-lead levels measured after modified abatements were an average of 360 μg/ft^2 (3875 μg/m^2) higher than pre-abatement levels. Thus, modified abatement procedures resulted in elevated floor dust-lead loadings, but not to the extent seen for traditional practices. At six months post-abatement, average dust-lead loadings were 65 μg/ft^2 (700 μg/m^2) higher than pre-abatement loadings for traditional abatements and 28 μg/ft^2 (300 μg/m^2) higher than pre-abatement loadings for modified abatements.

Pre- and post-abatement blood-lead concentrations were available for 46 children who lived in the abated residences and had not undergone any chelation therapy. The post-abatement samples were collected within one month following the completion of the abatement activities. For traditional abatements, average blood-lead levels in 27 children rose 6.84 μg/dL (from 36.88 μg/dL to 43.72 μg/dL) while a rise of only 1.03 μg/dL (from 34.40 μg/dL to 35.43 μg/dL) was observed for 19 children exposed to modified abatements. Six months after abatement, a subset of 29 children (14 traditional, 15 modified) who had not undergone any chelation therapy exhibited blood-lead concentrations (mean, 30.66 μg/dL) that were not significantly different from their pre-abatement levels (mean, 32.53 μg/dL).

Despite the implementation of improved practices, modified abatements, like traditional abatements, did not result in any long-term reductions of levels of lead in house dust or the blood of children with elevated pre-abatement blood-lead concentrations.

Boston Retrospective Paint Abatement Study

This study [5] in 1984-1985 sought to evaluate the extent to which the lead poisoning of children is exacerbated during the abatement of lead-based paint within their residence. The study population consisted of 114 children ranging in age from 11 to 72 months (median age of 24 months) with at least one blood-lead concentration above 25 μg/dL obtained prior to abatement, one blood-lead sample collected during abatement, and one blood-lead determination following the completion of the abatement. The abatement process consisted of the removal or permanent coverage of any paint with a lead content greater than 1.2 mg/cm^2 which was loose and peeling (at any height), or present on chewable surfaces accessible to the child (below 4 ft (1.22 m)). Clean-up using wet washing with trisodium phophate (TSP) was stressed, but not uniformly performed following the abatement. The blood-lead concentration measurements were collected via venipuncture.

The mean blood-lead level in the 114 children rose 5.7 µg/dL during abatement and then fell 8.6 µg/dL approximately two months following the completion of the intervention activities (Figure 5). The statistically significant (p<0.05) decrease in mean blood-lead concentration post-intervention is due in part to 42 children who underwent chelation therapy between the mid- and post-intervention measurements. In an effort to determine the effect of intervention activities alone, a subset of 59 children who underwent no chelation therapy were examined. In this subset, an additional follow-up measure was collected 236-264 days after completion of the abatement work. There was no evidence of a change in mean blood-lead concentration during abatement. However, blood-lead levels fell an average of 4.5 µg/dL at the post-intervention collection (approximately two months) and fell an additional 5.5 µg/dL by the follow-up (approximately eight months) intervention collection (Figure 5). For 80 of the children, the specific method of lead-based paint abatement was available. Blood-lead levels in affected children were considerably elevated by dry scraping methods (mean increase in 41 homes of 9.1 µg/dL) and heat gun torches (35.7 µg/dL in 9 homes). By comparison, children exposed to encapsulation, enclosure, or replacement abatement procedures (12 homes) experienced a mean decrease of 2.25 µg/dL in their blood-lead burden.

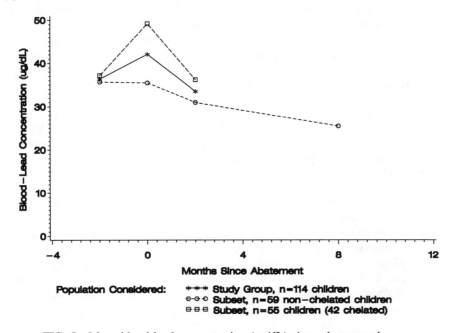

FIG. 5—Mean blood-lead concentration (µg/dL) since abatement by study population considered, Boston Retrospective Paint Abatement Study.

The study's results indicated that lead-based paint abatement may often produce a significant, transient elevation of blood lead in many children. It was most dangerous if accomplished with the use of torches, sanding, or dry scraping. The abatement may have been efficacious long-term, however, in that blood-lead concentrations had declined significantly by two months following the intervention.

Baltimore Experimental Paint Abatement Study

This study's [6, 7] objective was to evaluate experimental lead-based paint abatement practices developed in response to the inadequacies uncovered for traditional Baltimore abatement procedures. Six older dwellings in Baltimore City, built in the 1920s, were selected as the site of the experiment in 1986-1987. Each dwelling was a two-story six-room row home in poorly maintained condition with multiple lead-based paint hazards. Four of the residences were vacant and two housed lead-poisoned children. The experimental practices called for the floor to ceiling abatement of all interior and exterior surfaces where lead content of the paint exceeded 0.7 mg/cm^2 by XRF or 0.5% by weight by wet chemical analysis. Lead-contaminated dust was contained and minimized during the abatement, and extensive clean-up and disposal activities were utilized. Alcohol-treated wet wipes were used to collect dust-lead loading samples from household surfaces within each residence.

Serial measurements of lead in interior dust were made immediately before initiating abatement, during the abatement, after the final clean-up, and one, three, and six to nine months following the interventions. Floor dust-lead loadings immediately post-abatement were an average of 390 µg/ft^2 (4198 µg/m^2) lower than pre-abatement levels (Figure 6). By six to nine months following the interventions, average levels had decreased a further 74 µg/ft^2 (796 µg/m^2). All floor and window treatments were associated with significant ($p<0.05$) decreases in dust-lead loading over time. Results also suggested that window replacement may have been more effective in reducing dust-lead loading than stripping the lead-based paint. In addition, vinyl floor coverings may have produced lower dust-lead loadings than sealing old wooden floors with polyurethane.

The experimental methods resulted in substantial reductions in interior surface dust-lead levels immediately post-abatement which were found to persist throughout the six to nine month post-intervention period. However, dust-lead levels were not uniformly reduced to desired levels (<140 µg/ft^2 (1507 µg/m^2)), particularly on window sill and window well surfaces that were abated using paint removal methods. The magnitude of the decline in dust-lead loadings following intervention may have been exaggerated since vacant units are likely to contain more dust than occupied units.

Seattle Track-In Study

This study [8] sought to determine the extent to which low cost dust-control measures successfully lower household dust-lead loading. Forty-two homes in Seattle and Port Townsend, Washington built before 1950 formed the population studied from 1988-1990. The abatement procedures considered were strictly low-cost dust reduction

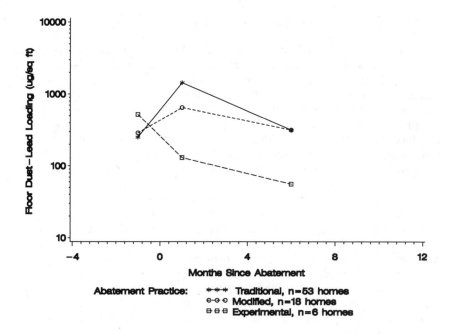

FIG. 6—Geometric mean floor dust-lead loading ($\mu g/ft^2$) since
abatement by abatement practice performed, Baltimore
Traditional/Modified and Experimental Paint Abatement Studies.

procedures: the use of a vacuum cleaner with an agitator bar, removing shoes at the
entrance to the residence, and an entrance mat. Dust samples were collected from
rugs within the residence using a Hoover Convertible vacuum cleaner. Soil samples
were scraped from within 1 ft (30.5 cm) of the residence's foundation.

The study employed step-wise regression analysis to assess which factors
determine the dust-lead loading within a residence. Significant pairwise correlations
were found between log transformed dust-lead loading and removing shoes at the door
(r=-0.62), and the presence of a floor mat at the home's entrance (r=-0.48). Lower
"fine" dust-lead levels were found in homes where the residents removed their shoes
(29 $\mu g/ft^2$ (312 $\mu g/m^2$)) and/or utilized an entrance mat (54 $\mu g/ft^2$ (581 $\mu g/m^2$))
compared to those in homes whose residents didn't (994 $\mu g/ft^2$ (10699 $\mu g/m^2$)). In
addition, the occupants of three homes tested in the study began removing their shoes
upon entry for at least five months prior to the collection of a second dust-lead
measurement from their carpets. The geometric mean dust-lead loading fell from
1588.6 $\mu g/ft^2$ (17100 $\mu g/m^2$) to 23.2 $\mu g/ft^2$ (250 $\mu g/m^2$) in these homes.

The data suggested that controlling external soil and dust track-in by removing
shoes or using an entrance mat will reduce the lead exposure from house dust. Lacking
blood measurements, it was difficult to assess the impact these interventions may have
had on childhood lead exposure.

1990 St. Louis Retrospective Paint Abatement Study

This 1989-1990 study [9] attempted to assess, via a retrospective cohort study, the effectiveness of lead-based paint abatement in reducing children's blood-lead levels. The sample population consisted of children under six years of age who were identified by the St. Louis City Health Department as having a blood-lead concentration of at least 25 µg/dL, and residing in dwellings with lead-based paint hazards. The intervention entailed the abatement of the lead-based paint hazard, identified using XRF, within the residence. Surfaces with peeling or broken lead-based paint were enclosed, replaced or had their lead-based paint removed. No extensive clean-up procedures accompanied the abatement. The blood-lead levels were collected via venipuncture.

The geometric mean blood-lead concentration among the 189 children selected was 33.6 µg/dL (range, 25-53 µg/dL). Among 71 children who had neither moved nor received chelation therapy and had their blood-lead concentration measured 10-14 months following the initial diagnosis, blood-lead concentrations fell following abatement. Children from abated homes (n=49) enjoyed a 23% reduction in blood-lead levels, while children residing in unabated homes (n=22) experienced a 12% decline. The difference between these reductions was statistically significant (p<0.10). A multiple regression analysis found that the geometric mean blood-lead levels of children residing in abated homes had decreased 13% more than children in unabated dwellings (p<0.10).

For lead-poisoned children in St. Louis, the decline in geometric mean blood-lead concentration was greater for children whose dwellings underwent lead-based paint hazard abatement than for children whose dwellings did not. The magnitude of the efficacy depended upon the child's initial blood-lead concentration. In addition, the differences between initial and follow-up samples were confounded with individual differences in the amount of time that passed between the sample collections and their timing relative to the abatement.

Boston 3-City Soil Abatement Study

This 1989-1991 project [10] endeavored to assess whether a significant reduction (≥1000 ppm) in the concentration of lead in residential soil will result in a significant decrease (≥3 µg/dL) in the blood-lead concentration of children residing at the premises. A total of 152 children were enrolled, each satisfying the following criteria: less than or equal to four years of age; blood-lead concentration between 10 and 20 µg/dL with no history of lead poisoning; and a minimum median residential soil-lead concentration of 1500 ppm. The project employed three intervention procedures: 1) interior paint stabilization by removing peeling or chipping paint; 2) interior dust abatement via wet mopping and HEPA vacuuming; and 3) soil removal (to a depth of six inches (15.24 cm)) and replacement. Dispersal of soil during the abatement was retarded by wetting the soil, preventing track-in by workers, containing the abatement site with plastic, and washing all equipment. Extensive environmental media and body burden samples were collected: composite core soil samples; vacuum dust samples; first draw water samples; interior and exterior paint assessment via portable XRF; venipuncture blood samples; and, hand-wipe samples.

Each child enrolled was randomly assigned to one of three experimental groups: Study (54 children), Comparison A (51 children), or Comparison B (47 children). The Study group received interior paint stabilization, interior dust abatement, and soil abatement. Comparison Group A received interior paint stabilization and interior dust abatement. Comparison Group B residences received only interior paint stabilization. Environmental media and body burden samples were collected at various times surrounding these intervention activities.

Average blood-lead concentrations in all three experimental groups decreased at the first post-abatement measurement (Figure 7). The statistically significant decreases were: 2.9 µg/dL - Study, 3.5 µg/dL - Comparison A, 2.2 µg/dL - Comparison B. The following increases in average blood-lead concentration were recorded between the first and second post-abatement measurement: 0.5 µg/dL - Study, 2.6 µg/dL - Comparison A, 1.5 µg/dL - Comparison B. Only the increases for the two control groups were significantly different from zero. The mean dust-lead levels from hand wipes for all groups followed a similar pattern, though they exhibited greater variability.

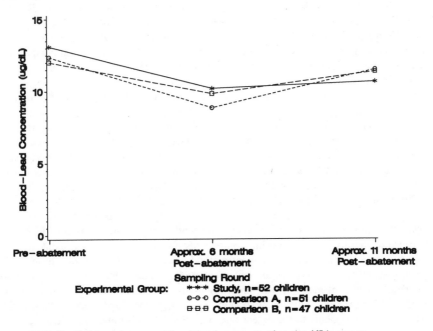

FIG. 7—Arithmetic mean blood-lead concentration (µg/dL) across sampling rounds and experimental groups, Boston 3-City Soil Abatement Study.

Mean soil-lead concentration did not change significantly for Comparison A or Comparison B residences. The decline in median soil-lead concentration among Study group residences immediately post-abatement, in contrast, ranged from 160 ppm to 5360 ppm, with a mean of 1790 ppm. There was no significant increase by nine months post-abatement. Composite floor dust-lead loadings and concentrations declined significantly during the study. Comparable declines were seen in all three groups, despite Comparison Group B not receiving any interior house dust abatement. Window well dust-lead levels declined immediately following abatement, but increased significantly by the final post-abatement sampling.

These results suggested that abatement of lead-contaminated soil around homes may result in a modest decline in blood-lead levels. The decline, however, was confounded with the efficacy of lead-based paint stabilization and the possibility of seasonal variation in blood-lead levels. Seasonal variations in blood-lead concentrations of comparable magnitude have been cited for Boston and Milwaukee [11, 12].

HUD Abatement Demonstration (HUD Demo) Study

This study [13, 14] was designed to determine and evaluate the overall suitability and effectiveness of various methods of lead-based paint abatement. These methods were tested in 1989-1990 in 172 FHA-foreclosed, single-family housing units in seven urban areas: Baltimore, Washington, D.C., Seattle, Tacoma, Indianapolis, Denver, and Birmingham. Six abatement procedures were employed: 1) encapsulation — coating and sealing of surfaces with durable coatings; 2) abrasive removal — removal of lead-based paint using mechanical removal equipment; 3) hand-scraping with a heat gun — removal of lead-based paint using a heat gun to loosen the paint; 4) chemical removal — removal of lead-based paint using a chemical stripper; 5) enclosure — resurfacing or covering of the surface; and 6) removal and replacement — removing contaminated substrates and replacing with new or deleaded components. XRF determination of lead content in paint, wet wipe sampling of surfaces within a defined area, and soil core samples were collected. No blood-lead measures were collected since the units were vacant at the time of abatement.

The specific units included were older housing found (using XRF) to have many structural components covered by paint with a high concentration of lead. Because of the diversity of housing components containing lead-based paint, it was generally true that no single abatement method could be used uniformly throughout a given housing unit. Therefore an abatement strategy, consisting of decision rules for choice of abatement method, was randomly assigned to each house. The method used to characterize the unit abatement strategy was always the first-choice method and was used on all components to the extent feasible. Second, third and fourth choice methods were specified for each strategy. Following completion of the abatement, the units were extensively cleaned using HEPA vacuums and TSP wet washings.

Pre-abatement dust-lead loadings generally were not collected. Once the lead-based paint had been abated and the area cleaned, clearance wipe samples were collected to verify acceptable dust-lead levels. The resulting dust-lead loading was compared to the appropriate standard in the HUD Guidelines [15]: 200 $\mu g/ft^2$ (2153 μg/m^2) for floors, 500 μg/ft^2 (5382 μg/m^2) for window sills, and 800 μg/ft^2 (8611 μg/m^2) for window wells. On average 80% of floor wipe clearance samples passed by measuring below the 200 μg/ft^2 (2153 μg/m^2) standard [13]. The highest failure rates among window sill wipe clearance samples were for chemical stripping (24%) and heat gun removal (24%) components. There were significant differences among the different abatement methods. Window well clearance wipe samples were more problematic than the other sample types; on average only 65% were measured below 800 μg/ft^2 (8611 μg/m^2). Units predominantly abated using chemical stripping and heat gun removal methods had approximately 45% of their clearance wipes above the standard. This is significantly different than the 21% failure rate encountered for units predominantly abated using replacement methods.

With the exception of abrasive sanding (the machines kept clogging), all the methods were successfully implemented. To do so, however, required varying degrees of effort. Chemical stripping and sanding methods had lower success rates in meeting the HUD Guidelines' clearance standards than did encapsulation, enclosure and replacement methods.

Comprehensive Abatement Performance (CAP) Study

The CAP Study [16], conducted in 1992-1993, sought to assess the long-term effectiveness of two lead-based paint abatement strategies: 1) encapsulation and enclosure methods, and 2) removal methods. Fifty-two FHA foreclosed, single family residences in Denver, Colorado were examined. Thirty-five of the residences were abated using the aforementioned methods as part of the HUD Demo Study. Each house was primarily classified according to the abatement category (i.e., encapsulation/enclosure versus removal methods) accounting for the largest square footage of interior abatement. The remaining 17 residences were control (unabated) homes identified in the HUD Demo Study to contain little or no lead-based paint. Vacuum dust-lead levels were measured at the interior and exterior entryways, floor perimeters, window sills, window wells, and air ducts of each residence. Core soil samples were collected at the foundation, entryway, and boundary of the home. No blood-lead measures were collected because the units were not reoccupied until several months after abatement.

The CAP Study found that for many sampling locations geometric mean dust-lead concentrations at houses abated during the HUD Demo Study were higher than those at control houses (Figure 8). The differences were statistically significant for the air ducts, window sills, and all three soil sampling locations. Air ducts and the surrounding soil, however, were not abated during the HUD Demo Study. Geometric mean dust-lead loadings on floors and exterior entryways were also significantly higher in abated houses than control houses, but these differences were attributed to higher dust loadings. It should be noted that both floor and window sill dust-lead loadings in abated houses were found to be below their respective HUD interim standards of 200 μg/ft^2 (2153 μg/m^2) and 500 μg/ft^2 (5382 μg/m^2). In contrast, window well dust-lead loadings in both abated and control houses were found to be well above the HUD value of 800 μg/ft^2 (8611 μg/m^2).

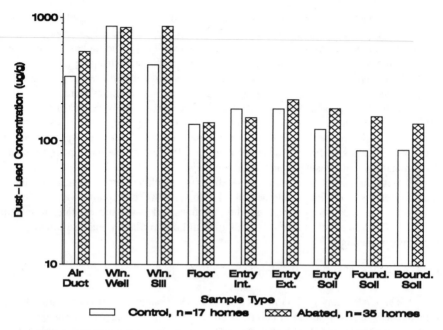

FIG. 8 —Estimated geometric mean dust-lead concentration (µg/g) in typical abated and control homes by sampling location, CAP Study.

Lead levels were somewhat higher, though not significantly higher, in houses abated by encapsulation/enclosure methods than in houses abated by removal methods. When interpreting these results it should be noted that encapsulation/enclosure houses typically had larger amounts of abatement performed than removal houses. Therefore, the differences in lead levels noted above may have been largely a result of the more severe initial conditions in encapsulation/enclosure houses.

Milwaukee Retrospective Paint Abatement Study

This study examined the effectiveness of the lead-based paint abatement strategies implemented in Milwaukee in 1989-1992. Damaged, painted surfaces with lead loadings exceeding 1.0 mg/cm^2 were abated. Clean-up procedures varied depending upon the practices of the particular abatement contractor. Only preliminary results from this study were available, but they are worth noting. Blood-lead concentrations were collected from 104 children before and (mostly) 3-12 months after the lead-based paint abatement. The arithmetic mean blood-lead concentration was reduced from 34 µg/dL pre-abatement to 26 µg/dL post-abatement which represents a 24% decline in their averages.

New York Chelation Study

This study [17, 18, 19] in 1989-1990 was an effort to ascertain the efficacy of a particular chelation therapy procedure on moderately lead-poisoned children. Two hundred and one children with blood-lead levels between 25 μg/dL and 55 μg/dL were administered a lead mobilization test (LMT) to determine whether chelation therapy might prove effective. Children with a positive LMT underwent chelation therapy. For all children enrolled, visual and XRF inspections of the paint in their residences were performed. Residences of 89% of the children had sufficient lead-based paint to warrant an abatement.

The reported results for this study emphasized overlapping subsets of the enrolled population. The first set of analyses examined a subset of 174 children (71 chelated, 103 control). Six to seven weeks following enrollment, blood-lead levels among the 103 non-chelated children had fallen an average 2.5 μg/dL (mean at enrollment, 29.0 μg/dL) and bone-lead levels had fallen an average 3.3 CNET (mean at enrollment, 125.3 CNET). The second set of analyses considered a subset of 154 children (61 chelated, 93 control). The cognitive index rose 3.6 points (from 79.0 to 82.6), on average, among a subset of 126 children (both chelated and non-chelated) six months following enrollment. The authors concluded that the cognitive index increased approximately one point for every 3 μg/dL decrease in blood-lead level. The third subset was of 59 children, 30 of whom were non-chelated. Mean blood-lead levels among the 30 non-chelated children had fallen 6 μg/dL by 6 weeks post-enrollment (from 29 μg/dL to 23 μg/dL) and fell an additional 2 μg/dL (to 21 μg/dL) by 24 weeks post-enrollment. This represents a 28% decline compared to an average decline of 37% among the chelated children (39.5 μg/dL to 25 μg/dL). Mean bone-lead levels did not change among the non-chelated children during this time period.

Though sifting through the various subsets is difficult, there was evidence that lead-based paint abatement lowered blood-lead levels. Furthermore, the authors concluded that the results suggest an association between declines in blood-lead levels and positive health outcomes (in addition to the lowered blood-lead concentrations).

Granite City Blood Lead Study

This 1991 study [20] included an effort to evaluate the efficacy of educational interventions to reduce blood-lead concentrations in exposed individuals. Children, under six years of age, recruited in Granite City, Illinois constituted the sampled population. Extensive educational efforts were aimed at the children and families exposed to elevated levels of lead in the surrounding environment. Instruction included identifying where lead-based paint was commonly found, how to perform house cleaning procedures, and hygienic procedures for young children. Venous blood samples, soil samples, dust samples from within the residence, tap water samples, and an assessment of the lead content in interior paint were collected.

Blood-lead concentrations were initially measured in August-September 1991. For children with blood-lead concentrations greater than 10 μg/dL, a follow-up measure was collected four months later. In the interim, the families of these children received extensive counseling in the prevention of lead exposure. The four month follow-up blood-lead concentrations were significantly lower than the initial levels for all age groups considered (Figure 9): arithmetic mean decrease for children 6-71 months of age, 7.2 µg/dL; 6-14 years, 5.9 µg/dL; and ≥15 years, 7.0 µg/dL. The results of one year follow-up blood samples were not yet reported.

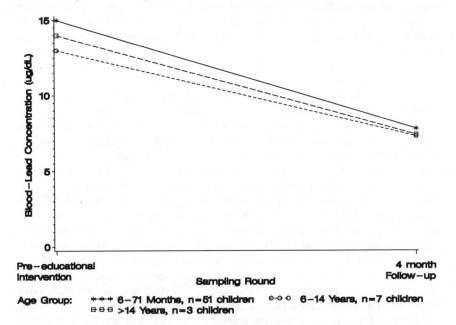

FIG. 9—Pre-educational and four month follow-up arithmetic mean blood-lead concentration (µg/dL) by age group, Granite City Blood Lead Study.

These striking declines in blood-lead levels provided evidence of the possible effectiveness of educational efforts. The full implications of these declines in blood-lead concentration, however, were difficult to ascertain since no measurements were collected for a control group of children.

CONCLUSIONS

The available literature on the effectiveness of lead hazard intervention focused on impeding the hand-to-mouth pathway of childhood exposure to environmental lead sources. The emphasis on this exposure pathway seems appropriate since it is recognized in the literature as the predominant pathway in young children. The pathway may be disrupted by a variety of means including the abatement of lead-based paint, dust-lead level reduction procedures and elevated soil-lead abatement.

The literature is limited in its scope. It only covers some of the intervention types and methods used in practice. However, the studies suggest that both in-place management and source isolation or removal methods were at least partially effective in reducing blood-lead concentrations. There was no definitive evidence in the literature that one of these categories of methods was more efficacious than the other. Source isolation or removal methods often had an accompanying risk of at least short-term elevation of residents' blood-lead levels that must be factored into any summary of intervention efficacy. In-place management methods, in turn, usually required sustained effort to retain their effectiveness.

The nine paint abatement studies examined all employed source removal or isolation methods to abate the lead-based paint hazard. The literature suggests that the efficacy of these methods depends in part on the safeguards employed to protect the occupants and their residential environment during abatement. In the Boston Retrospective [5] and Baltimore Traditional/Modified [4] Paint Abatement Studies, average blood-lead levels were observed to increase 16%-19%, on average, during abatement and remain elevated following the intervention. The levels in Baltimore were elevated one month following intervention, but in Boston had decreased by two months post-intervention. In the case of the Baltimore study, the authors suggested that the increase stemmed from incomplete abatement or insufficient clean-up following the abatement. Dust-lead levels within the dwelling were exacerbated, which led the authors to the conclusion that environmental exposure had merely been shifted from one media to another. In both the Boston and Baltimore studies, elevated blood-lead levels were associated particularly with the dry scraping and heat gun methods of source removal which were performed at the time (1984-1985).

In the Boston Retrospective Paint Abatement Study [5], lead-based paint isolation methods such as encapsulation, enclosure, and replacement were associated with an average reduction of 2-3 µg/dL in blood-lead concentrations. The results of the HUD Demo Study [13, 14] also suggest that clearance standards may be easier to meet via encapsulation and enclosure methods than via removal methods. The CAP Study [16] indicated that long-term interior dust-lead levels were somewhat higher, though not statistically higher, in encapsulation/ enclosure homes than in removal homes. However, as was noted earlier, this may have been largely a result of the more severe initial conditions in encapsulation/enclosure houses. Still, for two of three sampling locations, both types of abatement methods reduced long-term follow-up dust-lead levels below HUD Guidelines [15] standards. Since the HUD Demo and CAP studies followed units that were vacant before abatement, no changes in residents' blood-lead levels were available.

Lead-based paint removal methods were shown to lower the blood-lead levels of inhabitants in the Boston Retrospective [5], 1982 St. Louis Retrospective [3], 1990 St. Louis Retrospective [9], New York Chelation [17, 18, 19], and Milwaukee Retrospective Studies. These studies reported 20-29% declines in the blood-lead concentration of affected residents. The declines were manifest as soon as six weeks after intervention. The remaining lead in the blood (20-29% declines leave about ¾ still present) may be due to any number of reasons including the mobilization of bone-lead stores, the incomplete abatement of the lead-based paint and elevated dust lead, and the potential for exposure from non-residential sources.

Evidence that incomplete lead-based paint abatement may not be fully effective was found in the CAP Study [16]. Recall that significantly higher geometric mean lead concentrations were found in abated houses as compared to control houses in sampling locations that underwent no abatement (i.e., air ducts and soils). In addition, geometric mean dust-lead loadings at window wells were above HUD Guideline levels (800 μg/ft^2 (8611 μg/m^2)) for both abated and control houses.

The three dust abatement studies primarily employed in-place management methods. The Baltimore Dust Control Study [2] focused on managing the dust lead hazard after removing or isolating the lead-based paint hazard identified within the residence. These in-place management methods do not appear to aggravate childhood lead exposure if performed improperly. Once such techniques were discontinued though, the literature indicated the dust-lead hazard returned rapidly. The Baltimore Dust Control Study [2] noted that, "in most homes the initially high [dust-lead] levels were again present within two weeks after the first visit." Similarly, the one-time dust abatement and paint stabilizations performed in the Boston 3-City Soil Abatement Study [10] reduced window well dust-lead loadings for only a short period of time.

Regular, extensive dust-lead hazard management efforts by trained personnel produced an 18% decline in mean blood-lead concentration for affected residents (see Baltimore Dust Control Study [2]). The Granite City Blood-Lead Study [20] reported a 48% drop in mean blood-lead level from extensive educational outreach (a drop from 15 μg/dL, on average). The implication of this decline was difficult to ascertain, however, since no measurements were collected for a control group of children. The Seattle Track-In Study [8] reported significantly lowered dust-lead levels after residents removed their shoes and used an entrance mat (no blood-lead measures were collected).

The one study of soil abatement employed both source isolation or removal methods and in-place management methods. The Boston 3-City Soil Abatement Study [10] removed and replaced soil exhibiting elevated lead levels, but also stabilized the peeling paint and wet mopped the interior dust. Soil-lead and floor dust-lead levels in the abated residences remained low following the interventions. Blood-lead concentrations among affected inhabitants oscillated after intervention, but did not return to pre-intervention levels. In fact, a modest decline of 1-2 μg/dL in average blood-lead concentration (19% of pre-intervention levels, on average) was reported approximately one year following the interventions. This decline, however, coincided with comparable temporal variation in the average blood-lead levels of residents of unabated dwellings used as controls in the study. The control residences also underwent the same one-time paint stabilization procedure as the study residences. It was unclear exactly why the unabated residents experienced temporal variation, though seasonal variation of a comparable magnitude has been identified previously in children's blood-lead levels [11, 12]. This was a significant potential confounder in several of the efficacy studies.

A number of factors in addition to the effectiveness of the intervention impact the magnitude of a post-intervention decline in blood-lead concentration. Unless the residential lead hazards targeted by the intervention represent the full range of the child's exposures, the intervention can only be partially successful. The mobilization of some of the accumulated lead in a child's bones following an intervention may be capable of partially masking the effectiveness of the intervention. Seasonal variation in blood-lead and environmental-lead levels may moderate or magnify the perceived effectiveness of an intervention, depending upon the timing of the intervention and its follow-up measures. There appears to be little available information on the potential impact of these factors.

Some studies are currently under way to further examine the efficacy of lead hazard interventions, including in-place management methods. The EPA is conducting the Lead-Based Paint Abatement and Repair and Maintenance Study in Baltimore to compare comprehensive and low-cost methods for lead-based paint abatement in terms of their efficacy for reducing the levels of lead in residential house dust and children's blood. EPA is also completing a study in Milwaukee to determine the impact of common lead-based paint abatements, as well as a study in Jersey City of strategies requiring lower up-front abatement costs. The 10 first-year recipients of HUD Abatement Grants will also soon provide information on currently implemented intervention practices. In a joint effort, the Centers for Disease Control and the EPA are sponsoring low-cost lead-based paint abatement evaluations in Baltimore, Cleveland, and Boston. In addition, results of the EPA 3-City Soil Abatement Demonstration Projects in Cincinnati and Baltimore should be released soon. The results of these studies will shed additional light on the effectiveness of lead hazard intervention, its mitigating factors, and the trade-offs between different in-place management and source isolation or removal strategies.

REFERENCES

[1]   Yankel, A. J., von Lindern, I. H., Walter, S. D., "The Silver Valley Lead Study: The Relationship Between Childhood Blood Lead Levels and Environmental Exposure," Journal of the Air Pollution Control Association, Vol. 27, No. 8, 1977, pp. 763-767.

[2]   Charney, E., Kessler, B., Farfel, M., Jackson, D., "Childhood Lead Poisoning: A Controlled Trial of the Effect of Dust-Control Measures on Blood Lead Levels," New England Journal of Medicine, Vol. 309, 1983, pp. 1089-1093.

[3]   Copley, C. G., "The Effect of Lead Hazard Source Abatement and Clinic Appointment Compliance on the Mean Decrease of Blood Lead and Zinc Protoporphyrin Levels," Mimeo, City of St. Louis, Department of Health and Hospitals, Division of Health, Office of the Health Commissioner, St. Louis, MO, 1983.

[4]   Farfel, M. R., Chisolm, J. J. Jr., "Health and Environmental Outcomes of Traditional and Modified Practices for Abatement of Residential Lead-Based Paint," American Journal of Public Health, Vol. 80, No. 10, 1990, pp. 1240-1245.

[5]   Amitai, Y., Brown, M. J., Graef, J. W., Cosgrove, E., "Residential Deleading: Effects on the Blood Lead Levels of Lead-Poisoned Children," Pediatrics, Vol. 88, No. 5, 1991, pp. 893-897.

[6]   Farfel, M. R., Chisolm, J. J. Jr., "An Evaluation of Experimental Practices for Abatement of Residential Lead-Based Paint: Report on a Pilot Project," Environmental Research, Vol. 55, 1990, pp. 199-212.

[7]   U.S. Environmental Protection Agency, "Baltimore Integrated Environmental Management Project - Phase II Report: Reducing the Hazards from Abatement of Lead Paint," Final Report, 1987.

[8]   Roberts, J. W., Camann, D. E., Spittler, T. M., "Reducing Lead Exposure from Remodeling and Soil Track-in in Older Homes," Presented at the 84th Annual Meeting of the Air and Waste Management Association, June 16-21, 1991.

[9]   Staes, C., Matte, T., Copley, G., Flanders, D., Binder, S., "Retrospective Study of the Impact of Lead-Based Paint Hazard Remediation on Children's Blood Lead Levels in St. Louis, Missouri," American Journal of Epidemiology, Vol. 139, No. 10, 1994, pp. 1016-1026.

[10] Weitzman, M., Aschengrau, A., Bellinger, D., Jones, R., Hamlin, J. S., Beiser, A., "Lead-Contaminated Soil Abatement and Urban Children's Blood Lead Levels," Journal of the American Medical Association, Vol. 269, No. 13, 1993, pp. 1647-1654.

[11] Kinateder, J., Menton, R., "Seasonal Rhythms of Blood-Lead Levels," Final Report from Battelle to U.S. Environmental Protection Agency, May 1994.

[12] Schultz, B. D., "Variation in Blood Lead Levels by Season and Age," Draft Memorandum on data from the Milwaukee blood screening program, June 1993.

[13] U.S. Department of Housing and Urban Development, "The HUD Lead-Based Paint Abatement Demonstration (FHA)," Washington, DC, August 1991.

[14] U.S. Department of Housing and Urban Development, "Comprehensive and Workable Plan for the Abatement of Lead-Based Paint in Privately Owned Housing: Report to Congress," Washington, DC, December 1990.

[15] U.S. Department of Housing and Urban Development, "Lead-Based Paint: Interim Guidelines for the Hazard Identification and Abatement in Public and Indian Housing," Office of Public and Indian Housing, September 1990.

[16]   Buxton, B. E., Rust, S. W., Kinateder, J. G., Schwemberger, J. E., Lim, B., Constant, P., Dewalt, G., "Post-Abatement Performance of Encapsulation and Removal Methods for Lead-Based Paint Abatement," Lead in Paint, Soil, and Dust. Health Risks, Exposure Studies, Control Measures, Measurement Methods, and Quality Assurance, ASTM STP 1226, Michael E. Beard and S. D. Allen Iske, Eds., American Society for Testing and Materials, Philadelphia, 1994.

[17]   Markowitz, M.E., Bijur, P.E., Ruff, H.A., Rosen, J.F., "Effects of Calcium Disodium Versenate (CaNa$_2$EDTA) Chelation in Moderate Childhood Lead Poisoning," Pediatrics, Vol. 92, No. 2, 1993, pp. 265-271.

[18]   Ruff, H.A., Bijur, P.E., Markowitz, M.E., Ma, Y., Rosen, J.F., "Declining Blood-Lead Levels and Cognitive Changes in Moderately Lead-Poisoned Children," Journal of the American Medical Association, Vol. 269, No. 13, 1993, pp. 1641-1646.

[19]   Rosen, J., Markowitz, M., Bijur, P., Jenks, S., Wielopolski, L., Kalef-Ezra, P., Slatkin, D., "Sequential Measurements of Bone Lead Content by L-X-Ray Fluorescence in CaNa$_2$EDTA-Treated Lead-Toxic Children," Environmental Health Perspectives, Vol. 91, 1991, pp. 57-62.

[20]   Kimbrough, R. D., Statement to the Subcommittee on Investigations and Oversight, Committee on Public Works and Transportation, U.S. House of Representatives, June 9, 1992.

Control Measures

Aaron L. Sussell,[1] Angela Weber,[2] Deanna Wild,[3] David Wall,[3] and Kevin Ashley[4]

AN EVALUATION OF AIRBORNE AND SURFACE LEAD CONCENTRATIONS FROM PRELIMINARY CLEANING OF A BUILDING CONTAMINATED WITH DETERIORATED LEAD-BASED PAINT

REFERENCE: Sussell, A. L., Weber, A., Wild, D., Wall, D., and Ashley, K., "An Evaluation of Airborne and Surface Lead Concentrations from Preliminary Cleaning of a Building Contaminated With Deteriorated Lead-Based Paint," Lead in Paint, Soil and Dust: Health Risks, Exposure Studies, Control Measures, Measurement Methods, and Quality Assurance, ASTM STP 1226, Michael E. Beard and S. D. Allen Iske, Eds., American Society for Testing and Materials, Philadelphia, 1995.

ABSTRACT: Researchers from the National Institute for Occupational Safety and Health (NIOSH) conducted a hazard evaluation of a pilot project to examine three methods for cleaning a building that was grossly contaminated with lead-based paint, prior to future renovation work. Three two-man crews cleaned six rooms each, using each method for two rooms. Personal and area air samples were obtained during each cleaning activity, and surface wipe samples were taken before and after cleaning. Also, paint samples were obtained and analyzed. Although the overall reduction in floor surface lead concentration was found to be significant, post-cleaning surface lead concentrations did not vary significantly with the method, concentrations of lead in paint, area air, or pre-cleaning surface concentrations. Overall the method, mean paint lead concentration, pre-cleaning surface lead concentration, and work crew were jointly significantly associated with observed variation in mean personal breathing zone (PBZ) and area airborne lead concentrations. However, the correlation between mean paint lead concentration and PBZ exposures was very weak. Results indicated the potential for worker overexposures with all three cleaning methods.

KEYWORDS: abatement, airborne particulate, atomic spectrometry, lead, lead-based paint, renovation, surface dust.

[1]Supervisory Industrial Hygienist, [2]Industrial Hygienist, [3]Statistician, and [4]Research Chemist, U.S. Department of Health and Human Services, Centers for Disease Control and Prevention,* National Institute for Occupational Safety and Health, Cincinnati, OH 45226.

*Disclaimer: Mention of company names or products does not constitute endorsement by the Centers for Disease Control and Prevention.

The National Institute for Occupational Safety and Health (NIOSH) received a request for technical assistance from Ohio University (Athens, OH) to evaluate methods for cleaning buildings that were grossly contaminated with deteriorated lead-based paint (LBP). NIOSH researchers evaluated worker exposures and cleaning effectiveness during a pilot project for three LBP cleaning methods which were under consideration by the university. The results of the evaluation are of interest because many construction workers may perform similar activities during renovation and implementation of interim controls for LBP hazard reduction in public housing. One NIOSH site visit was made for this evaluation. The purpose of the visit was to observe work practices, and to conduct air, surface, and bulk sampling for lead.

BACKGROUND

This pilot project to evaluate LBP cleaning methods and worker exposures took place in unoccupied buildings which were part of a former state residential hospital complex, acquired by Ohio University from the State of Ohio. The university planned to renovate the buildings, portions of which had been unoccupied and without utilities for many years. The buildings were three-story brick, built between 1873 and 1888, and contained many patient rooms of similar size which had painted plaster walls and ceilings, with terrazzo floors. Due to weathering, much of the paint which had been applied over the years was loose and peeling, and large amounts of paint chips and dust had fallen to the floors. Visual inspection revealed that some of the rooms had been painted many times with different colors and types of paint. A previous building inspection conducted by university staff had suggested that many of the walls, ceilings, and painted wood trim surfaces in the rooms were coated with LBP. Previous sampling of the plaster walls and ceilings had not detected asbestos, a possible constituent of plaster in older buildings.

The university planned to clean gross lead contamination in the buildings prior to future renovation work, in order to reduce the potential lead hazard for inspectors, architects and engineers who would need to enter the buildings. The LBP cleaning pilot project was designed to evaluate cleaning methods under consideration. The three cleaning methods (and designations) used were:

▸   dry scraping followed by broom sweeping (dry sweeping)--This was selected to demonstrate exposures with no use of engineering or work practice controls.

▸   wet scraping (painted surfaces were wetted with water mist) followed by high-efficiency particulate air-filtered (HEPA) vacuuming (wet HEPA).

▸   wet scraping followed by HEPA vacuuming, with a HEPA-filtered air-filtration device (AFD) placed in the room (adjacent to a window) to exhaust room air to the outside. The AFDs, which were provided by the abatement contractor, were HEPA-AIRE® 2000, Model H2000C (Abatement Technologies). According to the manufacturer, these AFDs provide a maximum volume flow rate of 1550-1750 ft^3/min (43.9-

49.6 m³/min) with a clean filter, irrespective of the additional resistance provided by the 12 in (30.4 cm) diameter flexible exhaust ducts which were used. The actual flow rates vary with the line voltage, and resistance to airflow at the inlets and outlets. These AFDs provided an estimated average of about 37 air changes per hour in the rooms cleaned (assuming complete mixing).

The final step for each of the above methods was wet-mopping of the floor (once) with fresh trisodium phosphate (TSP) detergent solution (mixed according to label directions), using a new string mop head for each room cleaned. The rooms' doors were kept open throughout the pilot project, except for brief periods when it was necessary to close them to clean around the door. AFDs were rolled between rooms on casters; they were not decontaminated between rooms.

An asbestos and lead abatement contractor (Lepi Enterprises, Inc., Zanesville, Ohio) agreed to donate labor for the pilot project to the university; however, the labor was limited to six workers for one day. The workers wore appropriate protective clothing, including safety glasses, disposable coveralls and boot covers, and NIOSH-approved half-face respirators with HEPA filter cartridges.

EVALUATION DESIGN AND METHODS

Study Design

A previous NIOSH study of residential LBP abatement found that the geometric standard deviation (GSD) for personal breathing zone (PBZ) lead exposures during various cleaning activities was 3.6 [1]. NIOSH researchers estimated that, assuming a GSD of 3.6 and three work crews, a total of 63 rooms would be required to detect a four-fold difference between geometric mean PBZ exposures for the three methods (α=0.05). Since a pilot project of this size was not feasible, the project was limited to 18 rooms, which was the estimated maximum number that could be cleaned with the available labor (six workers x one day).

Eighteen rooms, in two adjoining hospital buildings, were non-randomly selected for cleaning at the outset of the study. To the extent possible, rooms of approximately the same size with similarly deteriorated paint were selected. Most of the rooms were about 9 ft x 15 ft (2.7 m x 4.6 m), with 12 ft (3.7 m) (minimum height) ceilings; although some were larger, up to 14 ft x 22 ft (4.3 m x 6.7 m). The workers were randomly assigned to three work crews of two workers each. Each work crew cleaned a total of six rooms; two rooms were cleaned consecutively with each of the three cleaning methods. Each work crew's assignments, including chronological order for the three methods and assignation of the rooms to be cleaned, were determined randomly.

Sampling

Environmental and personal samples were obtained by NIOSH investigators during the three-day site investigation. Pre-cleaning room and hall (floor) surface wipes, area air, and bulk paint chip samples were collected on the first day. PBZ and area air samples, as well as surface (hand lead) samples were collected during LBP cleaning on day two. Post-cleaning sampling (area air and floor surface wipe) was conducted on the third day. Sampling and analytical methods used in this evaluation are summarized below.

Bulk Samples--Two samples (which appeared to be representative) of loose or peeling paint were collected in each room from two different surfaces: usually a wall (or wood trim) and the ceiling. The paint chip samples (approximately 5 grams) were collected from surfaces with gloved hands and placed in sealable plastic food bags for shipment to the laboratory. Bulk samples of paint chips were analyzed for lead and other elements according to NIOSH Method 7300 (inductively coupled plasma atomic emission spectrometry, ICP-AES) [2]. The limit of quantitation (LOQ) for lead by this technique was 3 μg/sample.

Samples of wall plaster were collected from five randomly selected rooms. The samples were analyzed for percent and type asbestos with polarized light microscopy according to NIOSH Method 9002 [2].

Surface Samples--Floor surface lead concentrations were determined by wipe sampling 10 cm x 10 cm areas (defined by plastic templates) with individually wrapped towelettes (Wash'n Dri®) according to NIOSH Draft Method 0700 [3]. These towelettes have been found to be free of lead contamination, and result in good analytical recovery for lead [4]. Disposable 10 cm x 10 cm sampling templates, cut from 8.5 x 11 in (20.8 cm x 27.9 cm) plastic overhead transparency sheets, were used in an effort to avoid possible cross-contamination of samples. The templates were held in place with masking tape on the outside edges during sampling, and a fresh template was used for each sample collected. Single room surface wipe samples were collected on the terrazzo floors near the center of each room, and hall floor surface wipe samples were taken ca. 2 ft (0.6 m) outside the doorway of each room to be cleaned. Wipe samples were placed in sealable plastic food bags for shipment to the laboratory.

A brief study was conducted in an effort to estimate the sample variability of surface wipe samples collected using this method. Sets of five adjacent (in a row) wipe samples (100 cm^2 areas, as described above) were collected on the floors near the room center, in three randomly selected rooms (both pre- and post-cleaning).

Pre- and post-handwashing hand lead concentrations were measured by collecting samples immediately before and after handwashing, at the lunch break and the end of the shift. Handwashing was accomplished with hand soap, running water, and disposable towels at a staging area in one of the buildings being cleaned. The sampling procedure was to give each worker an individually-wrapped towelette, have the worker open the towelette package, wipe both hands thoroughly with it for a timed 30-sec period, and then place the towelette in a sealable, heavyweight plastic food bag. Samples were analyzed by NIOSH Method 7105 (graphite furnace atomic absorptions spectrometry, GFAAS) [2], modified for sample matrix as per NIOSH Draft Method 0700 [3]. The limits of detection (LODs) and limits of quantitation (LOQs) for lead were 0.09-5 μg/wipe and 0.31-15 μg/wipe, respectively, depending on dilution during sample preparation.

Air Samples--PBZ and area samples were collected on 0.8 μm cellulose ester membrane filters (SKC, Inc.) with personal sampling pumps (Mine Safety Appliances, Inc.) at a flow rate of 2.0 L/min. The pumps were calibrated immediately before and after sampling with a mass flowmeter (Gelman Instruments) which had been calibrated with a primary standard (bubble flowmeter, Scientific Glass & Instruments). The means of the measured pre- and post-sampling flow rates were used to calculate sample volumes. PBZ samples were collected in workers' breathing zones by attaching the media on the workers' shirt collars. One PBZ sample was taken per worker per room cleaned, and another long-term (whole workday) PBZ sample was obtained per worker. Area samples (one per room) were collected ca. 5 ft (1.5 m) above the floor near the room center during each cleaning activity. Samples were analyzed according to NIOSH Method 7105 [2]. The LOD and LOQ were 0.08 and 0.28 μg/sample, respectively.

Data Analyses

The primary outcomes of interest were the PBZ and area airborne lead concentrations, and the change (post- minus pre-cleaning) in floor surface lead concentrations in the rooms and hallways. The analyses, by analysis of covariance (ANCOVA), which were performed with the data are presented in Table 1. Due to the relatively small sample size, the analyses did not include consideration of potential interactions between independent variables.

TABLE 1--<u>Primary data analyses, Ohio University pilot project.</u>

ANCOVA[*] No.	Independent Variables	Dependent Variables
1	method (3 categories) crew (3 categories) mean paint Pb (%) pre-cleaning surf. Pb (mg Pb/m^2)	mean PBZ air Pb (μg/m^3)
2	"	area airborne Pb (μg/m^3)

3	method (3 categories)
	crew (3 categories)
	mean paint Pb (%)
	pre-cleaning room surf. Pb
	  (mg Pb/m^2)
	area air Pb (μg Pb/m^3)
		(log) room post-cleaning
		  surf. Pb (mg Pb/m^2)

4	method (3 categories)
	mean paint Pb (%)
	Pre-cleaning hall surf. Pb
	  (mg Pb/m^2)
	area air Pb (μg Pb/m^3)
		(log) hall post-cleaning
		  surf. Pb (mg Pb/m^2)

[*]Analysis of covariance; test for significance: F-test, $\alpha = 0.05$.

EVALUATION CRITERIA

General

The primary sources of evaluation criteria for the workplace are: NIOSH Criteria Documents and Recommended Exposure Limits (RELs) [5], the American Conference of Governmental Industrial Hygienists (ACGIH) Threshold Limit Values (TLVs) [6], and the Occupational Safety and Health Administration (OSHA) Permissible Exposure Limits (PELs) [7]. Employers are required to comply with the OSHA PELs and other OSHA standards. These values are usually based on a time-weighted average (TWA) exposure, which refers to the average airborne concentration of a substance over an entire 8-hour (PEL-TWAs, TLV-TWAs) or up to 10-hour (REL-TWAs) workday. Concentrations are usually expressed in parts per million (ppm), milligrams per cubic meter (mg/m^3), micrograms per cubic meter (μg/m^3), or fibers per cubic centimeter (fibers/cm^3). To compare results with the NIOSH REL-TWAs and OSHA PEL-TWAs, it is sometimes useful to extrapolate an equivalent 8-hr TWA exposure for sampling times of shorter than 8-hr duration. In extrapolating an 8-hr TWA, an assumption is made that there was no other exposure to the compound of interest over the remainder of the 8-hr work shift.

Lead--Inhalation (breathing) of dust and fume, and ingestion (swallowing) resulting from hand-to-mouth contact with lead-contaminated food, cigarettes, clothing or other objects, are the major routes of worker exposure to lead. Once absorbed, lead accumulates in the soft tissues and bones, with the highest accumulation initially in the liver and kidneys [8]. Lead is stored in the bones for decades, and may cause toxic effects as it is slowly released over time. Overexposure to lead results in damage to the kidneys, gastrointestinal tract, peripheral and central nervous systems, and the blood-forming organs (bone marrow). The frequency and severity of symptoms associated with lead exposure increase with increasing blood lead levels (BLLs).
New regulations have revised the OSHA PEL for lead in the construction industry. Under the new OSHA standard regulating occupational exposure to inorganic lead in the construction industry, the PEL is 50 μg/m^3 as an 8-hour TWA [9]. The standard requires monitoring of BLL for employees exposed to airborne lead at or above the Action Level of 30 μg/m^3 (8-hour TWA), specifies medical removal of employees whose average BLL is 50 μg/dL or greater, and provides economic protection for medically removed workers. NIOSH and OSHA have recently published recommendations for construction workers potentially exposed to lead [10,11]. An ASTM subcommittee is developing consensus standards for lead abatement and related activities; the status of the draft ASTM protocols has recently been summarized [12].
High BLLs in resident children, and elevated concentrations of lead in the house dust, have been found in the homes of workers employed in industries associated with high lead exposure [13]. Particular effort must be made to ensure that children of workers with lead poisoning, or who work in areas of high lead exposure, are not exposed to "take-home" lead from occupational settings.

Lead in Surface Dust--There are presently no Federal standards governing the level of lead in surface dust in either occupational or non-occupational (i.e., residential) settings. However, lead-contaminated surface dust in either setting represents a potential exposure to lead through ingestion, especially by children. This may occur either by direct hand-to-mouth contact with the dust, or indirectly from hand-to-mouth contact via clothing, food, and other objects that are contaminated by lead dust. Previous studies have found a significant correlation between resident children's BLLs and house dust lead levels [14]. Based on previous standards established in Massachusetts and Maryland, the U.S. Department of Housing and Urban Development (HUD) has recommended final clearance standards for lead in house dust on specific interior surfaces following lead abatement [15].

RESULTS AND DISCUSSION

General

Bulk Samples--The overall mean paint lead concentration was 4.3% (n=36); the data are summarized in Table 2. However, paint lead concentrations varied widely, as the overall relative standard deviation (RSD) was 184%. Nine of the 18 rooms selected for cleaning had mean paint lead concentration greater than the federal LBP criteria of 0.5% lead by weight (range: 2.8% to 19%) [15], as defined under Section 302 of the Lead-Based Paint Poisoning Prevention Act (42 United States Code 4822). In four of these nine rooms, both paint samples were LBP (>0.5% lead), in the other five only one sample was LBP, and in the remaining nine rooms neither paint sample was LBP.

TABLE 2--Environmental sampling results, Ohio University pilot project.

Method	Paint %Pb (Mean)	Room Surf. Pb (Mean, mg/m^2) Pre-@	Post-@	Hall Surf. Pb (Mean, mg/m^2) Pre-@	Post-@	Airborne Pb* (Mean, μg/m^3) Area Room	Hall#	PBZ
dry swp.&	3.2	29.1	8.6	48.2	43.0	74	13	100
wet HEPA	3.4	23.7	11.2	28.5	43.2	20	12	24
wet HEPA/ AFD	6.2	30.1	21.5	54.0	90.7	38	10	73
Overall Mean	4.3	27.5	13.8	43.6	59.0	44	12	66

*Results are TWAs for sampling periods of 13-55 min.
@Pre-/Post-: before and after (respectively) room cleaning.
#Hall area samples were obtained 2 ft (0.6 m) outside rooms.
&Dry sweeping.

Although rooms were assigned randomly to each of the three methods, paint lead concentrations may have differed among the methods. Of the six rooms assigned to each method, one of the rooms for dry sweeping, three of the rooms for wet HEPA, and five of the rooms for wet HEPA/AFD had a mean paint lead >0.5%. To account for these differences in data analyses, covariates (per room) were adjusted for mean paint lead concentrations (see Data Analyses section below). Since only two paint samples per room were collected, the mean paint lead concentrations may not have been representative of all surfaces cleaned.

No asbestos was detected in five samples of plaster collected from walls in five randomly selected rooms.

Surface Samples--Room surface lead concentrations were measured on the floor near the center of each room; results are summarized in Figure 1 and Table 2. Pre-cleaning, the rooms had a mean (floor) surface lead concentration of 28.0 mg/m^2 (range: 6.7 to 88.2 mg/m^2) indicating gross lead contamination. Overall, the post-cleaning room surface lead concentrations were significantly reduced, mean 14.0 mg/m^2 (range: 2.7 to 45.2 mg/m^2), p=0.018, Wilcoxon signed ranks test. All 18 post-cleaning room surface lead levels exceeded the HUD residential surface lead clearance criteria of cs. 2.2 mg/m^2 for floors [15]. It should be noted that the more extensive containment and final cleaning procedures that have been recommended by HUD for residential LBP abatement [15] were not followed in the pilot project. The changes in room surface lead concentration (post- minus pre-cleaning) among the 18 rooms varied widely; surface lead concentrations decreased in 14 rooms (range: -72.0 to -1.2 mg/m^2), there was no change in one room, and in three rooms the surface lead concentrations appeared to increase (range: 6.5 to 22.0 mg/m^2), see Figure 1. The floor surfaces which were sampled appeared to be less contaminated with paint chips and dust after cleaning, so it is likely that the post-cleaning surface lead consisted of primarily of small particles not removed by the cleaning. Additionally, the apparent increases may have been due to the high variability of adjacent surface samples (see below).

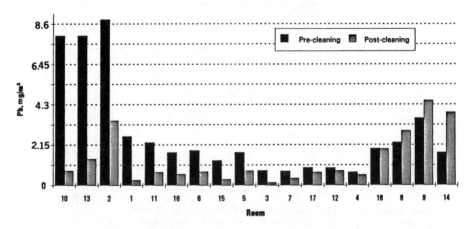

FIG. 1--Environmental sampling results, Ohio University pilot project; room surface lead concentrations.

The pre-cleaning hall (two feet outside room doors) surface lead concentrations, with an overall mean of 43.6 mg/m² (range: 10.0 to 108 mg/m²), were generally even higher than that of the rooms. Overall the post-cleaning hall surface lead concentrations, mean 59.0 mg/m² (range: 10.8 to 215 mg/m²) did not differ significantly from the pre-cleaning concentrations, p=0.35, Wilcoxon signed ranks test. It should be noted that cleaning the hallways was not an objective of the pilot project, although in many cases the HEPA vacuuming and mopping was extended at least two feet outside the rooms. The change in hall surface lead concentration (post- minus pre-cleaning) ranged from -62.4 to 215 mg/m², and was an increase in lead contamination for 12 of the 18 hall areas. It is likely that increases were due to lead contamination which was tracked out by workers, carried out on equipment, and, to a lesser extent, fugitive airborne lead (hall area airborne lead levels during cleaning were relatively low--see Area Air Sampling below).

TABLE 3--Adjacent and single surface sample results, Ohio University.

Room	Adjacent Wipes,* [Pb] (mg/m²)			Single Wipe,# [Pb] (mg/m²)
	Range	Mean	RSD	
Pre-cleaning				
5	9.6-39.8	20.7	62%	17.2
10	57.0-161.4	90.6	46%	79.6
8	8.1-43.0	23.2	69%	22.6
Post-cleaning				
4	2.7-20.4	14.5	48%	5.5
6	10.0-29.1	19.8	44%	7.2
11	5.6-8.8	7.8	17%	7.0

*Five adjacent wipe samples collected by a single investigator.
#Separate, non-adjacent, single wipe sample result.

The results of the study of surface sample variability (five adjacent wipes collected in six rooms) are presented in Table 3. It can be seen from these data that the field sample variability is quite high. In some rooms, the quantities of dust or paint chips on adjacent surface areas sampled were visibly non-uniform. Variability of adjacent surface samples, as measured by the RSD, was 46% to 69% in the three rooms which were sampled pre-cleaning, and 17% to 48% in three rooms sampled post-cleaning. One set of post-cleaning wipe samples revealed rather low sample variability (RSD=17%, Table 3). This may be due in part to the relatively low lead levels in this sample set. Of course, there are other contributions to the variability of field samples (e.g., type of substrate surface, individual variations in sampling technique, etc.), but these sources of variability are difficult to eliminate. In all 18 rooms, a single surface sample (non-adjacent) was also collected, see

Table 3. In all six rooms where adjacent wipe samples were collected, the result for the single surface sample was within the range of the adjacent sample results [16]. Results of single pre- and post-cleaning surface samples were used in the data analyses.

The results of sampling for hand lead pre- and post-handwashing were highly significant. All six workers were sampled at the lunch break and again at the end of the shift. Hand lead levels at the lunch break were quite variable, both pre-handwashing (mean 703 μg, RSD=74%) and post-handwashing (mean 55 μg, RSD=74%); similar results were found at the end of the shift (pre-: mean 748 μg, RSD=56%; post-: mean 87 μg, RSD=93%). However, for all six workers, measured hand lead levels were markedly reduced by handwashing with soap and water.

Area Air Sampling--Results for general area airborne lead concentrations during cleaning (day 2) are summarized in Table 2. Airborne lead concentrations were 1.6 and 3.8 μg/m^3 in the building during pre-cleaning bulk and surface wipe sample collection (day 1); and slightly lower, 1.1 and 0.60 μg/m^3, respectively, at the same locations during post-cleaning surface sample collection (day 3). During LBP cleaning activities (day 2) general area lead concentrations on the two affected floors in the building were somewhat higher, 3.1 and 4.6 μg/m^3. Airborne lead concentrations measured in an unaffected area outside the building were 0.095 μg/m^3 and none detected, on days 2 and 3, respectively. Since the building hallways were grossly contaminated with lead, and only small portions of the halls were cleaned, it is likely that the source of airborne lead measured in the building during pre- and post-cleaning (days 1 and 3) was lead-containing dust on the hall floors which was stirred up by occupant and equipment movement. On the actual day of cleaning, somewhat higher area airborne lead levels were probably due to the higher activity level in the halls and by fugitive dust from LBP cleaning activities in the rooms.

During cleaning, the mean for short-term (13-55 min) area airborne lead concentrations measured inside rooms was 44 μg/m^3 (range: 4.1 to 180 μg/m^3); see Table 2. Ten of 18 room area concentrations exceeded the OSHA Action Level of 30 μg/m^3; six of six for dry sweeping method, one of six for wet HEPA method, and three of six for wet HEPA/AFD method [16].

The mean hall area lead concentration, for six areas immediately outside rooms during cleaning, was 12 μg/m^3 (range: 1.9 to 18 μg/m^3). Both the highest and lowest hall concentrations measured were for rooms cleaned with the wet HEPA/AFD method. Unlike the other five hall area measurements, one hall measurement for wet HEPA/AFD (18 μg/m^3) was greater than the corresponding room area measurement (8.6 μg/m^3), which suggests that it may have been due to entrainment of emissions from another nearby room being cleaned. The results show that airborne lead was released to surroundings during all three cleaning methods, although all hall concentrations were relatively low, below the OSHA construction industry Action Level of 30 μg/m^3. Further study is needed to determine the effectiveness of general exhaust ventilation with AFDs in reducing fugitive airborne lead emissions during LBP cleaning and abatement.

PBZ Air Sampling--The overall mean for short-term (13-55 min) PBZ airborne lead exposures inside rooms during cleaning was 66 μg/m^3 (range: 5.0 to 360 μg/m^3), see Table 2. The results indicated the

potential for worker overexposures during all three LBP cleaning
methods. Sixteen of 36 short-term PBZ exposures equalled or exceeded 50
$\mu g/m^3$; 9 of 12 for dry sweeping, one of 12 for wet HEPA, and six of 12
for wet HEPA/AFD.

Short-term lead exposures (per room) among the 2-man work crews
were reasonably well correlated overall ($r^2=0.59$), see Figure 2. The
average of the two PBZ exposures (per room) was used as a variable (see
Data Analyses section below). Short-term area lead concentrations were
well correlated with the mean PBZ exposures ($r^2=0.72$), see Figure 3.

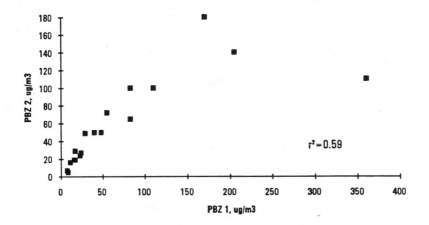

FIG. 2--Airborne lead, Ohio University pilot project; personal breathing
zone (PBZ) sample 1 plotted vs. PBZ sample 2.

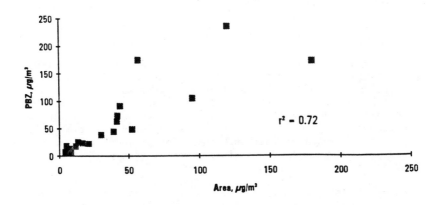

FIG. 3--Room area airborne lead concentration vs. PBZ airborne lead
concentration; Ohio University pilot project.

The range for five long-term (approximately 5 hours) PBZ lead exposures measured on the day of cleaning was 9.4 to 110 $\mu g/m^3$, see Table 4. Because the sampling periods were less than a full 8-hr shift (sampling did not include a lunch break and some setup time), 8-hr TWAs were extrapolated by assuming no other airborne lead exposure during the workshift. Since that assumption was not always valid, the extrapolated 8-hr TWAs reported should be considered minimum values. One of the five extrapolated 8-hr TWAs exceeded the OSHA PEL-TWA of 50 $\mu g/m^3$ (range: 6 to 73 $\mu g/m^3$). The 8-hr TWA exposures among the two workers on crew 2 (who cleaned the same rooms) were quite different, 24 $\mu g/m^3$ and 73 $\mu g/m^3$. This result is primarily due to exposures in one of the six rooms the crew cleaned (room 9), where the workers' short-term (55 min) PBZ exposures were 110 and 360 $\mu g/m^3$, respectively [16]. The differences indicate that individual work practices are an important determinant of lead exposures during LBP cleaning.

TABLE 4--Full-Shift PBZ Lead Exposures, Ohio University Pilot Project

Crew	Worker	Sampling Period (min)*	TWA ($\mu g/m^3$)	8-hr TWA# ($\mu g/m^3$)
1	C	313	46	30
1	E	321	26	18
2	A	319	110	73
2	B	317	36	24
3	D	327	9.4	6
3	F	@	@	@

*Sampling period did not include lunch break.
#Extrapolated 8-hr TWA, assuming no other exposure during workshift.
@Sample lost due to pump failure.

Data Analyses

The parameters for each of the four analyses presented below are given in Table 1. Overall, the variability of PBZ exposures measured during this project (GSD=2.9) was less than what was expected, based on the results for LBP cleaning activities in a previous NIOSH study of lead abatement workers (GSD=3.6) [1]. The previous study included far more workers, abatement contractors, and structures over a much longer time period. Accordingly, although the pilot project size was limited to cleaning 18 rooms, the statistical power of this project was greater than expected.

ANCOVA 1--Overall, the method, mean paint lead concentration, pre-cleaning surface lead concentration, and crew were jointly significantly associated with observed variation in mean PBZ lead exposures, p=0.023, degrees of freedom (df) 6, 11. Both method and crew variables, after

adjusting for the other variables in the model, were borderline
significant, p=0.056 and 0.054, respectively. The adjusted (least
squares) mean PBZ exposure for dry sweeping (107 $\mu g/m^3$) was
significantly greater than that for wet HEPA (34 $\mu g/m^3$) p=0.021, but not
wet HEPA/AFD (56 $\mu g/m^3$), p=0.095. The use of AFDs in rooms (with an
estimated average of 37 air changes per hour), which was expected to
lower workers lead exposures, did not provide any measurable benefit,
and may have increased exposures. This may be because use of the AFDs
in the relatively small rooms actually stirred up dust, either with air
turbulence created by the exhaust, or because it was necessary to move
them frequently during cleaning. Furthermore, the workers often
operated some distance away from the AFDs, yet (obviously) near where
the lead-containing paint was being disturbed. The adjusted (least
squares) mean PBZ exposure for crew 3 (14 $\mu g/m^3$) was significantly lower
than either of those for crews 1 and 2, which did not differ
significantly (103 and 81 $\mu g/m^3$), p=0.026 and 0.045, respectively. The
measured difference between crews indicates that work practices are
important determinants of personal exposures.

It has been suggested that renovators test surfaces for LBP in
older housing as a means to determine the potential for personal lead
overexposures during various renovation and demolition activities [17].
However, the correlation between mean paint lead concentrations and mean
PBZ exposures overall was weak (r^2=0.13), as were the corresponding
correlations by method: dry sweeping (r^2=0.33), wet HEPA (r^2=0.013),
and wet HEPA/AFD (r^2=0.15), see Figure 4. In fact, the mean PBZ
exposure was greater than 50 $\mu g/m^3$ in four of the nine rooms with mean
paint lead concentrations below 0.5%. Similar results have been
reported recently by other researchers [18]. The results of Figure 4
should be interpreted with caution due to small sample sizes, and may
be, at least in part, because paint sampling was not representative of
all surfaces with LBP.

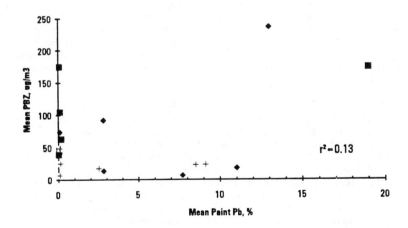

FIG. 4--Plot of mean paint lead concentration vs. PBZ exposure.
■: dry sweeping; +: wet HEPA; ♦: wet HEPA/AFD.

However, the results are consistent with the finding in this study that PBZ exposures are dependent on several variables, in addition to the mean paint lead concentrations. This finding is also supported by a previous NIOSH study of lead abatement workers, in which testing for LBP was comprehensive, which also found a very weak overall correlation between mean paint lead and (log) mean airborne lead concentrations (r^2=0.175) [1].

ANCOVA 2--Overall, the method, mean paint lead concentration, pre-cleaning surface lead concentration, and crew were jointly significantly associated with observed variation in area airborne lead, p=0.015, df 6, 11. The method variable, after adjusting for the other variables in the model, was significant, p=0.016. The adjusted (least squares) mean area concentration for dry sweeping (80 μg/m^3) was significantly higher than those for either wet HEPA (26 μg/m^3) and wet HEPA/AFD (25 μg/m^3), p=0.011 for both, and the latter two methods did not differ significantly. The use of AFDs in rooms (with an estimated average of 37 air changes per hour), which was expected to lower room airborne lead concentrations, did not provide any measurable benefit. As mentioned earlier, this may be because use of the AFDs in the relatively small rooms actually stirred up dust, either with air turbulence created by the exhaust, or because it was necessary to move them frequently during cleaning. The crew variable, after adjusting (least squares means) for other variables, was not significant, p=0.10.

ANCOVA 3--Overall, the method, mean area airborne lead concentration, mean paint lead concentration, pre-cleaning surface lead concentration, and crew were not jointly significantly associated with observed variation in (log) room post-cleaning surface lead concentrations, p=0.13, df 7, 10. The adjusted (least squares) means for dry sweeping (2.7 mg/m^2), wet HEPA (16.1 mg/m^2), and wet HEPA/AFD (22.6 mg/m^2) did not differ significantly, p=0.15, due in large part to the amount of variability observed. Although the results are not statistically significant, the majority of rooms cleaned showed decreases in surface lead concentrations (Figure 1). A greater number of samples may potentially have provided statistically significant results. Unfortunately, it was not possible to obtain a large number of surface wipe samples owing to the time and personnel constraints of the study.

ANCOVA 4--Overall, the method, mean area airborne lead concentration, mean paint lead concentration, pre-cleaning surface lead concentration, and crew) were not jointly significantly associated with observed variation in (log) hall post-cleaning surface lead concentrations, p=0.48. The adjusted (least squares) means for dry sweeping (30.1 mg/m^2), wet HEPA (50.6 mg/m^2) and wet HEPA/AFD (97.9 mg/m^2) did not differ significantly, p=0.24, due in large part to the amount of variability observed. Although the results are not statistically significant, the majority of hall areas outside rooms that were cleaned showed increases in surface lead concentration. A greater number of samples may be required to generate results that would be statistically significant. Unfortunately, it was not possible to obtain a large number of surface wipe samples given the time and personnel contraints of this study.

CONCLUSIONS

▸ Workers are potentially overexposed to lead during all of the LBP cleaning activities evaluated: dry scraping followed by sweeping with a broom; wet scraping followed by use of a HEPA vacuum; and wet scraping followed by HEPA vacuuming, with an AFD placed in the room.

▸ PBZ and area airborne lead concentrations during LBP cleaning are dependent on several variables, including the method, mean paint lead concentration, pre-cleaning surface lead concentration, and crew. The mean paint lead concentrations (obtained from sampling two surfaces per room) were a poor predictor of personal exposures during cleaning, as high airborne lead exposures occurred even in rooms with low (<0.5%) mean paint lead concentrations.

▸ Of the three cleaning methods evaluated (after adjusting for other variables), the wet scraping (followed by HEPA vacuuming) method appeared to offer the best control for worker lead exposures, and room airborne lead concentrations.

▸ The significant differences between mean PBZ exposures among work crews, and between workers on a single crew, indicate that individual work practices are important determinants for personal lead exposures during LBP cleaning activities.

▸ The use of air filtration devices (AFDs) in the rooms with the wet HEPA method did not provide any additional reduction of worker lead exposures or area lead concentrations; and may have, in some cases, increased personal lead exposures.

▸ Overall, room surface lead concentrations were significantly reduced by the LBP cleaning; the cleaning effectiveness of the three methods, as measured by the change in room surface lead concentrations, did not differ significantly.

▸ Overall, hall surface lead concentrations were not significantly increased by the LBP cleaning, although there was an apparent increase outside some of the rooms. The effectiveness of the three methods, as measured by change in hall surface lead concentrations, did not differ significantly.

▸ Post-cleaning surface lead concentrations indicated that all of the rooms were still contaminated with lead dust. Better containment of dust and debris, and/or repeated vacuuming and mopping, would be necessary to meet the HUD final clearance criteria for (residential) floor surfaces.

▸ Bulk sampling of plaster did not indicate a potential for asbestos exposure during LBP cleaning at this facility.

▸ The variability of lead concentrations among bulk paint samples from different component surfaces, and adjacent floor surface samples, even within rooms was quite high. No attempt was made to examine any potential correlation between bulk paint and surface lead concentrations, since comparatively few paint and surface lead samples were obtained, and the variabilities in lead concentrations from paint and surface wipe samples were extremely high.

▸ Worker hand lead concentrations were markedly reduced by handwashing on-site with soap, running water, and disposable towels.

ACKNOWLEDGMENTS

The authors thank Leo Blade and John Kelly of NIOSH for field assistance. We also acknowledge invaluable technical help provided by Chuck Hart and Debbie Thornsberry of Ohio University. Atomic absorption spectrometric analyses were performed by DataChem Laboratories, Salt Lake City, UT.

REFERENCES

[1] Sussell, A. L., Elliot, L. J., Wild, D., and Freund, E., Health Hazard Evaluation Report: HUD Lead-Based Paint Abatement Demonstration Project; U.S. Department of Health and Human Services (DHHS), Public Health Service (PHS), Centers for Disease Control (CDC), National Institute for Occupational Safety and Health (NIOSH), Cincinnati, OH, 1992.

[2] Eller, P. M., Ed., NIOSH Manual of Analytical Methods, 3rd ed.; DHHS/PHS/CDC/NIOSH, Cincinnati, OH, 1984.

[3] Eller, P. M., Ed., NIOSH Manual of Analytical Methods, 4th ed.; DHHS/PHS/CDC/NIOSH, Cincinnati, OH (in press).

[4] Millson, M., Eller, P. M., and Ashley, K., "Evaluation of Wipe Sampling Materials for Lead in Surface Dust," American Industrial Hygiene Association Journal, Vol. 55, pp. 339-342, 1994.

[5] NIOSH, Recommendations for Occupational Safety and Health, Compendium of Policy Documents and Statements; DHHS/PHS/CDC/NIOSH, Cincinnati, OH, 1992.

[6] American Conference of Government Industrial Hygienists (ACGIH), 1992-1993 Threshold Limit Values for Chemical Substances and Physical Agents and Biological Exposure Indices; ACGIH, Cincinnati, OH, 1992.

[7] Code of Federal Regulations, "Air Contaminants-Permissible Exposure Limits," 29 CFR Part 1910.1000; Federal Register, U.S. Government Printing Office, Washington, DC, 1989.

[8] NIOSH, Occupational Health Guidelines for Chemical Hazards; DHHS/ PHS/CDC/NIOSH, Cincinnati, OH, 1981.

[9] Code of Federal Regulations, "Lead Exposure in Construction: Interim Final Rule," 29 CFR Part 1926.62; Federal Register, U.S. Government Printing Office, Washington, DC, 1993.

[10] OSHA, and NIOSH, Working with Lead in the Construction Industry; U.S. Department of Labor (DOL)/OSHA, and DHHS/PHS/CDC/NIOSH, Washington, DC, 1990.

[11] NIOSH, Alert: Request for Assistance in Preventing Lead Poisoning in Construction Workers; DHHS/PHS/CDC/NIOSH, Cincinnati, OH, 1991.

[12] Ashley, K., and McKnight, M. E., "Lead Abatement in Buildings and Related Structures: ASTM Standards for Identification and Mitigation of Lead Hazards," ASTM Standardization News, Vol. 21, No. 12, pp. 32-39, 1993.

[13] Grandjean, P., and Bach, E., "Indirect Exposures: the Significance of Bystanders at Work and at Home," American Industrial Hygiene Association Journal, Vol. 47, pp. 819-824, 1986.

[14] Farfel, M. R., and Chisholm, J. J., "Health and Environmental Outcomes of Traditional and Modified Practices for Abatement of Residential Lead-Based Paint," American Journal of Public Health, Vol. 80, pp. 1240-1245, 1990.

[15] U.S. Department of Housing and Urban Development (HUD), Lead-Based Paint: Interim Guidelines for Hazard Identification and Abatement in Public and Indian Housing; HUD, Office of Public and Indian Housing, Washington, DC, 1990.

[16] Sussell, A. L., Weber, A., Wild, D., Ashley, K., and Wall, D., Health Hazard Evaluation Report: Ohio University, Athens, Ohio; DHHS/PHS/CDC/NIOSH, Cincinnati, OH, 1993.

[17] National Association of Home Builders (NAHB), What Remodelers Need to Know and Do About Lead: An Interim Guide; NAHB, Washington, DC, 1992; pp. 20-21.

[18] Rucker, S. W., and Clark, C. S., "Worker Exposures During Lead-Based Paint Abatement;" paper presented at the American Industrial Hygiene Conference and Exhibition, New Orleans, LA, 1993; Paper No. 190.

Bruce E. Buxton,[1] Steven W. Rust,[1] John G. Kinateder[1], John G. Schwemberger,[2] Ben S. Lim,[2] Paul Constant,[3] and F. Gary Dewalt[3]

COMPREHENSIVE ABATEMENT PERFORMANCE STUDY, PART II: COMPARISON OF ENCAPSULATION/ENCLOSURE AND REMOVAL METHODS FOR LEAD-BASED PAINT ABATEMENT

REFERENCE: Buxton, B.E., Rust, S.W., Kinateder, J.G., Schwemberger, J.G., Lim, B., Constant, P., and Dewalt, G., "Comprehensive Abatement Performance Study, Part II: Comparison of Encapsulation/Enclosure and Removal Methods for Lead-Based Paint Abatement," Lead in Paint, Soil, and Dust: Health Risks, Exposure Studies, Control Measures, Measurement Methods, and Quality Assurance, ASTM STP 1226, Michael E. Beard and S. D. Allen Iske, Eds., American Society for Testing and Materials, Philadelphia, 1995.

ABSTRACT: In 1989 the U.S. Department of Housing and Urban Development (HUD) initiated the Lead-Based Paint Abatement Demonstration Study in seven urban areas across the U.S. in order to assess the cost, worker hazards, and short-term efficacy of various lead-based paint abatement methods. One question which was not answered by the HUD Abatement Demonstration was that of the long-term efficacy of the abatement methods. Therefore, in 1990 the U.S. Environmental Protection Agency (EPA) initiated the Comprehensive Abatement Performance (CAP) Study to address this question. This paper presents conclusions from the CAP Study regarding the efficacy of the HUD Demonstration abatement procedures, as well as results concerning the correlations among lead levels observed in dust and soil at various household locations.

KEYWORDS: Lead-based paint abatement, encapsulation methods, enclosure methods, removal methods

[1]Program Manager, Research Leader, and Research Scientist, Battelle, 505 King Avenue, Columbus, OH 43201
[2]Statistician and Chemist, U.S. Environmental Protection Agency, 401 M Street, SW, Washington, D.C. 20460
[3]Program Manager and Senior Research Chemist, Midwest Research Institute, 425 Volker, Kansas City, MO 64110

INTRODUCTION

In response to requirements mandated by the Lead-Based Paint Poisoning Prevention Act (as amended by Section 566 of the Housing and Community Development Act of 1987), the Residential Lead-Based Paint Hazard Reduction Act of 1992, and other legislation, the U.S. Environmental Protection Agency, U.S. Department of Housing and Urban Development, U.S. Department of Health and Human Services, and other federal agencies are conducting a broad-based program of research, demonstration, and policy actions aimed at reducing the incidence of childhood lead poisoning in the U.S. An important part of the federal program is to identify and abate lead-based paint hazards in privately-owned and public housing. Toward this end, HUD initiated two important studies in 1989, the HUD National Survey of the incidence of lead-based paint in housing [1], and the HUD lead-based paint Abatement Demonstration [2] .

The HUD Abatement Demonstration was a research program in ten cities assessing the costs and short-term efficacy of alternative methods of lead-based paint abatement. However, although the HUD Abatement Demonstration did assess the short-term efficacy of certain lead-based paint abatement strategies, it was not intended to evaluate the longer-term performance of these approaches. Therefore, in 1990 the EPA Office of Pollution Prevention and Toxics (formerly the Office of Toxic Substances) decided to conduct the Comprehensive Abatement Performance (CAP) Study to further evaluate the abatement strategies used in the HUD Abatement Demonstration.

This paper presents statistical modeling results from the EPA CAP Study. The focus of this paper is primarily the performance of the studied lead-based paint abatement methods, as well as observed correlations among lead levels in household dust and soil measured at different locations. Two other papers concerning the CAP Study can also be found in this volume. Kinateder, et al. [3] describe in detail the study objectives and design, as well as the CAP Study measured lead levels as they compare with levels reported from other studies. Dewalt, et al. [4] describe the field sampling and chemical analysis methods used during the CAP Study. Complete results from the CAP Study are presented in EPA's final report [5].

STUDY OBJECTIVES

As discussed more fully by Kinateder, et al. [3], there were three primary objectives of the CAP Study:

1. Compare abatement methods or combination of methods relative to performance. Assess whether there are differences in performance.

2. Characterize levels of lead in household dust and exterior soil for HUD Demonstration and control homes.

3. Investigate the relationship between lead in household dust and lead from other sources, in particular, exterior soil and air ducts.

These objectives were intended to address at least three important concerns presented in the HUD Comprehensive and Workable Plan [1]: the durability of various abatement methods over time, the importance of adequate dust control during the abatement process, and the possible recontamination of housing units from a variety of locations, such as exterior soil and dust, as well as air ducts. This paper presents results related to study objectives 1 and 3.

RESULTS CONCERNING ABATEMENT EFFECTS

The first objective of the CAP Study was to compare the performance of different abatement methods used in the HUD Abatement Demonstration. To assess performance, Table 1 presents statistical estimates which can be used to compare lead levels between abated and control houses. Three blocks of estimates are displayed, and within each block are estimates for lead loading, lead concentration, and dust loading. The first block presents the estimated geometric mean lead levels in control houses. The second block presents the multiplicative factors by which geometric mean lead levels for typical abated houses were higher (or lower) than geometric mean lead levels in control houses. The last block presents the ratio of lead levels found in typical houses abated by encapsulation and/or enclosure (E/E) methods to those found in typical units abated by removal methods.

Four primary conclusions regarding abatement effects can be made from the CAP Study results. First, mean dust lead levels were often higher in abated houses than in control houses, but the main component for which the differences were statistically significant was air ducts, which were not abated. For air ducts the ratios of lead concentrations, lead loadings, and dust loadings in abated houses to those in control houses were significantly different from 1. Air ducts were not abated during the HUD Demonstration (they were covered with tape during the abatement). Therefore, if residual pre-abatement leaded dust were left in the air ducts, it would not be surprising that there is now a difference in lead levels between abated houses and control houses for this component. For exterior entryways, lead loadings were also marginally significantly higher in abated houses than in control houses. However, for this component, the significant difference found for lead loadings is largely explained by the fact that the dust loadings were significantly higher in the abated houses. Dust loadings on the floors of abated houses were also marginally significantly higher than those in control houses. It is interesting that in several cases, such as window channels, lead levels at abated houses were similar to those in control houses. This means that two years after abatement was performed, the window channels in abated houses looked like the window channels in control houses where there was relatively little lead-based paint.

TABLE 1--Summary of Significant Abatement Effects.
(Note: 1μg/ft² = 10.76 μg/m² and 1 mg/ft² = 10.76 mg/m².)

Component	Geometric Mean in Control Houses Based on Model Estimates			Ratio of Levels in Abated Houses[1] to Those in Control Houses			Ratio of Levels in E/E Houses to Those in Removal Houses		
	Lead Load μg/ft²	Lead Conc. μg/g	Dust Load mg/ft²	Lead Load	Lead Conc.	Dust Load	Lead Load	Lead Conc.	Dust Load
Dust									
Air Duct	76	332	202	4.70**	1.59**	3.11*	3.99**	2.01**	1.80
Window Channel	1604	851	1857	0.86	0.98	0.88	0.54	1.46	0.37
Window Stool	38	416	92	1.84	1.70	1.09	2.51	1.77	1.42
Floor (Wipe)	...	...	...	...	...	...	0.93	...	...
Floor (Vacuum)	16	137	118	1.76	1.03	1.65*	2.02*	1.30	1.55
Interior Entryway	191	183	1054	1.05	0.85	1.19	1.15	0.95	1.24
Exterior Entryway	220	184	1152	2.24*	1.19	1.95**	1.09	1.01	1.07
Soil									
Entryway (Soil)	...	126	...	...	1.48*	...	...	1.26	...
Foundation (Soil)	...	86	...	...	1.82**	...	...	0.81	...
Boundary (Soil)	...	86	...	...	1.63**	...	...	1.27	...

1   For interior samples, these represent ratios of levels in abated rooms of abated houses to those in control houses.
*   Significant at 10% level.
** Significant at 5% level.

The second conclusion from the CAP Study was that lead levels were typically higher in houses abated by encapsulation/enclosure methods than in houses abated by removal methods, but, except for air ducts, the differences were not statistically significant. Lead loadings and lead concentrations were significantly higher in the air ducts of E/E houses than in removal houses. In addition, lead loadings on the floors of E/E houses were marginally significantly higher than in removal houses. Two facts are important to note here. First, houses at which E/E methods were used generally had more lead-based paint present than houses at which removal methods were used. E/E houses had an average 910 ft^2 (84.6 m^2) of abatement performed, while removal houses had on average 321 ft^2 (29.8 m^2) of abatement. Second, as noted above air ducts were not abated in the HUD Demonstration.

The third CAP Study finding was that in the soil outside abated homes, lead concentrations were consistently and significantly higher than corresponding levels outside control homes. Although lead concentrations in soil were greater at the foundation, entryway, and boundary of abated houses, one point to note is that on average abated houses in this study were 17 years older than control houses. The average year built for abated houses was 1926, while the average year built for control houses was 1943. Therefore, these differences between the soil lead levels at abated and control houses could be due to the differences in age, the current or past presence of leaded paint, or both.

The fourth CAP Study conclusion was that lead levels were often lower in control rooms of abated houses (i.e., rooms that did not require abatement) than in abated rooms of these same houses, but the differences were not statistically significant. Table 2 lists the ratios of the geometric means of the dust lead levels in control rooms to those for the abated rooms. Note that most of the ratios are less than 1. An obvious exception is interior entryways. None of the lead concentration ratios was significantly different from 1. However, lead loadings for window channels and floors were marginally significantly lower in the control rooms, as was the dust loading for floors. These results may suggest that some leaded dust generated either before or during abatement was not completely controlled during the HUD Abatement Demonstration.

TABLE 2--Ratio of Dust Levels of Control Rooms to those in Abated Rooms.

Component	Lead Loading	Lead Concentration	Dust Loading
Air Duct	0.73	0.79	0.91
Window Channel	0.39*	0.61	0.65
Window Stool	0.67	0.69	0.96
Floor (Vacuum)	0.56*	0.87	0.65*
Interior Entryway	1.63	1.28	1.31

*Significant at the 10 percent level.

COMPARISONS WITH HUD ABATEMENT DEMONSTRATION DATA

In addition to comparing lead levels at abated and control houses, abatement performance was assessed by comparing CAP Study dust and soil lead levels with similar measures taken in the same locations for testing during the earlier HUD Abatement Demonstration. Two sources of HUD data considered here include abatement clearance dust lead loadings, and soil lead concentrations taken either before or shortly after abatement. The dust samples were collected from individual components within a room, and the soil core samples were collected on all four sides of the unit. The HUD Demonstration dust and post-abatement soil samples were collected between November 1989 and July 1990; while the pre-abatement soil samples were collected between August and December 1989. The CAP Study results, in turn, were collected in March and April 1992. Though a seasonal effect may be influencing the comparisons that follow, it cannot be separated from other differences between the projects such as sampling and chemical analysis protocols.

Figure 1 contrasts the CAP Study floor dust lead loading results to those from the HUD Demonstration clearance testing. For the CAP Study, geometric mean dust lead loadings were calculated for all floor dust vacuum and wipe samples collected within a room and unit. Since the dust samples collected in the HUD Demonstration were part of the clearance procedure with potentially multiple sampling iterations, only the final floor dust wipe sample collected in a room was retained. Figures 2 and 3 present similar comparisons for window stools and window channels, respectively. Recall that in the CAP Study, both wipe and vacuum dust samples were collected on the floors of abated units, while only vacuum dust samples were collected from window stools and channels.

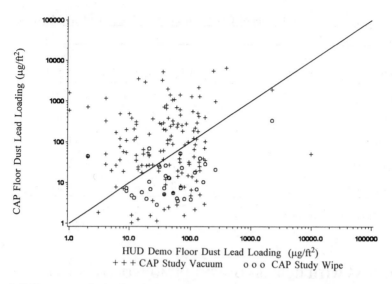

Figure 1--CAP vacuum and wipe floor lead loading versus HUD Demonstration wipe clearance testing results: geometric mean lead loading ($\mu g/ft^2$) by room. (Note: 1 $\mu g/ft^2$ = 10.76 $\mu g/m^2$.)

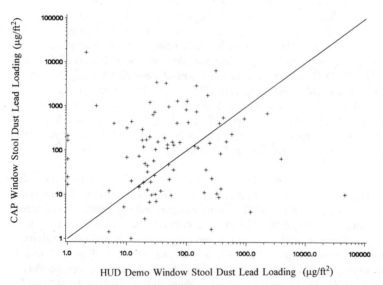

Figure 2--CAP vacuum window stool lead loading versus HUD Demonstration wipe clearance testing results: geometric mean lead loading ($\mu g/ft^2$) by room. (Note: 1 $\mu g/ft^2$ = 10.76 $\mu g/m^2$.)

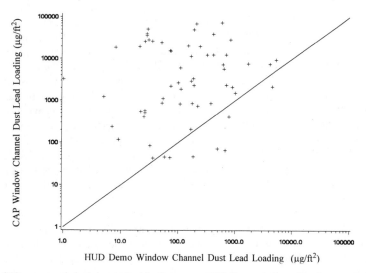

Figure 3--CAP vacuum window channel lead loading versus HUD Demonstration wipe clearance testing results: geometric mean lead loading ($\mu g/ft^2$) by room. (Note: 1 $\mu g/ft^2$ = 10.76 $\mu g/m^2$.)

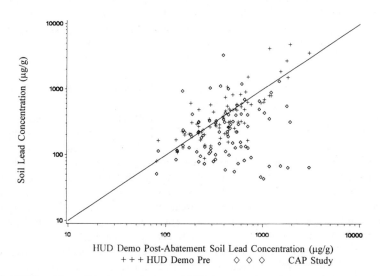

Figure 4--CAP foundation soil lead concentration and HUD Demonstration pre-abatement results versus HUD Demonstration post-abatement results: geometric mean lead concentration ($\mu g/g$) by side of unit.

As is evidenced in the figures, there is often little agreement between the CAP Study results and those from the HUD Demonstration. It is interesting to note in Figure 1 that the CAP Study wipe sampling lead loadings for floors were generally lower than those from clearance testing in the HUD Demonstration, while in Figure 3 the CAP Study results for window channels were generally higher than those from HUD Demonstration clearance testing. The higher dust lead loadings from the CAP Study, most apparent for the window channel samples, may be due to several reasons, including increased lead concentration in the dust, greater efficiency of the vacuum sampler employed, or more dust accumulating since the units were reoccupied. In contrast, the lower CAP Study wipe sampling results for floors might be due to differences in the sampling and/or chemical analysis protocols, or to the fact that the housing units were occupied during the CAP Study but unoccupied during HUD abatement activities.

Figure 4 compares the HUD Demonstration and CAP studies relative to soil lead concentrations collected at the foundation on the same side of each housing unit. Both HUD pre-abatement and post-abatement soil samples are included as a basis of comparison. Note that the HUD Demonstration pre- and post-abatement results appear relatively well correlated. The CAP soil lead concentrations, in contrast, exhibit a higher degree of scatter, and are generally lower than the HUD Demonstration post-abatement soil lead levels. Possible reasons for the lower CAP Study results include differences in sampling and chemical analysis protocols, as well as possible changes in the true soil lead concentrations over time.

RESULTS CONCERNING CORRELATIONS AMONG LEAD LEVELS

The third objective of the CAP Study was to investigate the relationship between lead levels in different media (i.e., dust and soil) and different sampling locations (e.g., floors, window channels, foundation soil). These relationships were quantified by housing unit-level and room-level correlation coefficients. Unit-level correlations reflect house-to-house relationships among different sample types, such as between air ducts and window channels. Room-level correlations are similar measures, except they are based on room-to-room differences within a house, after controlling for house average lead levels. Correlation coefficients were calculated for both lead loadings and lead concentrations. Only a relatively small number of correlation coefficients were found to be significant, and almost all of the significant correlations were found at the unit level. Therefore, only these unit-level correlation results are presented in Tables 3 and 4.

At the house level, significant correlations in dust lead loadings (Table 3) were found for three pairs of sample types. These were between lead loadings in window channels and window stools (correlation coefficient of 0.56), in air ducts and exterior entryways (0.41), and between floor (wipe) samples and exterior entryways (0.44). Significant correlations in lead concentrations at the house level (Table 4) were found for four pairs of sample types. These were between lead concentrations in window

TABLE 3--Correlations* Among Sample Types for Unit-Level Effects: Lead Loading.

	Air Duct	Window Channel	Window Stool	Floor (Wipe)	Entryway Exterior (Dust)
Air Duct		.16 33 .37	.13 37 .43	.25 21 .26	.41 36 .01
Window Channel			.56 41 <.01	-.08 25 .68	.12 40 .43
Window Stool				-.03 27 .87	.09 45 .55
Floor (Wipe)					.44 27 .02
Entryway Exterior (Dust)					

* Top number is estimated correlation; middle number is degrees of freedom; and bottom number is significance level.

TABLE 4--Correlations* Among Sample Types for Unit-Level Effects: Lead Concentration.

	Vacuum				Soil		
	Window Channel	Window Stool	Entryway Interior	Entryway Exterior	Entryway	Foundation	Boundary
Window Channel		.40 41 .01	.27 40 .08	.26 40 .10	.23 41 .13	.07 24 .72	.15 39 .35
Window Stool			.07 44 .63	-.06 45 .70	.18 46 .22	.12 29 .53	.38 44 .01
Entryway Interior				.25 43 .09	.29 44 .05	.26 28 .16	.22 43 .15
Entryway Exterior					.18 45 .22	.32 28 .08	-.12 43 .44
Entryway						.29 29 .11	.56 44 <.01
Foundation							.09 29 .93
Boundary							

* Top number is estimated correlation; middle number is degrees of freedom; and bottom number is significance level.

channels and window stools (0.40), between entryway soil and boundary soil (0.56), between boundary soil and window stools (0.38), and between entryway soil and interior entryway dust (0.29). At the room level, no significant correlations in dust lead loadings were found. However, significant correlation in lead concentrations was observed between interior and exterior entryway dust lead concentration (0.37, not shown in tables).

DISCUSSION OF RESULTS

The CAP Study results provide potentially important information about the role of relatively high-cost abatement procedures for eliminating, or controlling, residential lead-based paint which may contribute to cases of childhood lead poisoning. The CAP Study found that in several cases lead levels at houses abated during the HUD Demonstration study were higher than those at control houses. In addition, lead levels in abated rooms were sometimes higher than those in control rooms of the same houses. Both of these results seem to suggest that lead introduced to a housing environment by lead-based paint can not be completely controlled by abatement. However, in soil samples and air ducts, no lead abatement was done in the HUD Demonstration. Therefore, one would expect the lead levels to be different in these cases. Also, the CAP Study results suggest that the HUD Abatement Demonstration procedures may, in many cases, be able to maintain future lead levels below the HUD interim standards for dust. Both floor and window stool dust lead loadings at abated houses were found to be below their respective HUD interim standards of 200 and 500 $\mu g/ft^2$ (2152 and 5380 $\mu g/m^2$). However, window channel lead loadings at both abated and control houses were found to be well above the HUD value of 800 $\mu g/ft^2$ (8608 $\mu g/m^2$).

Furthermore, one needs to recognize that the "abatement effects" estimated from this study are not increases in lead loading and lead concentrations due to abatement. They are estimates of the ratios of lead levels observed in houses which were abated to levels observed in a group of control houses which never needed to be abated. This group of control houses had different characteristics. For example, abated houses were an average of 17 years older. The study results indicated that lead levels were typically higher in houses abated by encapsulation/enclosure methods than in houses abated by removal methods. These results may suggest that encapsulation/enclosure methods are less effective, either because they raise more dust during the abatement, or because they can not contain the lead-based paint hazard as time goes on. However, an unfortunate confounding factor in the CAP Study was that encapsulation/enclosure methods were generally used on houses requiring significantly more abatement. That is, more lead-based paint was present in HUD Demonstration houses abated with encapsulation/enclosure methods than in houses abated with removal methods. Therefore, the higher lead levels observed at encapsulation/enclosure houses may be due more to the greater amounts of lead-based paint present than to the performance of the abatement methods.

REFERENCES

[1]   U.S. Department of Housing and Urban Development, Comprehensive and Workable Plan for the Abatement of Lead-Based Paint in Privately Owned Housing, report to Congress, Washington, DC, December 7, 1990.

[2]   U.S. Department of Housing and Urban Development, The HUD Lead-Based Paint Abatement Demonstration (FHA), Office of Policy Development and Research, Washington, DC, 1991.

[3]   Kinateder, J.G., Kumar, P., Buxton, B.E., Rust, S.W., Schwemberger, J.G., Lim, B.S., Dewalt, F.G., and Constant, P., "Comprehensive Abatement Performance Study: Part I -- Study Design and Characterization of Soil-Lead and Dust-Lead Levels", Lead in Paint, Soil, and Dust: Health Risks, Exposure Studies, Control Measures, Measurement Methods, and Quality Assurance, ASTM STP 1226, Michael E. Beard and S.D. Allen Iske, Eds., American Society for Testing and Materials, Philadelphia, 1994.

[4]   Dewalt, F.G. and Constant, P., Buxton, B.E., Rust, S.W., Lim, B., Schwemberger, J.G., "Sampling and Analysis of Lead in Dust and Soil for the Comprehensive Abatement Performance Study (CAPS):, Lead in Paint, Soil, and Dust: Health Risks, Exposure Studies, Control Measures, Measurement Methods, and Quality Assurance, ASTM STP 1226, Michael E. Beard and S.D. Allen Iske, Eds., American Society for Testing and Materials, Philadelphia, 1994.

[5]   Battelle Memorial Institute and Midwest Research Institute, 1993, "Draft Final Report, Comprehensive Abatement Performance Study", report to U.S. EPA Office of Pollution Prevention and Toxics, prepared under Contract No. 68-D2-0139 and Contract No. 68-D0-0137.

David E. Jacobs[1]

LEAD-BASED PAINT AS A MAJOR SOURCE OF CHILDHOOD LEAD POISONING: A REVIEW OF THE EVIDENCE

REFERENCE: Jacobs, D. E., **"Lead-Based Paint As A Major Source of Childhood Lead Poisoning: A Review of the Evidence,"** Lead In Paint, Soil and Dust: Health Risks, Exposure Studies, Control Measures and Quality Assurance, ASTM STP 1226, Michael E. Beard and S.D. Allen Iske, Eds, American Society for Testing and Materials, Philadelphia, 1995.

ABSTRACT: The current and historical evidence that lead-based paint constitutes a major source of lead poisoning in young children in the United States today is reviewed. Lead-based paint was recognized as a proximate cause of childhood lead poisoning before the turn of the century in Australia. Evidence continued to accumulate in this country that lead-based paint was associated with lead poisoning in residences. Congress attempted to correct this problem by passing the 1971 Lead-Based Paint Poisoning Prevention Act. Recent case studies, studies of environmental correlates of blood lead in children, and stable isotope ratio studies have all indicated that old deteriorated lead-based paint still in residences contributes significantly to levels of lead found in house dust and soil, especially during routine renovation and inadequate abatement activity. There is now evidence that the principal pathway of childhood lead exposure is from lead in paint and soil to house dust to hand dust to ingestion through normal childhood hand-to-mouth contact. There is also some evidence that direct ingestion of lead paint chips through pica behavior is responsible for some cases of lead poisoning. This body of historical, epidemiological and analytical evidence is contrasted with an unsubstantiated theoretical approach which argues that lead-based paint cannot be a major source of childhood lead poisoning. The current weight of the scientific evidence indicates that failure to control lead-based paint in older dwellings will result in continued exposure to lead for a large number of children.

KEYWORDS: lead, lead poisoning, lead-based paint, childhood lead poisoning, history

---

[1]Deputy Director, National Center for Lead-Safe Housing, Columbia, MD 21044

HISTORY OF POISONING FROM LEAD-BASED PAINT

The evidence that old deteriorated residential lead-based paint is a principal cause of childhood lead poisoning now spans a century. Nearly one hundred years ago, Australian researchers diagnosed lead poisoning in children [1] and identified lead-based paint as the source [2]. Gibson and his colleagues published several papers explaining how other potential sources of lead had been eliminated in those cases [3, 4, 5, 6]. In October 1991, the U.S. Centers for Disease Control indicated that "lead-based paint remains the major source of high-dose lead poisoning in the United States" [7]. The clinical literature of the last 60 years is replete with case reports documenting severe lead poisoning through evidence of lead in blood, paint chips in the gastro-intestinal tract, and no indication of other environmental sources of lead exposure [8, 9].

The first reported U.S. case of childhood lead poisoning due to lead-based paint was a fatality [10]. The case bears some striking similarities to current conditions, where the patient is returned to an environment where the source of lead exposure remains uncontrolled. The boy was admitted to the hospital comatose and with seizures, treated, and released to the same home environment, only to return with the same symptoms five months later. The physicians' report states that "We were much puzzled as to the source of the lead, until he was found with his mouth covered with white lead paint which he had bitten from the railings of his crib."

Other case reports appeared in the early part of this century, usually prompted by fatalities [11, 12, 13, 14]. By 1926, 15 separate U.S. medical publications described lead-based paint as a major source of childhood lead poisoning [15]. Similar reports appeared in other countries and many of them adopted regulations to control lead exposures for both children and industrial workers. Austria specifically banned the use of white lead in domestic interiors around 1910 [16] and a number of governments ratified a ban of white lead paint prepared by the International Labour Organization [17]. The governments ratifying the ban included Austria, Belgium, Bulgaria, Chile, Czechoslovakia, Estonia, France, Latvia, Poland, Romania, Spain, and Sweden. In the 1920's, other governments either banned the use of lead paint indoors or severely restricted children's contact with, including Great Britain, Tunisia, Cuba, Yugoslavia, and Greece [15]. However, in the U.S., the National Paint, Oil, and Varnish Association opposed it, and the US never ratified the ban. The result was that lead-based paint continued to be widely used for residential purposes, mostly up to 1950 - 1960; residential lead paint was not fully banned until 1978.

Despite these reports of adverse health effects, the use of lead paint for residential purposes was promoted by both industry and government due to its durability, washability, and aesthetic appearance. Government agencies recommending lead-based paint for residential purposes included the National Bureau of Standards, Federal Security Agency, U.S. Housing Authority, the Public Works Administration [15] and the US Department of Commerce [18]. By the late 1920's the number of lead poisoning cases received the attention of at least one insurance company and the US Bureau of Labor Statistics began to track the incidence of lead poisoning in both children and adult workers [19, 20].

Although the concentration of lead in paint started to decline in the 1940's and 1950's, reports of widespread childhood lead poisoning became more prevalent as physicians became more adept at diagnosing the illness.   Studies of numerous cases of lead-based paint poisoning were conducted in Baltimore [21, 22], Boston [23], New York City [24], and Chicago [25].   By the end of the fifties, over 6,000 cases had been reported.

Finally recognizing the hazard associated with the use of residential lead-based paint and lead-based paint on children's toys, the American National Standards Institute adopted a voluntary standard limiting the lead content in surface coatings to 1% [26].   However, the standard was unenforceable and no standards addressing old lead-based paint already applied to dwellings were developed.   Throughout the fifties the concentration of lead in new paint declined as new materials such as titanium gradually replaced the use of lead in residential paint [15, 27].

In 1970, the issue of lead-based paint was addressed by Congress.   At that time, it was estimated that 200 children died each year from lead poisoning, and of the 12,000 - 16,000 children who did not die, half were left mentally retarded.   Further, it was estimated that 6 - 28% of urban children had blood lead levels greater than 50 µg/dl [28].

CURRENT EVIDENCE OF LEAD POISONING FROM LEAD-BASED PAINT

Throughout the seventies and eighties, the paint and gasoline industries pointed fingers at each other and suggested that the other was responsible for the large numbers of children with lead poisoning.   The vice-president of the International Lead Zinc Research Organization stated that childhood lead poisoning is caused by "old lead-based paint which poor children eat either in the form of paint dust or chips." [29] A paint chemist associated with Sherwin Williams argued that "the excessive lead in the blood of small children derives at least 90% from vapor, dust, and soil spewed out from gasoline combustion and less than 10 percent from historic lead in old paint." [30].   Both groups argued that solutions were simple: "Simple, vigorous, periodic scrubbing of floors, sills, walls of inner home surfaces...can reduce dramatically and sufficiently the perceived and persistent lead now detected in homes of children.... 'Cleanliness is next to Godliness' was practiced by those legendary Dutch housewives who vigorously scrubbed their homes [and is] now needed above all other aspects of the lead-in-child[ren] problem..." [30].

It is now clear that the phase down of lead content in gasoline has been accompanied by a significant decline in average population blood lead levels [31].   However, it is also clear that large numbers of children still have blood lead levels associated with adverse health effects.   In 1984, the Agency for Toxic Substances and Disease Registry estimated that 17% of all American pre-school children had blood lead levels above 15 µg/dl [32].   Although it is likely that average blood levels have continued to decline over the past decade, large numbers of children are still believed to have blood lead levels above 10 µg/dl, the current threshold of concern.   Lead poisoning remains the most common childhood environmental disease [33] and can be prevented by controlling sources of lead in old paint, and the contaminated dust and soil it generates.

What exactly is the current evidence that old lead-based paint remains the major source of lead poisoning, especially for those populations at greatest risk?   There are three types of studies that yield insights into this question: Case study reports of the effect of disturbing or abating lead-based paint, studies of environmental correlates of blood lead levels in children, and analytical source identification studies through use of stable isotope ratio techniques.

Case Reports

First, there have been a number of case reports indicating that when old lead-based paint is disturbed in the course of ordinary housing rehabilitation, repainting or in the course of improper abatement activities, large quantities of lead dust are generated and often result in elevated blood lead levels. Rabinowitz et al. reported that mean blood lead correlated significantly with the amount of lead in indoor paint (p<0.01) and that refinishing activity in homes with lead paint was associated with an average 69 percent increase in blood lead level in the 249 infants studied [34]. Shannon and Graef reported that in a study of 370 newly lead-poisoned children, sources of lead poisoning included household renovation and paint chip ingestion (p<0.0001) [35]. Other researchers have reported cases where remodeling or renovation activity resulted in elevated blood lead levels [36, 37].

Inadequate cleanup and abatement of lead-based paint have also been associated with increases in blood lead levels. Amitai et al. reported that abatement measures involving dry scraping of lead-based paint resulted in a statistically significant increase of blood lead levels from a mean of 36.4 μg/dl to 42.1 μg/dl (p<0.001) in a cohort of 114 preschool children. However, when abatement was accomplished by covering or replacement of building components (i.e., minimizing the abrasion of the lead-based paint), blood lead levels declined by 2.25 μg/dl (p<0.005). In both cases, the long-term effect of abating lead-based paint was a decrease in blood lead levels from 36 μg/dl to 26 μg/dl (p<0.001) [38]. Farfel et al. found that improved abatement techniques resulted in lower blood lead levels than did so-called "traditional" abatement measures, which included torching and sanding of lead-based paint, although this result could not be detected over a long period of time [39]. He also demonstrated that "traditional" abatement actually increased blood lead levels in many cases. Charney demonstrated that post-abatement dust lead cleaning is important in reducing blood lead levels [40].

Environmental Correlate Studies

A number of recent studies have also examined the environmental correlates of children's blood lead levels. Rabinowitz reported that the blood lead level of 249 newborns in a two-year longitudinal study were highly correlated with lead in dust (r=0.4, p<0.01), soil (r=0.3, p<0.001) and paint (r=0.2, p<0.01). Furthermore, refinishing activity in the presence of lead paint was also significantly correlated with blood lead level [41]. Interestingly, total dust was not predictive of blood lead levels, suggesting that the quality of housekeeping may be less important than suggested by industry spokesmen such as Weaver.

Paint lead levels were also correlated with blood lead levels in a prospective study in Cincinnati, as was hand dust lead and interior dust lead. The correlation coefficients between paint lead and blood lead were between 0.3 and 0.4 for children aged 6 to 24 months and was significant (p<0.0001). Interior dust loading (mg/m^2) was also correlated with blood lead, with a range of correlation coefficients from 0.37 to 0.48 for ages 12-42 months, also significant at p=0.0001 [27]. This same group also demonstrated that housing that had been rehabilitated (i.e., housing which had most of the lead paint removed) had lower dust lead levels and lower blood lead levels than did private non-rehabilitated housing that still contained lead-based paint and that was deteriorated and dilapidated. The highest blood lead levels were found in children living in deteriorated pre-WWII housing where lead paint concentrations were highest. Importantly, the general location of the rehabilitated housing and the dilapidated private housing was the same [42]. If it were true that exposures were due primarily to historic deposition of lead gasoline particulate into soil and not lead-based paint, there should have been no difference in blood lead levels between these two groups of children living in areas with similar traffic patterns. Furthermore, in the EPA three cities study, soil removal resulted in a very small decline in blood lead levels only when baseline soil lead levels were approximately 2,000 µg/g [43].

Chisolm et al. also found that there were statistically significant differences in blood lead levels for those children who had been treated for lead poisoning and released to "lead-free" public housing (average blood lead level = 28.8 µg/dl) and gut rehabilitated housing (average blood lead level = 28.7 µg/dl) on the one hand and older homes that had been "traditionally" abated and still contained some lead-based paint (average blood lead level = 38.5 µg/dl) [44].

In 1990, the Department of Housing and Urban Development released the results of a major national survey of the extent of lead-based paint and leaded dust in private housing. The study found that a dwelling was 4 times more likely to have dust lead levels above HUD clearance standards if lead-based paint was present than if the dwelling contained no lead-based paint. Seventeen percent of occupied housing with lead-based paint had excessive dust lead levels, while only 4 percent of the houses without any lead based paint had high dust lead levels. Similarly, the chance of exterior soil containing lead levels greater than EPA guidelines was 4 to 5 times greater if there was exterior lead-based paint [45].

Data on the prevalence of lead paint in 80,000 Chicago housing units and blood lead levels in children showed a relative risk of approximately 15 for lead toxicity for children who reside in homes with lead-based paint [48, 49].

Taken as a group, these environmental correlate studies indicate that the most likely route of exposure is from lead-based paint to dust and soil to hand lead to blood lead. Some portion of the soil and exterior dust lead is also likely to be due to deposition of lead from past use of gasoline, nearby demolition activity and industrial point sources. Table 1 summarizes a number of studies showing that lead in paint contributes substantially to lead in dust and soil.

Source Identification Studies

There is one additional source of evidence that lead-based paint is a major source of lead poisoning in children today. Yaffe et al. have reported that the isotopic ratios of lead in the blood of a small group of children in California were close to the average lead ratios of paint from exterior walls and the ratios of lead in soil. The study concluded that the lead in the soil was derived mainly from weathering of lead-based exterior paints and that the lead-contaminated soil was the proximate source of lead in the blood of children [46].

TABLE 1 -- Studies of the Contribution of Leaded Paint to Lead in Dusts and Soils

Study Site	Study Design	Results	References
Lead-painted frame and brick homes, Detroit, Mich. area	Soil lead vs. distance from test buildings (N=18 each type)	Lead in soil 2 ft. away was 5 times higher than in samples 10 ft. away.	Ter Haar and Aronow, 1974 [53]
Lead-painted rural barns and urban homes with leaded paint	Soil lead vs. distance from two painted building types	Similar soil lead content for both building types	Ter Haar and Aronow, 1974 [53]
Outside areas around homes in small town	Dust lead samples, curbside vs. at building line; electron microscopic chemical and surface analysis with element markers	24-85% of dwelling-line lead particles were from paint flakes	Linton et al., 1980 [54]
House dust from homes, Christchurch, New Zealand	Housedust lead as function of home age and type: painted surface, brick, etc.	In homes with leaded paint in interiors, paint lead adds 45% to total dust lead content	Fergusson and Schroeder, 1985 [55]
Neighboring soils, bridge in Mystic, Conn.	Distance-stratified soil lead (1-cm layer) from bridge during and after lead paint removal	Soil lead 8,127 µg/g at bridge; 3,272 µg/g up to 3 m away; 457 µg/g 30-80 m away; and 197 µg/g 100 m away	Landrigan et al., 1982 [56]

TABLE 1 (continued) -- Studies of the Contribution of Leaded Paint to Lead in Dusts and Soils

Study Site	Study Design	Results	References
Variable-quality housing, Cincinnati, Ohio	Dust lead (internal and external) and dust fall rate vs. house age, paint lead, and condition	All measures much higher in poor housing with paint lead	Clark et al., 1985 [42]
Variable-quality housing, Cincinnati, Ohio	Statistical analysis (structural equation modeling) of lead pathway in 18-month-olds	Paint lead and external-dust lead explain 52% of dust-lead variation; paint lead correlated with external-dust lead	Bornschein et al., 1987 [57]
Various residential areas and homes undergoing deleading	Analysis of housedust lead or child blood lead from paint dust generated during and after paint lead removal	Such dust formation has substantial effect on child exposure and blood lead	Rey-Alvarex and Menke-Hargrave, 1987 [58]; Amitai et al., 1987 [59]; Farfel and Chisolm, 1987 [39]; Rabinowitz et al., 1985 [41]; Charney et al., 1983 [40]
Playground areas at schools undergoing lead-paint removal and repainting	279 schools in London, England, tested for play-area dust lead before, during and after removal of old paint	Substantial increases in play-area dust lead after old-paint removal	Schwar and Alexander, 1988 [60]

SOURCE: "Measuring Lead Exposure in Infants, Children and other Sensitive Populations," National Research Council, National Academy Press, Washington DC, 1993.

ARGUMENTS THAT LEAD IN PAINT IS NOT A MAJOR SOURCE

A few other arguments are sometimes advanced to support the idea that in spite of all the evidence to the contrary, lead-based paint cannot be responsible for childhood lead poisoning. The first is that we are "overwhelmed" by larger amounts of lead from gasoline, since much more lead was used in gasoline than in paint [30]. However, a tabulation of industry data indicates that about seven million tons of lead have been used in the US for white lead paint, with a roughly equal amount used for leaded gasoline [47, 27]. This does not include about 400,000 additional tons of red lead that may have been used in residential lead paint. In short, the data show that similar amounts of lead were used in both paint and gasoline and that gasoline could not "overwhelm" paint as a significant source.

Another argument the idea that lead in paint is in an intact or "bound" form and therefore not available to young children. However, it should be fairly obvious that intact paint does not stay that way. In fact, there are a number of deteriorated paint conditions formally used by the painting and decorating industries to describe routine paint failures [50]. These include "aligatoring, blistering, checking, cracking, flaking, chalking and peeling." The idea that old lead-based paint will remain intact forever and not become available for ingestion, especially in dilapidated housing, is naive at best. In fact, it is more likely that most houses exhibit at least some deteriorated paint routinely. Additionally, there is evidence that a significant proportion of children exhibit pica behavior, i.e., direct ingestion of non-food items, in this case deteriorated lead-based paint that is removed from a surface or has fallen to the floor or the soil. Estimates of pica behavior among children range from 6% in some populations [51] to as much as 30% to 50% in others [52].

CONCLUSION

There is a substantial body of historical, epidemiological, and analytical evidence indicating that lead-based paint is the major source of lead poisoning in children in the United States today. The main pathway of exposure appears to be from lead in paint to lead in house dust and soil to lead hand dust to blood lead through normal hand to mouth contact. Another important pathway is through direct ingestion of paint chips. The current weight of the scientific evidence indicates that failure to control lead-based paint in older dwellings will result in continued exposure to lead for a large number of children.

Soil also contains some lead from previous use of leaded gasoline, from industrial point sources in some locations, and from paint during demolition and repainting activities.

While exposures conceivably can be interrupted at any step along these pathways (e.g., by controlling dust and soil and deteriorated paint only), lead-based paint will eventually deteriorate or be removed through renovation and repainting activities and re-enter the pathways, presenting an immediate hazard. The removal of lead from gasoline produced enormous public health benefits and is instructive as an example of effective source control through removal. However wholesale removal of all lead-based paint in housing is unlikely in the near term, given the existing crisis in affordable housing and the difficult (though not impossible) engineering problems associated with dust control during removal. Nevertheless, this review should make it clear that it was a serious error to permit lead-based paint to be used in housing in the first place. The cost of this error will be borne over the next century by more costly housing renovations, increased repainting safety practices, the on-going costs of vigilant management controls to ensure that intact lead-based paint does not deteriorate and become an immediate hazard, and, of course, the continuing costs incurred by lead-poisoned children. Further research is needed to quantify the rate of entry of lead from paint into the various exposure pathways to provide better guidance on the type and extent of the management and maintenance controls needed.

In spite of these substantial costs, there are signs that the nation is struggling to achieve the proper balance. Lead-based paint is no longer being ignored as an important source of lead exposure. Exposures in the nation's public housing program are being controlled through a reasonable combination of abatement and interim control efforts. The Residential Lead Hazard Reduction Act of 1992 provides a means of bringing major control efforts to most federally-supported housing and also provides a means for formal disclosure of lead-based paint hazards in all private housing. The Act also provides for some important research endeavors that should provide insights on the most cost-effective means of treating lead-based paint hazards. These are all important steps forward in the twin efforts to provide lead-safe housing and eliminate childhood lead poisoning.

REFERENCES

[1]   Turner, J. A., "Lead Poisoning Among Queensland Children," Australasian Medical Gazette, Vol. 16, 1897, pp. 475-479.

[2]   Gibson, J. L., "A Plea for Painted Railings and Painted Walls of Rooms as the Source of Lead Poisoning Amongst Queensland Children," Australasian Medical Gazette, Vol. 23, 1904, pp. 149-153.

[3]   Gibson, J. L., "Plumbic Ocular Neuritis in Queensland Children," British Medical Journal, Vol. 2, 1908, pp. 1488-1490.

[4]   Gibson, J. L., "The Importance of Lumbar Puncture in the Plumbar Ocular Neuritis of Children," Transactions of the Australasian Medical Congress, Vol. 2, 1911, p. 750.

[5]   Breinl, A., and Young, W. J., "The Occurrence of Lead Poisoning Amongst North Queensland Children," Annals of Tropical Medicine and Parasitology, Vol. 8, 1914, pp. 575-590.

[6]   Gibson, J. L., "The Diagnosis, Prophylaxis and Treatment of Plumbic Ocular Neuritis," Medical Journal of Australia, Vol. 2, 1917, pp. 201-204.

[7]   Centers for Disease Control, Preventing Lead Poisoning in Young Children, Atlanta, Georgia, U.S. Department of Health and Human Services, 1991.

[8]   Agency for Toxic Substances and Disease Registry, The Nature and Extent of Lead Poisoning In Children in the United States, A Report to Congress, Atlanta, Georgia, 1988.

[9]   Airborne Lead in Perspective, National Research Council, National Academy Press, Washington, D.C., 1972.

[10]   Thomas, H. M. and Blackfan, K. D., "Recurrent Meningitis, Due to Lead, in a Child of Five Years," American Journal of Diseases of Children, Vol. 8, 1914, pp. 377-380.

[11]   Blackfan, K. D., "Lead Poisoning in Children," American Journal of Medical Science, Vol. 153, 1917, pp. 877-887.

[12]   Strong, R. A., "Meningitis Caused by Lead Poisoning in a Child of Nineteen Months," Archives of Pediatrics, Vol. 37, 1920, pp. 532-537.

[13]   Holt, H. E., and Howland, J., The Diseases of Infancy and Childhood, 8th Edition, New York, D. Appleton-Century Co., 1923.

[14]   Weller, C. V., "Some Clinical Aspects of Lead Meningo-Encephalopathy," Annals of Clinical Medicine, Vol. 3, 1925, pp. 604-613.

[15]   Reich, P., "The Hour of Lead," Environmental Defense Fund, 1992, Washington D. C.

[16]   Oliver, T., "Lead Poisoning: From the Industrial, Medical, and Social Points of View," 1914, New York, Paul B. Hoeber.

[17]   International Labour Office, White Lead, Studies and Reports Series F (Industrial Hygiene), No. 11, Geneva, 1927.

[18]   Walker, P., and Hickson, E., Paint Manual, With Particular Reference to Federal Specifications, Washington D.C., 1945, U. S. Department of Commerce.

[19]   Hoffman, F. L., "Deaths from Lead Poisoning," Bulletin No. 426, Bureau of Labor Statistics, 1927, Washington, D.C., Government Printing Office.

[20]   Metropolitan Life Insurance Company, "Chronic Lead Poisoning in Infancy and Early Childhood," Statistical Bulletin, Vol. 11, No. 10, 1930, p. 4.

[21]   Williams, H., Kaplan, E., Couchman, C. E., and Sayres, R. R., "Lead Poisoning in Young Children," Public Health Reports, Vol. 67, 1952, pp. 230-236.

[22]   Chisolm, J. J., and Harrison, H. E., "The Exposure of Children to Lead," Pediatrics, Vol. 18, 1956, pp. 943-958.

[23]   Byers, R. K., "Urinary Excretion of Lead in Children," American Journal of Diseases of Children, Vol. 87, 1954, pp. 548-558.

[24]   McLaughlin, M. C., "Lead Poisoning in Children in New York City, 1940 - 1954," New York State Medical Journal, Vol. 56, 1956, pp. 3711-3714.

[25]   Jenkins, C. D., and Mellins, R. B., "Lead Poisoning in Children," American Medical Association Archives of Neurological Psychology, Vol. 77, 1957, pp. 70-78.

[26]   ANSI Z66.1-1955, "Specifications to Minimize Hazards to Children from Surface Coating Materials," American National Standards Institute, Inc., New York, 1955.

[27]   Clark, S., Bornschein, R., Succop, P., Roda, S., and Peace, B., "Urban Lead Exposures of Children in Cincinnati, Ohio," Chemical Speciation and Bioavailability, Vol. 3, 1991, No. 3, pp. 163-171.

[28]   Hearings before the Subcommittee on Health of the Committee on Labor and Public Welfare, Nov. 23, 1970, Washington DC, Government Printing Office.

[29]   Cole, J., "Old Paint, Not Gasoline, Is the Problem in Lead Poisoning", The New York Times, August 23, 1982.

[30]   Weaver, J. C., "A White Paper on White Lead," ASTM Standardization News, April 1989, pp. 34-38.

[31]   Annest, J. L., "Trends in the Blood Lead Levels of the US Population," In: Lead versus Health, Rutter, M., and Jones, R. R., editors, 1993, John Wiley and Sons, Chichester and New York, pp. 33-58.

[32]   U. S. Agency for Toxic Substances and Disease Registry. Nature and Extent of Childhood Lead Poisoning in the United States - Report to Congress. Washington, D. C. Department of Health and Human Services, 1988, p. II-5.

[33]   Centers for Disease Control, Strategic Plan for the Elimination of Childhood Lead Poisoning, U. S. Department of Health and Human Services, Atlanta, 1991.

[34]   Rabinowitz, M., Leviton, A., and Bellinger, D., "Home Refinishing, Lead Paint, and Infant Blood Lead Levels," American Journal of Public Health, Vol. 75, 1985, No. 4, pp. 403-404.

[35]   Shannon, M. W., and Graef, J. W., "Lead Intoxication in Infancy," Pediatrics, Vol. 89, No. 1, 1992, pp. 87-90.

[36]   Fischbein, A., Anderson, K. E., Shigeru, S., Lilis, R., Kon, S., Sarkoi, L., Kappas, A., "Lead Poisoning from "Do It Yourself" Heat Guns for Removing Lead-Based Paint: Report of Two Cases," Environmental Research, Vol. 24, 1981, pp. 425-431.

[37]   Marino, P. E., Landrigan, P. J., Graef, J., Nussbaum, A., Bayan, G., Boch, K., and Boch, S., "A Case Report of Lead Paint Poisoning during Renovation of a Victorian Farmhouse," American Journal of Public Health, Vol. 80, No. 10, 1990, pp. 1183-1185.

[38]   Amitai, Y., Brown, M. J., Graef, J. W., and Cosgrove, E., "Residential Deleading: Effects on the Blood Lead Levels of Lead-Poisoned Children," Pediatrics, Vol. 88, No. 5, 1991, pp. 893-897.

[39]   Farfel, M. R., and Chisolm, J. J., "Health and Environmental Outcomes of Traditional and Modified Practices for Abatement of Residential Lead-Based Paint," American Journal of Public Health, Vol. 80, No. 10, 1990, pp. 1240-1245.

[40]   Charney, E., Kessler, B., Farfel, M., and Jackson, D., "A Controlled Trial of the Effect of Dust-Control Measures on Blood Lead Levels," New England Journal of Medicine, Vol. 309, No. 18, 1983, pp. 1089-1093.

[41]   Rabinowitz, M., Leviton, A., Needleman, H., Bellinger, D., and Waternaux, C., "Environmental Correlates of Infant Blood Lead Levels in Boston," Environmental Research, Vol. 38, 1985, pp. 96-107.

[42]   Clark, S., Bornschein, R. L., Succop, P., Que Hee, S. S., Hammond, P. B., and Peace, B., "Condition and Type of Housing as an Indicator of Potential Environmental Lead Exposure and Pediatric Blood Lead Levels", Environmental Research, Vol. 38, 1985, pp. 46-53.

[43]   Weitzman, M., Aschengrau, A., Bellinger, D., Jones, R., Hamlin, J. S., and Beiser, A., "Lead-Contaminated Soil Abatement and Urban Children's Blood Lead Levels," Journal of the American Medical Association, Vol. 269, No. 13, 1993, pp. 1647-1654.

[44]   Chisolm, J. J., Mellits, E. D., and Quaskey, S. A., "The Relationship between the Level of Lead Absorption in Children and the Age, Type and Condition of Housing," Environmental Research, Vol. 38, 1985, pp. 31-45.

[45]   US Department of Housing and Urban Development, Comprehensive and Workable Plan for the Abatement of Lead-Based Paint in Privately-Owned Housing: A Report to Congress, December 7, 1990, Washington DC.

[46]   Yaffe, Y., Flessel, C. P., Wesolowski, J. J., Rosario, A. D., Guirguis, G. N., and Matia, V., "Identification of Lead Sources in California Children Using the Stable Isotope Ratio Technique," Archives of Environmental Health, Vol. 38, No. 4, 1983, pp. 237-245.

[47]   Minerals Yearbook 1932-33 through 1988, U. S. Bureau of Mines 1989, Washington DC in Clark 1991.

[48]   Annest, J. L., and Mahaffey, K., "Blood Lead Levels for Persons Aged 6 Months to 74 Years, United States 1976-80," Vital and Health Statistics, Series 11, 1984, No. 233, DHHS Publ. No. (PHS) 84-1683, Washington, D.C.

[49]   Schwartz, J., and Levin, R., "The Risk of Lead Toxicity in Homes with Lead Paint Hazard," Environ. Research, Vol. 54, 1991, pp. 1-7.

[50]   NDPA, "Paint Problem Solver" (Fourth Edition), National Decorating Products Association, St. Louis, 1990.

[51]   Mahaffey, K. R., and Annest, J. L., "Association of Blood Lead Level, hand-to mouth activity and pica among young children," In: 69th Annual Meeting of the Federation of American Societies for Experimental Biology, Anaheim, Fed. Proc. Vol. 44, April 21-26, p. 752.

[52]   Barltrop, D., "The prevalence of pica," American Journal of the Disabled Child, Vol. 112, 1966, pp. 116-123.

[53]   Ter Har, G. and Aronow R., "New Information on Lead in Dirt and Dust as Related to the Childhood Lead Problem," Environmental Health Perspectives, May 1974, p. 83-89.

[54]   Linton, R.W., Natusch D.F.S., Solomon, R.L., Evans, C.A., "Physicochemical Characterization of Lead in Urban Dusts: A Microanalytical Approach to Lead Tracing," Environmental Science and Technology, 14, 1980, p. 159-164.

[55]   Fergusson, J.E. and Schroeder, R.J., "Lead in House Dust of Christchurch, New Zealand: Sampling, Levels and Sources," Science of the Total Environment, 46, 1985, p. 61-72.

[56]   Landrigan, P.J., Baker, E.L., Himmelstein, J.S., Stein, G.F., Weddig, J.P. and Straub, W.E., "Exposure to Lead from the Mystic River Bridge: The Dilemma of Deleading," New England Journal of Medicine, 306, 1982, p. 673-676.

[57]   Bornschein, R.L., Succop, P.A., Krafft, K.M., Clark, C.S., Peace, B., Hammond, P.B., "Exterior Surface Dust Lead, Interior House Dust Lead and Childhood Lead Exposure in an Urban Environment," Trace Substances in Environmental Health, 20, 1987, p. 322-332

[58]   Rey-Alvarez, S., Menke-Hargrave, T, "Deleading Dilemma: A Pitfall in the Management of Childhood Lead Poisoning," Pediatrics, 79, 1987, p. 214-217.

[59]   Amitai, Y., Graef, J.W., Brown, M.J., Gerstle, R.S., Kahn, N., and Cochrane, R.E., "Hazards of Deleading Homes of Children with Lead Poisoning, American Journal of the Disabled Child, 141, 1987, p. 758-760.

[60]   Schwar, M.J. and Alexander, D.J., "Redecoration of External Leaded Paint Work and Lead-In-Dust Concentrations in School Playgrounds," Science of the Total Environment, 68, 1988, p. 45-59.

Measurement Methods

Sharon L. Harper[1], William F. Gutknecht[2], and Michael E. Beard[1]

PERFORMANCE EVALUATIONS OF MEASUREMENT METHODS USED FOR LEAD-BASED PAINT CONTAMINATED MEDIA: CURRENT STATUS

REFERENCE: Harper, S.L., Gutknecht, W.F., and Beard, M.E., "Performance Evaluations of Measurement Methods Used for Lead-based Paint Contaminated Media," Lead in Paint, Soil and Dust: Health Risks, Exposure Studies, Control Measures, Measurement Methods, and Quality Assurance, ASTM STP 1226, Michael E. Beard and S.D. Allen Iske, Eds., American Society for Testing Materials, Philadelphia, 1995.

ABSTRACT: Evaluations of the performance of methods used to measure lead in paint and in paint-contaminated medias are being conducted by EPA's Atmospheric Research and Exposure Assessment Laboratory as part of an ongoing program to reduce the risks to lead exposures. The objectives of the program are (1) to improve the reliability of the measurements made in connection with soil, dust and paint abatement programs and (2) to reduce costs. Performance characteristics determined include bias, precision, interferences, working range, and throughput. Methods under evaluation include (1) the laboratory-based methods of atomic absorption, inductively-coupled plasma atomic emission, and X-ray fluorescence spectrometries and (2) the field-based methods of portable X-ray fluorescence spectrometry and test kits. Their performances were evaluated using, when available, Standard Reference Materials, method evaluation materials, and duplicate field samples. A review of the evaluations conducted to date is presented.

KEYWORDS: lead, paint, dust, soil, inductively coupled plasma emission spectrometry (ICP), atomic absorption spectroscopy (AAS), portable X-ray fluorescence (XRF), lead test kits, reference materials

---

---

[1]Chemist, Atmospheric Research and Exposure Assessment Laboratory, U.S. Environmental Protection Agency, Research Triangle Park, NC 27711

[2]Department Manager, Center for Environmental Measurements and Quality Assurance, Research Triangle Institute, Research Triangle Park, NC 27709

INTRODUCTION

It is estimated that 75% of U.S. housing contains leaded paint [1] and some residential neighborhoods have extensive soil lead contamination. These conditions put children and pregnant women at risk to exposure to lead and its adverse health effects. The US Environmental Protection Agency (EPA) publicly released its Strategy for Reducing Lead Exposures [2] in February, 1991 to address these and other lead risk factors. This strategy is interlinked and coordinated with the activities of other Federal Agencies. In support of these other programs, the EPA Office of Research and Development (ORD) has developed a Multimedia Lead Research Program that has identified lead-based paint abatement and urban soil-lead abatement as two of its most critical issues. In order to conduct wide-scale abatement programs, analytical methods are needed which are reliable, sufficiently sensitive, rapid, cost effective, readily available and capable of detection/measurement of lead in paint, dusts and soils. In addition, primary and secondary reference materials are needed to judge the performance of these methods. This paper presents a summary of the methods' performance evaluations that have been conducted to date in support of the ORD program by the Atmospheric Research and Exposure Assessment Laboratory (AREAL) and its contractor, the Research Triangle Institute (RTI).

APPROACH

Method Selection--First, the methods applicable to lead in paint and household dust, followed by methods for soil and street dust, are being evaluated for accuracy/bias, precision, working range, interferences and throughput. Methods typically used for these matrices, as well as methods used for lead in other medias, are being considered for evaluation. Methods with multimedia capability are of particular interest. Concurrent multimedia performance evaluations are conductd whenever possible. Both laboratory and field measurement techniques are included. As new technologies become commerically available, as well as refinements in existing technologies, they will be considered for incorporation into the evaluation process. Performance evaluations in the laboratory are performed first, followed by field evaluations as appropriate.

The initial step in the methods evaluation was the identification of the lead concentrations of concern to regulators and health scientists. Table 1 shows the lead concentrations of concern that were used as targets for methods development and evaluations. Methods were selected for evaluation if their working range included these lead levels of concern.

Performance Criteria-- Preliminary target performance criteria for quantitative and qualitative methods were developed. For quantitative methods, the target accuracy was 100 $\pm$10% on Standard Reference Materials and 100 $\pm$15-20% on secondary reference materials with target precision of $\pm$10% RSD. For qualitative methods [3] such as test kits, the target criteria were 95% positive responses at lead concentrations of 1.0 mg/cm^2 in paints and 95% negative responses at 0.1 mg/cm^2. For dusts, soils and street dust, target criteria were 95% positive responses at 450 ug Pb/g and 95% negative responses at 150 ug/g.

TABLE 1-- Lead Concentrations of Concern

Matrix		Concentration	Source
Paint			
Abatement		1.0 mg/cm^2 5000 ug/g	HUD [4][a]
New Paint		600 ug/g	CPSC [5][b]
Housedust			
Clearance	- Floor	200 ug/ft^2	HUD [4]
	- Window Sills	500 ug/ft^2	
	- Window Wells	800 ug/ft^2	
Soil and Dust		500-1000 ug/g	CDC [6][c]
Street Dust		Not determined	

[a] HUD- US Department of Housing and Urban Development [4]
[b] CPSC- Consumer Products Safety Commission [5]
[c] CDC - Centers for Disease Control [6]

Reference Materials--Judging the adequacy of the methods relative to these concentration and performance targets has been complicated by the lack of reference materials containing leaded paint contamination. At the start of the AREAL performance evaluations in late 1990, only one material was available - National Institute of Standards and Technology's (NIST) Standard Reference Material (SRM) 1579- Powdered Lead Based Paint at 11.87% Pb. The NIST paint films (shims) of 0.2 and 0.6 mg Pb/cm^2 were no longer available. No secondary reference materials existed for paints, dusts, or soils. Therefore, AREAL began the development of protocols that would result in the production of method evaluation (secondary reference) materials for paint and household dust. The EPA Environmental Monitoring Systems Laboratory in Las Vegas (EMSL/LV) will develop the protocols for soil and street dust. Target concentrations for the reference materials shown in Table 2 were identified at a workshop sponsored by EPA's Office of Pollution Prevention and Toxic Substances (OPPTS) in May 1991 [7]. These levels were chosen to bracket the concentrations typically analyzed. Real-world materials rather than synthetic matrices were specified for both SRMs as well as secondary reference materials.

NIST, through Interagency Agreements with EPA/ORD, is developing leaded paint contaminated Standard Reference Materials at multiple concentration levels for household dust, soil and street dust as well as three additional levels of powdered lead-based paint. Additionally, NIST is producing lead-paint research materials for use with test kits and other in-situ techniques. In July, 1992, NIST completed the production of the HUD-sponsored SRM 2579 Lead Paint Films on Milar for Portable X-ray Fluorescence Analyzers [8].

Production protocols for paint and housedust method evaluation materials have recently been completed and evaluated for AREAL by the

Research Triangle Institute (RTI). Details of these processes are given in references 9 and 10.

TABLE 2-- Target Concentrations for Reference Materials Containing Leaded Paint Contamination [7]

Matrix	Concentration	Rationale
Paint	500 ug/g	Near maximum Pb allowed in new paint [5]
	5000 ug/g	HUD action level [4]
	50000 ug/g	Typical laboratory sample concentration
Dust	50 ug/g	From exposure surveys
	500 ug/g	
	10000 ug/g	
Soil	20 ug/g	Found in rural areas
	1000 ug/g	Protective concentration - CDC [6]
	5000 ug/g	Typical laboratory sample concentration

As more and improved primary and secondary reference materials become available, they will provide an opportunity to reevaluate the laboratory and field methods to better characterize their overall performance across the lead concentrations typically encountered.

SUMMARY OF METHOD PERFORMANCE EVALUATIONS

Laboratory-based Methods--Laboratory-based methods of atomic absorption (AA) and inductively coupled plasma atomic emission (ICP) spectrometries were designated the confirmatory methods for paint analysis for abatement decisions by HUD [4]. Analysis of dust wipes used for clearance testing were also to be performed by AA or ICP. Although in wide use [4], neither the instruments' nor the extraction methods' performance had been thoroughly evaluated with leaded-paint containing materials.

A two-step evaluation was conducted at the levels of concern using the preliminary performance criteria as targets. Using solution standards, the AA and ICP sensitivity, working range, and precision were found adequate. No bias or interferences were observed. The extraction procedures were then evaluated for efficiency. The HUD Interim Guidelines [4] recommended six (6) methods for paint and four (4) for dust. The literature contained over 40 methods for lead, 26 for paint, dust and/or soil. Because of similarities, the extraction methods were assigned to one of three categories: 1) dry and wet ash (acid extracted); 2) wet ash; or 3) microwave. Ultimately, two methods from each category were evaluated. Details for selection are found in reference 11. Since leaded paint was the source of the lead contamination in the medias of concern, these six chosen extraction procedures were evaluated with 0.100 g aliquots of 11.87% Pb SRM 1579, Powdered Lead Based Paint. Triplicate extractions for each method were

performed. A >90% recovery criteria was used for the method to be
included in further performance evaluations. Three of the methods met
this criteria: ASTM D3335-85a, NIOSH 7082, and EPA AREAL/RTP-SOP-MRDD-
037. Their performance were futher evaluated using coarsely- and finely-
ground paint scrapings from old boards, leaded paint contaminated
housedusts and soils from EPA EMSL/LV, as well as SRMs 1648 (Urban
Particulate Matter) and 2704 (Buffalo River Sediment) as surrogates for
housedust and soil, respectively.

The ASTM 3335-85a consistently produced <90% recovery on the test
materials. The other two methods produced >94% recovery for the
materials tested. The details of the two methods used are found in
reference 12. Table 3 summarizes the performance of these two extraction
methods coupled with AA or ICP analysis for paints. Precision estimates
are from a round robin which used real-world materials as well as SRMs
as blind samples. Results for the bulk housedust samples in the round
robin are similar.

TABLE 3-- Lead Analysis of Paint

	Analysis	Extraction Method	
		Modified NIOSH 7082 Hotplate HNO_3/H_2O_2 100 ml final volume	EPA/AREAL Microwave HNO_3/HCl 20 ml final volume
Range	AA	0.2 - 20 ug/ml 200 - 20,000 ug/g	0.2 - 20 ug/ml 40 - 4,000 ug/g
	ICP	0.05 - 200 ug/ml 50 - 200,000 ug/g	0.05 - 200 ug/ml 10 - 40,000 ug/g
MDL[a]	AA	500 ug/g	100 ug/g
	ICP	50 ug/g	10 ug/g
Precision:[b] Repeatability	AA	7.8%	8.1%
	ICP	8.9%	6.7%
Reproducibility	AA	18.3%	12.5%
	ICP	17.8%	9.0%

[a] MDL- Method detection limit
[b] Precision from round robin of samples containing 1690 - 118,700
   ug Pb/g [12]; Repeatability is the within-laboratory precision and
   reproducibility is the between-laboratory precision.

Dust wipe materials and methods have been compared for relative
collection efficiency, lead blank levels, and analytical recovery of
lead collected on the wipes as well as from spikes of standard reference
and real world dust materials [13]. Additionally, three extraction

procedures were compared.

Description of the production of real-world matrix method evaluation samples and details of a round robin conducted to evaluate their performance are given in reference 14. These production protocols are being used to produce the performance evaluation audit samples for the Environmental Lead Proficiency Analytical Testing (ELPAT) program [15].

The performances demonstrated by these two extraction methods with AA or ICP analysis meet the target performance criteria outlined in the "Laboratory Accrediation Program Guidelines: Measurement of Lead in Paint, Dust and Soil" [16] for working range (0.1 to 10 x action level) and accuracy of 100 $\pm$10% for SRMs and 100 $\pm$15% on performance evaluation materials.

Procedures used for paint collection and removal are being investigated for their contribution to the total "laboratory" error. Additional investigations are continuing on the impacts of various paint preparation procedures on the performance of laboratory methods. Of special concern is the effect of grinding procedures on lead extractability as well as on subsampling homogeneity.

Additional types of laboratory instrumentation are capable of lead analysis. Laboratory X-ray fluorescence analysis has been used extensively in the Urban Soil Lead Abatement Demonstration Project (USLDP) [17] for soils. When one manufacturer's equipment was used and a rigorous protocol was followed, the results were comparable to AA and ICP. In another study incorporating a round robin [14], laboratories using three different brands of laboratory XRFs with varying operating conditions and sample preparation procedures demonstrated biases of less than 20% on paints and housedusts compared to AA and ICP results. Investigations are underway at the EPA EMSL/Las Vegas laboratory to generate a generic protocol to improve laboratory XRF performance. Additional techniques such as Inductively Coupled Plasma-Mass Spectrometry (ICP-MS) and Scanning Electron Microscopy-X-Ray Fluorescence (SEM/XRF) will be incorporated into the lead program due to their ability to produce additional types of information on Pb-containing samples.

Field Measurement Techniques--The most common field analysis devices used to measure lead in paint are portable X-ray fluorescence spectrometers (XRF) and lead test kits. Their analytical performance has been characterized only to a limited extent [1,4,18,19]. Precision and bias at or near the paint abatement level are of particular concern. These techniques have also been applied to a limited extent to dust and soil lead analysis [20,21]. These two field measurement techniques are included specifically in the ORD Multimedia Lead Research Program.

Other techniques that are nearing commerical introduction for the measurement of lead in paints, dusts and/or soils include lasers, ion specific electrodes, and various electrochemical techniques. These techniques will be considered for the evaluation process as they become commercially available for application to these medias.

Portable X-Ray Fluorescence Spectrometers--The performance of portable XRFs is being evaluated in stages. As previously mentioned, at the beginning of these evaluations in 1990, there were no available reference materials. The only source of known paint films for portable

XRF, the NIST-produced paint "shims", were exhausted. Therefore, before evaluations could begin, standards had to be developed. A series of synthetic paint films over the concentration range of 0.07 to 7.16 mg Pb/cm^2 were produced from new oil-based or latex paints spiked with white lead. Lead concentrations in the films were determined via random spot sampling, followed by extraction using the modified NIOSH 7082 procedure and ICP quantitation [12]. All of the XRF evaluations were conducted with these films.

The first XRF selected for laboratory evaluation [22] was the MAP-3, a spectrum analyzer manufactured by Scitec [23], due to its extensive use in the HUD National Survey [1]. Both K-shell and L-shell measurements were made during this laboratory evaluation. The impacts on the bias and precision were determined as changes were made to the parameters of measurement time, sample substrate, standard concentration and standard type. Additionally, the effect of varying the depth of the lead layer was examined.

The Scitec, which uses a ^{57}Co excitation source, was calibrated by the manufacturer in several different ways during the evaluations. The calibration ranges varied from 0.2 - 2.64 mg Pb/cm^2 to a maximum of 0.0 - 6.19 mg Pb/cm^2. The number of standards as well as the number of substrates used for the calibrations varied, with as many as 32 substrates for the maximum calibration range. Both "universal" as well as "substrate specific" calibration modes were used.

Measurement time is a controllable variable on the Scitec. Longer irradiation times normally give more precise results. However, a high throughput rate using the shortest measurement time that would produce precise results was desired. Therefore, measurement times of 30, 60 and 120 seconds were evaluated for precision using the K-shell and L-shell over the concentration range of 0.5 to 6.2 mg Pb/cm^2. No statistically significant improvement in precision was found by increasing the measurement time from 30 to 60 to 120 seconds [24]. The fact that Scitec uses a proprietary complex mathematical algorithm to process information from many parts of the emission spectrum may explain the lack of improvement with the increased measurement times.

The effect of substrates on this Scitec's bias and precision was determined in triplicate with 13 levels of paint films over eight substrates of varying densities [22]. Scitec does not recommend scraping of paint to get a substrate reading but uses a mathematical algorithm to correct for substrate interference. For the K-shell "universal" calibration mode of operation, with the exception of 4" cinderblock, all substrates showed a change in bias with a change in concentration of lead; the bias for 4" cinderblock was nearly constant. The bias values ranged from -0.7 mg Pb/cm^2 for 4" concrete to +4.4 mg Pb/cm^2 for solid cinderblock. The L-shell was less affected by the substrates.

The impact of the position of the lead layer of paint was evaluated. Lead-containing paint films laid over combinations of substrates showed higher results relative to single substrates. When three layers of no-lead paint films of ⁻0.3 mm thickness each were laid over the lead containing paint film, the lead signal was attenuated 100% for the L-shell and 50% for the K-shell. These three films equalled five to nine layers of old paint. The thickness of old paints were determined through measurement of individual layers of multilayed paint chips from old homes and found to be 0.1 - 0.2 mm thick. This is much thicker than the estimates of 0.025 - 0.050 mm derived from calculations using the spreading rate of 400 ft^2 per gallon of paint.

Variation in Pb concentrations across the component surface was checked for three different boards from an old house whose Pb concentrations ranged from 1.97 to 13.65 mg/cm^2. Six spots on each board were measured. Differences of 6.4 - 12.7% were found among the different spots on the individual boards. Remeasurements of the spots after scraping showed 50-99% of the Pb was removed. On one spot, ICP measurements were made on portions of the removed substrate as well as the removed paint. The XRF reading agreed with the ICP results if both the Pb from the paint and the substrate were added together.

The next phase of evaluation was to test the two other portable XRFs that were in wide commerical use [24, 25]. These also used ^{57}Co as the excitation source, but read the Pb X-ray emission directly, ie, "Direct Readers". They did not use software manipulations to correct for substrate effects. The Warrington MicroLead [26] used a scintillation counter as a detector while the Princeton-Gamma Tech XK-3 [27] used a Xe gas, proportional counter as a detector. Manufacturers' measurement procedures were also different. An experimental design was developed to compare these very different XRFs for bias and precision on as equal basis as possible. One instrument from each of the manufacturers was tested. Thirteen Pb concentrations of films covering 0.0 to 7.16 mg/cm^2 were used with the same eight substrates from the Scitec evaluation. Substrate corrections were made by manually subtracting the bare substrate reading. In this phase of the evaluation, the sequence of Pb concentrations and substrates were randomized.

The Warrington bias ranged from -0.03 mg Pb/cm^2 on plasterboard to 1.1 mg Pb/ cm^2 on concrete. The bias appeared to be concentration dependent for all substrates.

The PGT bias also exhibited a concentration-dependency with a minimum bias of 0.1 mg Pb/cm^2 for plasterboard and cinderblock to a maximum bias of -0.9 mg Pb/cm^2 for aluminum and steel. As an example, Table 4 shows the comparison of the three XRFs on plasterboard and plywood.

The performance characteristics determined were for in-laboratory evaluation of only one instrument for each manufacturer. To help determine if these characteristics were typical and to gather a larger information base upon which to design a set of experiments to generate or verify figures of merit for the technology, a workshop of government researchers and their contractors was sponsored by AREAL in January, 1993 [28]. Manufacturers were invited to send written input. Results of laboratory and field studies were reported by the participants. Technology needs as well as gaps were identified. From the 1 1/2 day workshop, the important parameters identified were: accuracy of manufacturer's calibration, precision, accuracy, detection limit, ruggedness, substrate effects and other interferences. Additional important parameters were identified that are difficult to measure experimently. Experiments to quantify these parameters were outlined as well as the need for real-world reference samples.

Building on the key findings of the XRF workshop, a pilot paint field study [29] was conducted in housing with target paint lead levels near 1 mg/cm^2 to acquire data on the key performance parameters. Results are being interpreted now.

TABLE 4-- Laboratory Performance Comparison of Portable XRFs Using Standard Paint Films on Substrates

	1/2" Plasterboard			3/4" Plywood		
	S[a]	W	P	S	W	P
Slope	1.04	0.92	0.81	0.93	0.87	0.80
Intercept	-0.11	0.10	0.10	-0.34	0.30	-0.20
Correlation Coefficient	0.985	0.998	0.986	0.972	0.998	0.986
Detection Limits (mg/cm^2)	0.2	0.4	0.6	0.2	0.4	0.8
Estimated Bias at 1 mg Pb/cm^2	-0.06	+0.03	-0.09	-0.41	+0.17	-0.40

[a] S, W, P indicate the results for Scitec, Warrington and Princeton-Gamma Tech XRFs, respectively

Evaluation of Lead Test Kits

Qualitative Test Kits-- In 1991, the first phase of the evaluation of commerically available lead test kits designed for homeowners and professional use was begun in the laboratory [30]. The manufacturers' directions were followed for the five test kits designed to test lead in solids. This initial investigation was designed only to determine the general behavior and responsiveness of the kits to a limited number of test parameters and with the very limited number of materials available at that time. Parameters that would not be controlled in the field, such as temperature, ionic strength or pH, were not controlled in the laboratory evaluations. Specific identification and investigation of causes of unexpected results were outside the scope of this first phase.

Four of the five kits were based on the reaction of lead with rhodizonate to form a pink complex. One kit used sodium sulfide's reaction with lead to form a black precipitate. Techniques of application varied by manufacturer and media to be tested. For paint, procedures ranged from in-situ testing such as rubbing the surface or cutting through all paint layers to removal of paint chips for overnight leaching and subsequent solution testing.

Dust and soil techniques used involved either direct contact of the solids with the indicator implement or leaching for two minutes to twenty-four hours with subsequent solution testing with the indicator implement.

To determine the lower limit of the response range of each kit, the kits were reacted with 10-80 microliter quantities of solution standard prepared from Pb(NO$_3$)$_2$ or Pb(Cl)$_2$ to generate thirteen concentration levels. Solution standards were chosen as they would not contain potential interferences nor be dependent on the extractability of the lead from the solid. Lead levels at which the kits changed from

100% negative results to 100% positive results for $Pb(NO_3)_2$ are shown in Table 5 by kit type for three trials each. $Pb(Cl)_2$ results were similar though not identical. Specifics by kit manufacturer are given in reference 30.

TABLE 5-- Qualitative Lead Test Kits Laboratory Evaluations

Media	Sample Type (# Levels) Conc Range[a]	Test Results		
		Response	Rhodizonate-based 4 Kit Types (# Responding)	Sulfide-based 1 Kit Type
Solution	$Pb(NO_3)_2$ (13) 0.1 - 4.0 ug	100% Neg 100% Pos	0.1 - 0.5 ug (4) 0.3 - 0.7 ug (4)	0.5 ug 2.0 ug
Paint	SRM 1579 (1) 11.87±0.04%	100% Neg 100% Pos	... 1187 ug (4)	... 1187 ug
	Synthetic film (6) 0.11-2.6 mg/cm^2	100% Neg 100% Pos	0.6-1.9 mg/cm^2 (4) 1.2-2.6 mg/cm^2 (4)	... <0.11 mg/cm^2
	Powdered Real (6) 18,000-55,000 ug/g	100% Neg 100% Pos	... 180 ug (4)	... 180 ug
Dust	SRM 1648 (1) 6,550±80 ug/g	100% Neg 100% Pos	65.5 ug (2) 65.5 ug (2)	... 65.5 ug
	Synthetic (4) 200-2300 ug/g	100% Neg 200% Pos	2.0 - 5.0 ug (4) 5.0 - 10.0 ug (4)	5.0 ug 10.0 ug
	Sieved Real (6) 60-2300, 21,000 ug/g	100% Neg 100% Pos	23.0 ug (4) 210.0 ug (4)	... <0.6 ug
Soil	SRM 2704 (1) 161±17 ug/g	100% Neg 100% Pos	1.61 ug (4) ...	... 1.61 ug
	Sieved Real (7) 330-15,000 ug/g	100% Neg 100% Pos	3.3 - 34.0 ug (4) 10.0 - 64.0 ug (4)	3.3 ug 10.0 ug

[a] 0.010 g sample aliquots used

Limited solution-based metal and salt interference tests were performed. Both positive (color-forming) as well as negative (color inhibiting) interferences were found and were in general agreement with the literature [31,32], considering the concentration ranges tested. With the rhodizonate kits, only the positive Ba^{+2} interference would be expected to potentially interfere in paint analysis. Subsequent evaluations by a kit manufacturer [33] have found $SO_4^=$ causes negative interferences. Positive interferences were not found for the rhodizonate kits for dusts and soils tested. The sodium sulfide kit exhibited positive responses for $Ag+$, $Co+^2$, $Cu+^2$, $Fe+^2$, $Fe+^3$, $Hg+^2$, $Ni+^2$, and $Tl+^2$. Paints, dusts, and/or soils may contain some of these metals. The kits were next evaluated with solid materials. Table 5 shows the lead levels found for 100% negative and 100% positive results. The levels are expressed as ug Pb for the 0.010 g sample aliquots for easier comparison to the solution results, with the exception of the synthetic paints. Kits results from solids testing showed response lead levels (100% positive) many times higher than the solution response. It must be noted again that only a few reference and real world materials were available for testing so that only a crude estimate of the characteristic response curve was obtainable.

Comparison of the results shown in Table 5 with the paint abatement target performance criteria [3] of 95% positive at >1.0 mg Pb/cm^2 or 5000 ug/g shows that for synthetic paints, some of the rhodizonate kits are only slightly above the target while the sulfide kit responded positively even to the "blank" paint film. No real-world samples nor SRMs were available for testing at concentrations close to the target concentration. For new/replacement paint as well as dusts and soils, a target of 95% positive results at 450 ug Pb/g was not achieved by any of the kits on the tested materials with the exception of the sulfide kit which appeared to give positive results even on the 60 ug/g real-world dust.

The results from this initial study have been shared with the manufacturers of the kits evaluated [30]. Current versions (1993) of the test kits appear to be greatly improved. Data provided by some of the test kit manufacturers to the participants at an AREAL-sponsored Test Kit Workshop [34] indicated consistent positive responses at the paint abatement target concentration. Independent field evaluations using test kits for paints and dusts are now being conducted by EPA [29]. Additionally, development and testing of experimental procedures designed to consistently produce the figures of merit across the test kit technology continue along the avenues recommended by the participants in the Test Kit Workshop. Key performance parameters identified for qualitative test kits included the defining of the performance curve (operating characteristic response curve) of the test kit and further identifying and characterizing interferences.

Quantitative Test Kit--Inconsistent extraction is one of the potential sources of varing responses of the test kits to Pb-containing solids. It was noted in the initial qualitative test kit study [30] that samples containing similar Pb concentrations from the same and from different medias did not respond identically. Therefore, a quantitative field extraction technique was developed that would be chemically compatable with Pb test kits [35]. It was then coupled to a commerically available quantitative field Pb analysis kit which had been used for water analysis, the Hach LeadTrak[R]. The LeadTrak[R] [36] is an eight (8) step water analysis kit which uses an ion exchange column to collect and concentrate the lead from the sample, followed by colorimetric analysis.

The quantitative field analysis system was therefore achieved by combining the two processes: the leaching of the solid sample with 25% v/v HNO_3 in an ultrasonic bath for 30 minutes, followed by dilution and detection using the LeadTrak[R]. For paints, the range of the method is from 0.03% to 0.60% Pb and, for bulk dusts and soils, from 0.01% to

0.24% Pb. The upper end of the ranges can be extended through dilution.
The results of this quantitative field analysis system were compared to
results from the microwave acid extraction/ICP procedure [12] to derive
the biases shown in Table 6 for the laboratory phase of this procedure's
evaluation. For SRMs and real-world samples of concentrations of 0.02%
to 11.9% Pb, biases of -11.9 to +11.7% were obtained, with the exception
of the lowest dust sample with a bias of +24.2%. Precisions for these
samples ranged from 3.7 to 16.4% RSD. Limited field testing indicates
that the achievable precision and bias are within a factor of two (2) of
those obtained in the laboratory, with the difficulty of field sample
preparation being the principal cause of the difference [35]. Complexity
of the sample and the colorimeter used may also affect the results.
Additional field studies are underway to better characterize the
system's performance.

Table 6-- Quantitative Field Analysis System Laboratory Evaluations

Media Aliquot size, g	Sample Type (# levels)	Concentration Range, ug/g (N)	Bias %	Precision % RSD
Paint 0.100	SRM 1579 (1)	118,700$\pm$400 (25)	-9.0	7.4
	Real World (3)	1620-36,000 (15)	-3.4 to +11.7	3.7 to 7.7
Dust 0.250	SRM 1648 (1)	6550$\pm$80 (5)	-5.8	7.0
	Real World (3)	351-9320 (5)	-1.7 to +24.2	4.7 to 11.9
Soil 0.250	SRM 2711 (1)	1162$\pm$31 (5)	-8.8	7.6
	Real World (3)	243-2940 (5)	-11.9 to -1.4	6.2 to 16.4

    The applicability of the quantitative field analysis system to
dust wipe samples is being tested [13]. The compatibility of the extract
from the field ultrasonic acid digestion procedure with the qualitative
test kits is also currently being investigated.

Conclusions

    A set of field as well as laboratory-based methods which respond
to Pb levels of concern have been identified and evaluated in the
laboratory with the available primary and secondary reference materials.
Limited field testing has been conducted. Evaluations have focused on
the performances of the methods at the concentrations of concern as well
as across the typical range of concentrations encountered. Preliminary
evaluation criteria have been developed. In addition, critical
performance parameters have been identified and experiments are being
designed that will consistently produce the figures of merit. Both
primary and secondary reference materials for paint and housedust are in
development, or have recently become available, to assist in the
determination of performance adequacy. Additional research continues to

better characterize the methods and their sources of error. Expanded
field studies are also underway.

ACKNOWLEDGEMENTS

We thank Dr. Robert Elias for his guidance, Mr. Warren Loseke for
his technical assistance, and the staff of RTI's Environmental Chemistry
Department for their experimental work.

DISCLAIMER

This paper has been reviewed in accordance with the U.S.
Environmental Protection Agency peer and administrative review policies
and approved for presentation and publication. Mention of trade names or
commerical products does not constitute endorsement or recommendation
for use.

REFERENCES

[1]   U.S. Department of Housing and Urban Development, "Comprehensive
       and Workable Plan for the Abatement of Lead-Based Paint in
       Privately Owned Housing, A Report to Congress." Washington, DC,
       December 1990.

[2]   U.S Environmental Protection Agency, "Strategy for Reducing Lead
       Exposures," Washington, DC, February 1991.

[3]   Williams, E.E., Estes, E.D., and Gutknecht, W.F., "Analytical
       Performance Criteria for Lead Test Kits and Other Analytical
       Methods," U.S. Environmental Protection Agency Contract 68-02-
       4550, Washington, DC, February, 1991.

[4]   "Lead-Based Paint: Interim Guidelines for Hazard Identification
       and Abatement in Public and Indian Housing," U.S. Department of
       Housing and Urban Development, Washington, DC, September 1990.

[5]   Consumer Product Safety Commission, "Consumer Product Safety Act,
       15 U.S.C., Part 16, Code of Federal Regulations 1303.1," pp.
       2057-2058, 1978.

[6]   Centers for Disease Control, "Preventing Lead Poisoning in Young
       Children," U.S. Department of Health and Human Services, 1985.

[7]   Williams, E.E., Groshe, P.M., Neefus, J.D., and Gutknecht, W.F.,
       "A Report on the Lead Reference Material Workshop." EPA 747/R-
       93/008, U.S. Environmental Protection Agency, Washington, DC,
       1991.

[8]   Pella, P.A., "Development of NIST Standard Reference Materials for
       Lead in Paint," _Lead in Paint, Soil, and Dust: Health Risks,
       Exposure Studies, Control Measures, Measurement Methods, and_

Quality Assurance, ASTM STP 1226, Michael E. Beard and S.D. Allen Iske, Eds., American Society for Testing Materials, Philadelphia, 1994.

[9]   Williams, E.E, Binstock, D.A., Estes, E.D., Neefus, J.D., Myers, L.E., and Gutknecht, W.F., "Preparation and Evaluation of Lead-Containing Paint and Dust Method Evaluation Materials. In: Proceedings of the Symposium of Lead Poisoning in Children: Exposure, Abatement and Program Issues, American Chemical Society, Washington, DC, 1992.

[10]   Binstock, D.A., Estes, E.D., Neefus, J.D., Williams, E.E., Gutknecht, W.F., Harper, S.L., and Beard, M.E., "Preparation and Evaluation of Lead-Contaminated Dust Method Evaluation Materials," Lead in Paint, Soil, and Dust: Health Risks, Exposure Studies, Control Measures, Measurement Methods, and Quality Assurance, ASTM STP 1226, Michael E. Beard and S.D. Allen Iske, Eds., American Society for Testing Materials, Philadelphia, 1994.

[11]   Binstock, D.A., O'Rourke, J.A., Hardison, D.L., White, J., Grohse, P.M., and Gutknecht, W.F., "Evaluation of Hotplate- and Microwave-based Methods for Extracting Lead in Paint, Dust and Soil with Measurement by Atomic Absorption Spectrometry and Inductively Coupled Plasma Emission Spectrometry," U.S. Environmental Protection Agency Contract 68-02-4550, Research Triangle Park, NC., 1992.

[12]   Binstock, D.A., Hardison, D.L., Grohse, P.M., and Gutknecht, W.F., Standard Operating Procedures for Lead in Paint by Hotplate- or Microwave-based Acid Digestion and Atomic Absorption or Inductively Coupled Plasma Emission Spectrometry. EPA 600/8-91/213, U.S. Environmental Protection Agency, Research Triangle Park, NC, 1991. Available from NTIS, Springfield, VA; NTIS PB92-114172.

[13]   Binstock, D.A., Hodson, L.L., Neefus, J.D., Gutkneckt, W.F., Harper, S.L., Pranger, L.J., and Beard, M.E., "Investigation of Wipe Methods Used for Collection on Lead-Based Paint Dust," presented at Lead in Paint, Soil, and Dust: Health Risks, Exposure Studies, Control Measures, Measurement Methods, and Quality Assurance, American Society for Testing Materials, Boulder, CO, July, 1994.

[14]   Williams, E.E., Binstock, D.A., and Gutknecht, W.F., "Preparation of Lead-Containing Paint and Dust Method Evaluation Materials and Verification of the Preparation Protocol by Round-Robin Analysis," EPA 600/R-93/235, U.S. Environmental Protection Agency, Research Triangle Park, NC, 1993.

[15]   Schlecht, P. and Grofe, J., "ELPAT Program Report: Background and Current Status," Applied Occupational Environmental Hygiene Journal, Vol 8, No. 8, 1993, p. 681.

[16] Task Group on Methods and Standards of the Federal Interagency Lead-based Paint Task Force, "Laboratory Accreditation Program Guidelines: Measurement of Lead in Paint, Dust, and Soil," EPA 747/R-92/001, U.S. Environmental Protection Agency, Washington, DC, March 1992.

[17] U.S. Environmental Protection Agency, "Urban Soil Lead Abatement Demonstration Project," EPA 600/AP-93/001, Vol. 1-4, Research Triangle Park, NC: Office of Health and Environmental Assessment, Environmental Criteria and Assessment Office, 1993.

[18] McKnight, M.E., Byrd, W.E., Roberts, W.E., "Measuring Lead Concentration in Paint Using a Portable Spectrum Analyzer X-Ray Fluorescence Device," NISTIR W90-650, National Institute of Standards and Technology, Gaithersburg, MD, May 1990.

[19] Pesce, J., Martin, K.P., Straub, W.E., "An Examination of Substrate Effect on Portable X-Ray Fluorescence Instrumentation," Star Environmental Services, Inc., P.O. Box 1027, Melrose, MA 02176, 1993.

[20] Bernick, M, Kaelin, L., Prince, G., Sprenger, M., and Campagna, P., "The U.S. Environmental Protection Agency Environmental Response Team's Use of Field-Portable X-Ray Fluorescence Instruments for Analyzing Lead in Soils", Lead in Paint, Soil, and Dust: Health Risks, Exposure Studies, Control Measures, Measurement Methods, and Quality Assurance, ASTM STP 1226, Michael E. Beard and S.D. Allen Iske, Eds., American Society for Testing Materials, Philadelphia, 1994.

[21] Frandon Enterprises, Inc., Pace Environs, 81 Finchdene Square, Scarborough, Ontario, Canada, M1X 1B4.

[22] Hardison, D.A., Neefus, J.D., Estes, E.D., and Gutknecht, W.F., "Report of the Evaluation of the Scitec Portable X-Ray Fluorescence Spectrometer", U.S. Environmental Prtotection Agency Contract 68-02-4550, Research Triangle Park, NC, 1993.

[23] Scitec Corporation, 2000 Logston Blvd., Richland, WA. 99352.

[24] Hardison, D.A., Whitaker,C.O., Neefus, J.D., Estes, E.D., and Gutknecht, W.F., "Evaluation of Portable X-Ray Fluorescence Spectrometer for Measurement of Lead in Paint, Soil and Dust, EPA 600/A-92/245, U.S. Environmental Protection Agency, Research Triangle Park, NC 1992. Available from NTIS, Springfield, VA; NTIS PB93-121010.

[25] Estes, E.D., Hardison, D.L., Whitaker, C.O., and Gutknecht, W.F., "A Preliminary Evaluation of the Scitec MAP-3, Warrington Microlead I, and Princeton Gamma-Tech XK-3 Portable X-Ray Fluorescence Spectrometers," EPA 600/R-94/016, U.S. Environmental Protection Agency, Research Triangle Park, NC, 1994.

[26] Warrington, Inc., 2113 Wells Branch Parkway, Suite 6700, Austin, TX 78728.

[27] Princeton Gamma-Tech, Inc., 1200 State Road, Princeton, NJ 08540.

[28] Estes, E.D., and Gutknecht, W.F., "Workshop Report: Identification of Performance Parameters for Portable X-Ray Fluorescence Measurement of Lead in Paint," EPA 600/R-92/130, U.S. Environmental Protection Agency, Research Triangle Park, NC, June 1993.

[29] Luk, K.K, Grohse, P.M., and Gutknecht, W.F., "Assessment of Techniques Used for Field Measurement of Lead in Paint," U.S. Environmental Protection Agency, Contract 68-D1-0009, Research Triangle Park, NC, May 1993.

[30] Luk, K.K., Hodson, L.L., O'Rourke, J.A., and Gutknecht, W.F., "Investigation of Test Kits for Detection of Lead in Paint, Soil, and Dust," EPA 600/R-93/085, U.S. Environmental Protection Agency, Research Triangle Park, NC, 1993.

[31] Feigl, F., and Suter, H.A., "Analytical Use of Sodium Rhodizonate," Industrial and Engineering Chemistry, Vol. 14, No. 10, October 1942, pp 840-842.

[32] Latimer, W.M., and Hildebrand, J.H., Reference Book of Inorganic Chemistry, 3rd ed., McMillan Co., NY, 1964.

[33] Hunter, M., "Field Test Methods: A Comparison of Four Test Methods," Hybrivet Systems, 4 Mechanic St., Natick MA 01760, 1993.

[34] Estes, E.D., and Gutknecht, W.F., "Workshop Report: Identification of Performance Parameters for Test Kit Measurement of Lead in Paint," EPA 600/R-92/129, U.S. Environmental Protection Agency, Research Triangle Park, NC, June 1993. Available from NTIS, Springfield, VA; NTIS PB 93-216604.

[35] Luk, K.K., Grohse, P.M., Hodson, L.L, Binstock, D.A., VanHise, C.C., and Gutknecht, W.F., "Standard Operating Procedure for the Field Analysis of Lead in Paint, Bulk Dust, and Soil by Ultrasonic, Acid Digestion and Colorimetric Measurement," EPA 600/R-93/200, U.S. Environmental Protection Agency, Research Triangle Park, NC, September 1993.

[36] Hach Co., 100 Dayton Ave., P.O. Box 907, Ames, Iowa 50010.

Mark B. Bernick,[1] George Prince,[2] and Rajeshmal Singhvi,[2]

THE U.S. ENVIRONMENTAL PROTECTION AGENCY'S ENVIRONMENTAL RESPONSE TEAM'S
USE OF FIELD-PORTABLE X-RAY FLUORESCENCE INSTRUMENTS FOR ANALYZING Pb IN
SOILS

REFERENCE: Bernick, M. B., Prince, G., and Singhvi, R., **"The U.S.
Environmental Protection Agency's Environmental Response Team's Use of
Field-Portable X-ray Fluorescence Instruments for Analyzing Pb in Soils,"**
Lead in Paint, Soil and Dust: Health Risks, Exposure Studies, Control
Measures, Measurement Methods, and Quality Assurance, ASTM STP 1226,
Michael E. Beard and S.D. Allen Iske, Eds., American Society for Testing
and Materials, Philadelphia, 1995.

ABSTRACT: The U.S. Environmental Protection Agency's (U.S.
EPA)/Environmental Response Team (ERT) has used field-portable X-ray
fluorescence (FPXRF) instruments extensively for analyzing lead (Pb) in
soils and sediments at hazardous waste sites nationwide. The U.S. EPA/ERT
has used both the Outokumpu Electronics Inc. (OEI) model X-MET 880 [1] and
the Spectrace Instruments model Spectrace 9000 FPXRF spectrometers. These
FPXRF analyzers have proven to be well suited for the analysis of Pb in
soils. U.S. EPA QA2 data objectives have been achieved providing quick
on-site multi-element analysis of large numbers of in-situ and prepared
samples. Additionally, statistical evaluations of in-situ and prepared
sample FPXRF analysis infer that both methods produce statistically
equivalent confirmation slopes (regression coefficients).
 The on-site availability of reliable FPXRF analyses provides
managers with near real-time data necessary for the guidance of critical
field decisions in removal actions. Time and cost savings over the
standard U.S. EPA CLP chemical methods are significant [2-4].
Consequently, by cost effectively increasing sampling densities, the
reliability of decisions based on spatial models delineating the extent of
contamination can be increased [5].

KEYWORDS: lead (Pb), lead in soil, X-ray fluorescence (XRF), field-
portable X-ray fluorescence (FPXRF)

 Historically, the chemical analytical methods approved for use by
the U.S. EPA Contract Laboratory Program (CLP) have been selected for the
analysis of the majority of environmental samples. As the successful

[1]Senior chemist, Roy F. Weston-REAC, GSA Raritan Depot, 2890
Woodbridge Avenue, Edison, NJ, 08837.

[2]Environmental scientist and chemist, respectively, U.S.
EPA/Environmental Response Team, Raritan Depot-Building 18, MS-101, 2890
Woodbridge Avenue, Edison, NJ 08837.

application of energy-dispersive XRF analysis of environmental samples is documented more frequently, FPXRF is becoming an accepted and viable analytical technique by the environmental community [2-8]. Time and cost savings over the standard U.S. EPA CLP chemical methods are significant [2-4]. Consequently, by cost effectively increasing sampling densities, the reliability of decisions based on spatial models delineating the extent of contamination can be increased [5].

Energy-dispersive XRF provides a nondestructive near real-time simultaneous multi-elemental analysis of liquid, powder, and solid samples. The U.S. EPA/ERT has used the OEI X-MET 880 and the Spectrace Instruments model Spectrace 9000 FPXRF analyzers for rapid on-site analysis of hazardous metallic wastes. These instruments were selected for their ability to provide multi-elemental analysis and sample matrix corrections. The instruments differ in their energy-resolving power and, consequently, in their calibration and analytical methodology. Both instruments have enabled the U.S. EPA/ERT to provide the following analytical services:

- Extent of contamination studies
- On-site metal analyses to direct removal actions
- Analysis of paint for Pb content
- Analysis of air filters for metals
- Post-cleanup surveys

Regression analyses of confirmatory vs FPXRF results, as well as precision and detection limit data are presented from hazardous waste sites containing metallic pollutants in a variety of soil and waste matrices. Typical target metals analyzed include: Pb, zinc (Zn), copper (Cu), chromium (Cr), nickel (Ni), cadmium (Cd), arsenic (As), and barium (Ba). Many of these elements are used in calculations to correct for sample matrix effects. Given the objective of this paper, only the Pb analytical results will be presented.

INSTRUMENTATION AND CALIBRATION

OEI X-MET 880

The OEI X-MET 880 was used equipped with a double-source surface (DOPS) probe for both in-situ soil and XRF sample cup analysis with the probe in the upright geometry and the safety shield attached. The DOPS probe was furnished with 100 mCi Cm^{244} and 30 mCi Am^{241} radioisotope sources. Only the Cm^{244} radioisotope spectrum was used for the analysis of Pb.

The OEI DOPS probe employs a gas proportional detector with a typical energy resolution of 850 eV at the full width at half of the maximum (FWHM) of the manganese (Mn) K X-ray line. The resolution of the detector does not allow for universal and efficient use of a fundamental parameters (FP)-based program to calculate elemental concentrations. An empirical or site-specific calibration employing elemental standards, a suite of site-specific calibration standards (SSCS), and regression mathematics are used to calibrate the instrument for elemental response and matrix effects. This provides the operator with the flexibility to configure the instrument to analyze for any element from aluminum (Al) to uranium (U).

The chemically analyzed [atomic absorption (AA) or inductively coupled plasma emission spectroscopy (ICP)] SSCS must be representative of the matrix and target element concentration range that will be sampled at the site. The highest and lowest SSCS samples are used to determine the linear calibration range.

The DOPS probe is temperature sensitive. The operator activates a software-controlled gain-control circuit for 5 minutes for every 5°F change in the ambient operating temperature, or every half hour during all operations to prevent possible errors due to gain shifts.

The electronic unit of the OEI X-MET 880 FPXRF is capable of holding 32 calibration models. Each model can be calibrated to analyze for six target elements. The electronic unit does not provide internal storage for spectrum and analytical results. An RS-232 serial port is provided for downloading data and spectra to a peripheral device.

U.S. EPA/ERT SOP 1707, "X-MET 880 Field Portable X-ray Fluorescence Operation Procedures," [9] and the OEI HAZ-MET [1] 880 Operator's Manual give guidelines for sampling and preparation of SSCS, calibrating, start-up, check-out, operation, calibration, and routine use of the X-MET 880 for field use in analysis of hazardous or potentially hazardous inorganic waste.

Spectrace 9000

The Spectrace 9000 surface probe provides for both in-situ soil analysis and XRF sample cup analysis with the probe in the upright geometry and the safety shield attached. It is furnished with 5 mCi Cd^{109}, 50 mCi Fe^{55}, and 5 mCi Am^{241} radioisotope sources.

The Spectrace 9000 utilizes a mercuric iodide (HgI_2) semiconductor detector with an energy resolution of less than 300 eV at the FWHM of the Mn K X-ray line. The improved energy resolution of the detector allows for efficient use of an FP-based program to calculate elemental concentrations. FP is a mathematical treatment of chemical matrix effects used in conjunction with pure element or known standard element responses to develop an iterative algorithm for analysis of a specific sample type (e.g., soil, oil, thin film, paint). The FP method does not require site-specific calibration samples. Calibration is not necessary; only selection of one of the FP-based applications from a menu is required. Applications for soils, K and L-line for Pb-in-paint, and thin-film are provided with the instrument. Only the soils application will be addressed.

X-ray intensities, derived from the spectra of the three sources, are processed for 25 elements simultaneously. Therefore, soil samples may be analyzed for any or all of these elements without developing a calibration model. The soil application presently analyzes for potassium (K), calcium (Ca), titanium (Ti), Cr, Mn, iron (Fe), cobalt (Co), Ni, Cu, Zn, As, selenium (Se), rubidium (Rb), strontium (Sr), zirconium (Zr), molybdenum (Mo), silver (Ag), Cd, tin (Sn), antimony (Sb), Ba, mercury (Hg), Pb, thorium (Th), and uranium (U).

A spectrum energy calibration is performed automatically with each analysis to prevent error due to gain shifts. The electronic unit provides internal nonvolatile memory for storage of 120 spectra and 300 multi-element analytical reports. An RS-232 serial port is provided for downloading data and spectra to a peripheral device. The multi-element analytical reports and the 2000-channel spectra can be displayed on the instrument's LCD panel.

U.S. EPA/ERT SOP 1713, "Spectrace 9000 Field Portable X-ray Fluorescence Operating Procedure," [10] and the Spectrace 9000 Operator's Manual gives guidelines for start-up, check-out, operation, calibration, and routine use of the Spectrace 9000 for field use in analysis of hazardous or potentially hazardous inorganic waste.

SAMPLE ANALYSIS METHODOLOGY

In-Situ FPXRF

Large rocks and organic debris are removed from the soil within a 10-in.-by-10-in. area to a 1-in. depth. The soil is mixed to reduce gross heterogeneity and flattened with a stainless steel trowel. Two or three different points in the area are analyzed with the FPXRF surface probe and the average is reported. A sample moisture content of up to 20 percent is acceptable for most elements including Pb [11]. Samples with a moisture content significantly higher than 20 percent have been successfully analyzed for Pb by FPXRF. This is attempted only when confirmation samples are going to be submitted to the laboratory for chemical analysis.

Alternatively, wet soils and sediments are placed in an aluminum pan and allowed to air dry. Large rocks and organic debris are removed from the soil and the sample is mixed to reduce gross heterogeneity. The sample is shaped into a 1-in.-thick cake and flattened with a stainless steel trowel. Two or three different points are analyzed with the FPXRF surface probe, and the average is reported.

Prepared Sample FPXRF

Soil or sediment within a 10-in.-by-10-in. area to a 1 in.-depth is collected and dried, if needed, either by air or in a conventional oven at 105°C [11]. The sample is broken up and passed through a 10-mesh sieve. The oversized material is discarded, and the remaining portion is mixed. A 31-mm sample cup is filled and covered with 0.2-mil polypropylene X-ray film. The cup is analyzed once with the FPXRF surface probe in the upright geometry.

Chemical Analysis

The confirmation samples (the same 31-mm sample cups analyzed by prepared FPXRF) are submitted to the laboratory for digestion and analysis as specified in the U.S. EPA publication, "Test Methods for Evaluating Solid Waste," SW-846, 3rd Edition.

DATA QA/QC

The FPXRF field method detection limit (MDL) is calculated from the measurement of a soils matrix blank at the start and end of sample analysis, and after approximately every tenth sample. The MDL is defined as three times the calculated standard deviation value of the mean for each target element [8,10].

Precision is monitored by analyzing a sample with target element concentrations above the MDL at the start and periodically throughout the analysis day. The coefficient of variation (COV) is used to calculate precision. The COV should be within ± 20 percent for the data to be considered adequately precise.

Three equally important QA objectives have been defined by the U.S. EPA for assessing and substantiating the collection of data. The characteristics of each of the QA objectives should be evaluated to determine which one or combination thereof fits the data use objective(s) established for the site. All three QA objectives provide useful and valid data for activities such as the following: enforcement, treatment and disposal, responsible party identification, extent of contamination, site characterization, and cleanup verification.

XRF data is accepted as U.S. EPA QA1, and QA2 according to OSWER Directive 9360.4-01, "Quality Assurance/Quality Control Guidance for Removal Activities-Sampling QA/QC Plan and Data Validation Procedures," April, 1990. Determining the appropriate QA objective depends upon site-specific project objectives. QA1 is a screening objective to afford a quick, preliminary assessment of site contamination. A calibration or performance check of the method is required in addition to the verification of the detection limit. No specific QA/QC check samples are required. QA2 is a verification objective that requires confirmation of a minimum of 10 percent of the XRF samples by U.S. EPA-approved laboratory (AA/ICP) methods. The regression analysis of AA/ICP vs XRF data sets must have a coefficient of determination (R^2) of 0.7 or greater to meet QA2 objectives [11].

RESULTS

The Pb MDL, precision, and confirmation regression data for the X-MET 880 FPXRF analyses of metal pollutants in a variety soil and waste matrix types are summarized (Table 1). Similar data for the Spectrace 9000 FPXRF analyzer have been calculated and are summarized (Table 2).

Additionally, several sites have been investigated with both instruments where most or all of the FPXRF and the confirmatory AA Pb results were below the FPXRF MDL; this data is not presented.

DISCUSSION OF RESULTS

Evaluation of In-situ and Prepared Sample Methodologies

The in-situ and prepared sample methodologies were evaluated at a battery breakage and a scrap metal site using the OEI X-MET 880 (the first and last sites in Table 1). Additionally, these methodologies were also evaluated with the Spectrace 9000 at the scrap metal site (the second site in Table 2). Both the in-situ and prepared sample FPXRF results for these sites met QA2 data objective requirements.

A statistical comparison of slopes (regression coefficients) was performed to compare AA/in-situ FPXRF and AA/prepared sample FPXRF regression results for data from the battery breakage and scrap metal sites. A methodology was utilized which is similar to that of testing the difference between two population means utilizing the Student's t [12]. The null hypothesis for this test is $ß_1 = ß_2$ where $ß$ represents the true population regression coefficient. The alternative hypothesis is $ß_1$ does not equal $ß_2$. In all cases, alpha, the probability of rejecting the null hypothesis when it is in fact true, was set equal to 0.05.

Comparison of X-MET 880 battery breakage AA vs in-situ FPXRF, and AA vs prepared sample FPXRF regression results indicated slopes of 0.92 and 0.84, respectively. When applying the Student's t methodology, no significant difference could be found between these two slopes (p-value>0.50) indicating that these slopes came from the same $ß$ population and that the regression lines can be assumed to be parallel.

Similar results were achieved for scrap metal comparisons for X-MET 880 regressions and Spectrace 9000 regressions. Results of the X-MET 880 in-situ FPXRF regression (slope=1.98) vs the prepared sample FPXRF regression (slope=1.78) also showed no statistical difference between the slopes with 0.10 <p-value< 0.20. Spectrace 9000 comparisons gave the same results as well, with in-situ FPXRF slope=1.09 and prepared sample FPXRF slope=1.04 and 0.20<p-value< 0.50.

In all three cases the null hypothesis could not be rejected which lends support to the theory that the true population regression coefficients are in fact the same between AA/in-situ and AA/prepared sample FPXRF results. Therefore, the pairs of regression lines can be assumed to be parallel in each case.

FPXRF Precision and Detection Limits

Lead detection limits in Table 1 and Table 2 are significantly below typical Pb action levels of 500-2000 mg/kg, and precision is normally less than 20 percent relative for analysis times of 30-60 seconds. FPXRF Pb results generally meet QA2 data objectives with close to 1:1 proportionality between AA/ICP and XRF data sets.

Table 1--<u>Lead Results of the OEI X-MET 880 FPXRF.</u>

Waste Type	Analysis Method	MDL mg/kg	Precision Conc[a]	COV%[b]	Meas Time[c]	Regression Statistics N[d]	R[2e]	Slope
Battery Breakage	P[f]	123	300	13.7	60	21	0.97	0.84
	I[g]	123	300	13.7	60	21	0.85	0.92
	I	81	...	...	60	46	0.85	0.85
Smelter Stack	I	165	485	11.3	60	9	0.84	0.53
Scrap Metal	P	111	159	23.3	60	22	0.78	1.16
Scrap Metal	P	606	...	...	60	24	0.64	1.01
Ind. Slag	P	73	1513	16.1	60	14	0.98	1.21
Battery Breakage	I	129	266	16.2	60	26	0.89	0.96
Smelter Slag	P	119	256	15.6	60	261	0.98	0.96
Plating	P	186	551	11.3	240	34	0.99	6.5
Scrap Metal	I	93	772	4.0	240	30	0.89	1.98
	P	93	772	4.0	240	70	0.92	1.78

Table 2-- <u>Lead Results of the Spectrace 9000 FPXRF.</u>

Waste Type	Analysis Method	MDL mg/kg	Precision Conc	COV%	Meas Time	Regression Statistics N	R[2]	Slope
Plating	P	114	1124	3.4	240	32	0.71	0.67
Scrap Metal	I	123	972	4.4	240	40	0.87	1.09
	P	123	972	4.4	240	72	0.83	1.04
Junkyard	P	30	136	19.1	60	12	0.86	1.17
Battery Breakage	I	42	1049	5.0	60	20	0.97	0.69
Battery Breakage	I	33	1750	4.3	60	13	0.99	1.62
Smelter Waste	P	38	1151	8.0	60	180	0.89	1.34
Burned Electronics	I	40	175	12.2	60	212	0.82	0.93
	P	59	164	16.4	30			

[a]Mean concentration in mg/kg, [b]Coefficient of variation in percent, [c]Source measurement time in seconds, [d]Number of observations, [e]Coefficient of determination for the regression, [f]Prepared sample, [g]In-situ analysis.

CONCLUSIONS

Lead is a primary target analyte in many extent of contamination studies and removal programs. FPXRF analyzers have proven to be well suited for the analysis of Pb in soils. QA2 data objectives have been achieved providing quick on-site multi-element analysis of large numbers of in-situ and prepared samples. Additionally, statistical evaluations of in-situ and prepared sample FPXRF analysis infer that both methods produce statistically equivalent confirmation slopes (regression coefficient).

The on-site availability of reliable FPXRF analyses provides managers with near real-time data necessary for the guidance of critical field decisions in removal actions. Time and cost savings over the standard U.S. EPA CLP chemical methods are significant [2-4]. Consequently, by cost effectively increasing sampling densities, the reliability of decisions based on spatial models delineating the extent of contamination can be increased [5].

ACKNOWLEDGEMENT AND DISCLAIMER

The authors wish to thank Joseph Lafornara, Allen Humphrey, Mark Sprenger, Philip Campagna, David Charters, JoAnn Camacho, Harry Compton, Gregory Powell, and William Coakley of the U.S. EPA/ERT and Dennis J. Kalnicky, Lawrence Kaelin, Donna Getty, and Jay Patel, of Roy F. Weston-REAC for their technical support. This work was performed under U.S. EPA Contract Number 68-03-3482. Mention of trade names of commercial products does not constitute endorsement or recommendation for their use.

REFERENCES

[1]   Registered trade mark of Outokumpu Electronics Inc., Bend, OR.

[2]   Furst, G.A., Spittler, T. and Tillinghast, V., "Screening for Metals at Hazardous Waste Sites: A Rapid Cost-Effective Technique Using X-ray Fluorescence," _Proceedings of 6th National Conference on Management of Uncontrolled Hazardous Waste Sites_, Hazardous Materials Control Research Institute, Silver Springs, MD, 1985.

[3]   Meiri, D., Bradfield, D. G. and Downs, D. M., "Delineation of Heavy Metals in Surface Soil by Portable X-ray Fluorescence Analysis Screening," _Fourth National Outdoor Action Conference on Aquifer Restoration, Ground Water Monitoring and Geophysical Methods_, Las Vegas, NV, 1990, pp 1067-1079.

[4]   Rabb, G. A., Kuharic, C. A., Cole III, W. H., Enwall, R. E. and Duggan, J. S., "The Use of Field-Portable X-ray Fluorescence Technology in the Hazardous Waste Industry," _Advances in X-ray Technology_, Vol. 33, C. S. Barrett et al., ed. Plenum Press, New York, 1990, pp 629-637.

[5]   Cole III, W. H., Enwall R. E., Raab, G. A. and Kuharic, C. A, "Rapid Assessment of Superfund Sites for Hazardous Materials with X-ray Fluorescence Spectrometry," _Proceedings of the Second International Symposium on Field Screening Methods for Hazardous Wastes and Toxic Chemicals_, U.S. Environmental Protection Agency, EMSL, Las Vegas, NV, 1991, pp 497-505.

[6]   Bernick M., Sprenger, M., Prince G., et al., "An Evaluation of Field Portable XRF Soil Preparation Methods," _Proceedings of the Second International Symposium on Field Screening Methods for Hazardous Wastes and Toxic Chemicals_, U.S. Environmental Protection Agency, EMSL, Las Vegas, NV, 1991, pp 603-607.

[7] Fribush, H. M., Frisk, J. F., "Field Analytical Methods for Superfund," Proceedings of the Second International Symposium on Field Screening Methods for Hazardous Wastes and Toxic Chemicals, U.S. Environmental Protection Agency, EMSL, Las Vegas, NV, 1991, pp 25-29.

[8] Bernick, M., Berry, P., Prince G., et al., "A High Resolution Portable XRF HgI_2 Spectrometer for Field Screening of Hazardous Metal Wastes," Advances in X-ray Technology, Vol. 35, C. S. Barrett et al, ed. Plenum Press, New York, 1992, pp 1047-1053.

[9] "X-MET 880 Field Portable X-ray Fluorescence Operation Procedures," U. S. Environmental Protection Agency/ERT, Raritan Depot-Building 18, MS-101, 2890 Woodbridge Avenue, Edison, NJ 08837, SOP #1707.

[10] "Spectrace 9000 Field Portable X-ray Fluorescence Operating Procedure," U. S. Environmental Protection Agency/ERT, Raritan Depot-Building 18, MS-101, 2890 Woodbridge Avenue, Edison, NJ 08837, SOP #1713.

[11] "Field Portable X-ray Fluorescence," U.S. Environmental Protection Agency/ERT, Quality Assurance Technical Information Bulletin, Vol. 1, No. 4, May 1991.

[12] Zar, J. H. "Biostatistical Analysis," Second Edition. Prentice-Hall, Inc., Englewood, NJ, 1984, pp 292-295.

Harold A. Vincent[1] and Dawn M. Boyer[2]

AN EXAMINATION OF AN XRF METHOD USED FOR THE DETERMINATION OF LEAD IN
URBAN SOIL AND DUST SAMPLES

REFERENCE: Vincent, H.A. and Boyer, D.M., "An Examination of an XRF
Method Used for the Determination of Lead in Urban Soil and Dust
Samples," Lead in Paint, Soil and Dust: Health Risks, Exposure Studies,
Control Measures, Measurement Methods, and Quality Assurance, ASTM STP
1226, Michael E. Beard and S.D. Allen Iske, Eds., American Society for
Testing Materials, Philadelphia, 1995.

ABSTRACT: X-ray fluorescence analysis (XRF), atomic absorption
spectroscopy (AAS), and inductively coupled plasma atomic emission
spectroscopy (ICP) were used for the measurement of lead in samples for
the Urban Soil Lead Abatement Demonstration Project (USLADP). This
paper focuses on the examination of the results from multi-sample XRF
lead determinations performed on soils and dusts for that project. The
purpose is to establish some accuracy and precision baselines for the
application of XRF analysis to "real world" samples using a prescribed
protocol. The contributions to variance were identified and measured.
Preparation of soil and dust samples is a very important parameter.
Variance for the XRF instrument is a minor contribution compared to
variance attributable to sample differences.

KEYWORDS: X-ray Fluorescence (XRF), Energy-dispersive X-ray
Fluorescence (EDXRF), lead, soil, dust, variance, quality control,
reference materials.

The purpose of this paper is to share some project-real, accuracy
and precision information regarding the determination of lead in soils
and dusts by X-ray Fluorescence Spectroscopy (XRF). These data were

---

[1]Chemist, Quality Assurance Research Branch, EMSL-LV, USEPA, P.O.
Box 93478, Las Vegas, NV 89193-3478.

[2]Scientist, Lockheed Environmental Systems and Technologies, 975
Kelly Johnson Drive, Las Vegas, NV 89119-3705

acquired for a project under normal routine conditions so that some realistic historical estimates and identifications of sources of error or imprecision can be extracted. These can be compared with work done on the same materials using Inductively Coupled Plasma Atomic Emission Spectroscopy (ICP) and Atomic Absorption Spectroscopy (AAS) methods.

The data were acquired as part of the Urban Soil Lead Abatement Demonstration Project (USLADP), which was coordinated by the U.S. Environmental Protection Agency (EPA) and carried out, cooperatively, by the EPA, The Center for Disease Control (CDC), and health-related groups in the test localities.

The EPA's Environmental Monitoring Systems Laboratory at Las Vegas, Nevada (EMSL-LV), participated in the USLADP by furnishing quality assurance materials, analytical determinations of lead, and statistical interpretations of the data for those materials. The materials included soil and dust samples, which were prepared into splits to be transmitted to laboratories performing analytical determinations for the project. The participating laboratories performed lead determination on these quality assurance samples, variously, as calibration, quality control, and as double blind audit samples. A project requirement for these materials was that the homogeneity of the sample splits be adequate for the applications. Because of the large number of replicate determinations obtained in the designed study of homogeneity, a statistical interpretation is possible which can yield valuable analytical information. Although developing and improving XRF techniques for lead analysis were not primary goals, the identification of error sources and magnitudes is valuable in considering such improvements.

The values obtained in this work for the various error components may be considered typical for the instrumental and other experimental conditions used and for the preparation and treatment given the sample materials. They may apply only for the experimental circumstances described but can be used as a guide for similar conditions.

EXPERIMENTAL

The collection, preparation and method of analysis by XRF has been described [1,2], so that only a few of the important options will be repeated here. Lead was determined by XRF in at least 50 sample splits of each of the sample materials. The samples were retreated and resplit if certain statistical criteria were exceeded.

The XRF instrument used for the determinations was a Kevex 7000. This is an laboratory-based energy-dispersive system with a lithium-drifted silicon detector and an air-cooled, rhodium-target X-ray tube with a silver secondary target for sample excitation. The X-ray tube was operated at 35 KV and 3 milliamperes. Spectra were acquired for each determination. Integration under the characteristic lines was done for both the lead L-alpha and L-beta lines and the silver Compton and Rayleigh X-rays.

Soil and dust samples which had been screened to pass 60 mesh size were loaded as loose powders into standard polyethylene 31mm diameter

sample cups. A minimum of 5 grams of each sample was used for
measurement in order to have samples that were infinitely thick for lead
X-rays.[1]   The XRF count time for most of the experimental work was 200
seconds, corrected for instrumental-detector dead time.

A non-project sample, used as a run monitor, was kept in the
instrument and the yttrium K-alpha line for that sample monitored to
determine the system stability. Data for the run monitor was used in
all calculations to correct for variation in the excitation. A series
of soil samples prepared for the USLADP were used for calibration.
Quality control samples were run with each batch to establish acceptance
of the calibration for that batch.

RESULTS

Analyses of dust samples:

Standard reference dust materials, similar in composition to
project-related samples, were not available at the beginning of the
USLADP project. Examinations of the XRF spectra for dusts obtained from
urban project sources revealed that they were similar in components to
the soils from those locations. Soil materials representative of
project locations were collected, prepared, and characterized to be used
for calibration and quality control. Dust materials were prepared and
used for quality control and as blind audit samples. Additionally, a
set of six reference soil samples had been provided by Rufus Chaney,
U.S. Department of Agriculture, and were available to aid in the
calibration for both dusts and soils. The lead content of these ranged
from approximately 400 to 4200 mg/kg. Characterization of these,
referred to as the RC reference samples, has been described earlier.[2]

Calibration for lead content in the dusts was accomplished using
XRF intensity ratios for the characterized soil materials versus the
lead values determined for them by ICP and AAS methods.

Quality control (QC) samples were used with each XRF batch run.
Two of these were from project bulk soil samples which were analyzed
extensively for lead using both ICP and AAS techniques to establish lead
values and their homogeneity. In order to create the high concentration
sample, one of the two bulk samples was spiked with lead oxide to create
a control sample at approximately 18,000 mg/kg. Homogeneity for the
distribution of total lead in the spiked sample was confirmed by
determinations in a large number of separate splits as was done for the
other materials. NIST SRM 1648, Urban Dust, was also used as a control
sample during most of the work.

A single split of each of these QC samples was used continuously
in the analyses, occupying the same position in the instrumental multi-
sample sample holder throughout the work. Between batch runs, each QC
sample was removed, tumbled within the sample container, and replaced to
the same position in the Kevex instrument sample holder. The data from
repetitions on the QC samples was used to establish reproducibility at
different lead concentration levels.

An X-ray fluorescence spectrum for one of the dusts (Fig. 1) shows the characteristic lead L-alpha, L-beta, and the silver Compton lines. The intensity ratio used in calibration was the ratio of the lead L-beta intensity (area under the peak) at 12.62 kev to the intensity of the silver Compton line at 20.7 kev. Calibration for this work was done using the XRF intensity ratios for the RC standards. XRF determinations of lead by several laboratories (Fig. 2) indicate linearity through approximately 14000 mg/kg.

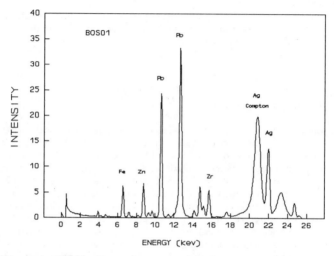

Figure 1 XRF spectrum for a lead-containing dust sample used for quality control in the USLADP project.

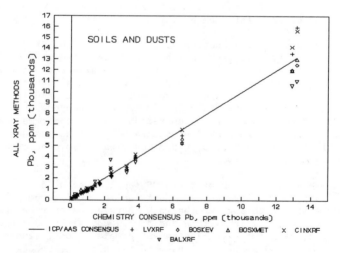

Figure 2 XRF results for soils and dusts.

The correspondence of XRF values versus AAS/ICP results for the RC standards, audit soil samples and dusts for the range from zero to 4000 mg/kg is shown in Figure 3. These data are for the EMSL–LV laboratory only and show that the data points for different kinds of samples conform to the same calibration line in this range.

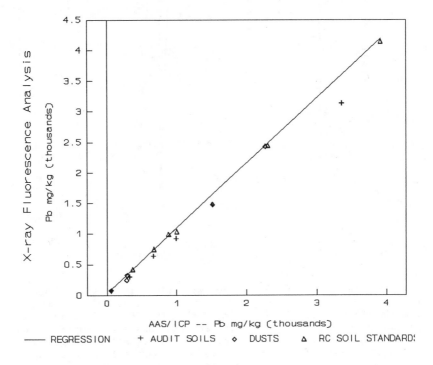

Figure 3 XRF results for soils and dusts versus AAS/ICP determinations.

During the 26 day analysis period for the dust samples, the counts accumulated for the yttrium K–alpha X–ray from the run monitor sample were on the order of 800,000 counts for 200 second livetime counting. This yields a calculated theoretical random count error level of about 0.11% relative standard deviation. The experimental variation measured over the 26 day period was 0.55% RSD. Figure 4 shows the variation with time of the run monitor response. This variation in run monitor intensity must be considered since all of the measured intensities for lead and the scatter peaks were corrected using run monitor values.

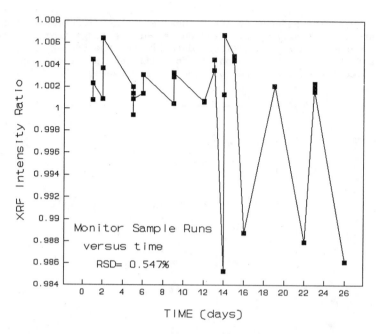

Figure 4   XRF intensity ratio for the run monitor sample.

Figure 5 shows the variation with time of the raw intensities for the lead L–beta peak, along with corresponding calculated values for lead in the NIST SRM 1648 sample, during the 26 day long analysis period. Intensities for the first several runs might appear to pose a problem for the analyses but another variable, silver Compton scatter, exhibited changes that corrected for the changes in lead intensities when the ratios of the two were used for the calculations of lead concentrations.

Principal component analysis (PCA) of the several variables considered in the calculation of lead concentration identified those initial X–ray intensities for lead L–beta as outliers.[3]   Silver Compton scatter values for the same runs were also identified as outliers by PCA.   No other variable was identified by PCA to be strongly related to these two.   The ratio calculations yield lead values for NIST SRM 1648 that fall in a narrow range.

No significant trends in calculated lead values for any of the control samples were observed.   This absence of trends can be seen in Figures 6 through 8, where calculated values for the three QC samples are shown in control charts.   Identifications of dust samples analyzed on specific days during the period are shown in the lower part of each graph.

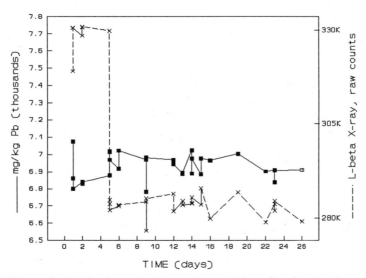

Figure 5 Variations in X-ray intensities for lead L-beta and calculated lead values for NIST 1648 versus time for 26 day analysis period.   True value is 6550 mg Pb/kg.   Measured values are retained for calculation consistency.

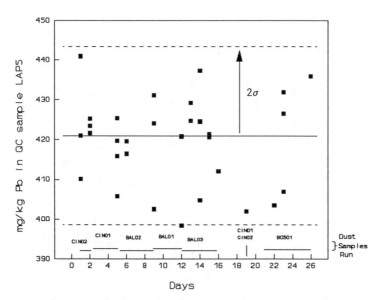

Figure 6 Control chart for lead determination in QC sample LAP5.

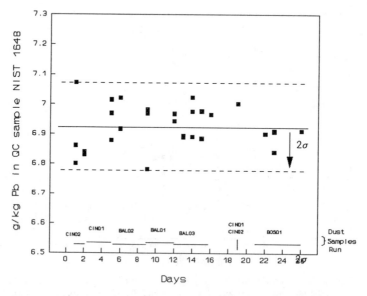

Figure 7 Control chart for lead determination in NIST 1648 used as a quality control sample over the analysis period.

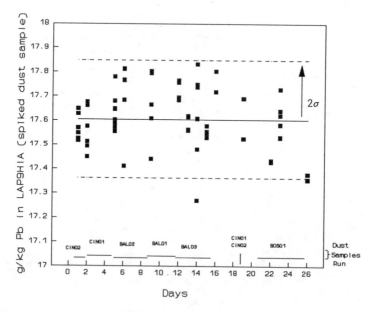

Figure 8   Control chart for lead determination for QC sample LAP9H1A.

A listing of relative standard deviations for the three quality control samples, acquired as they were used with the different dust sample runs, is given in Table 1.

TABLE 1—Variation of quality control sample values during Pb determinations in dusts.

DUST SAMPLE RUN	————————Quality Control Samples————————									ANALYSIS DATE
	——LAP5——			—NIST 1648—			——LAP9H1A——			—Mo/(Day)—
	AVG	STD	RSD	AVG	STD	RSD	AVG	STD	RSD	
CIN02	421	11	2.69	6890	96	1.39	17600	73	0.42	3/(15,16);4/(2)
CIN01	417	8	2.01	6920	79	1.15	17600	73	0.47	3/(16,19);4/(2)
BAL02	418	9	2.06	6950	75	1.07	17600	114	0.65	3/(19,20,23)
BAL01	415	13	3.06	6930	75	1.08	17700	104	0.59	3/(23,26)
BAL03	420	13	3.02	6940	48	0.70	17600	139	0.79	3/(26,27,28)
BOS01	421	13	2.66	6890	28	0.40	17500	103	0.66	4/(5,6,9)

The values shown in table 1 for NIST SRM 1648 are higher than the certified value of 6550 mg/kg.

Table 2 shows calculated values for the relative standard deviation expected for these determination if the contributions to variance were due only to random count errors. Since there were differences between the calculated and the experimental then there must be significant sources of variance to be identified that must be assignable to experimental parameters in the XRF analyses of soils and dusts.

TABLE 2—Calculated RSD values from random count error considerations.

	——LAP5——		—NIST 1648—		——LAP9H1A——	
	L-beta	Compton	L-beta	Compton	L-beta	Compton
COUNTS(Rounded average)	7.2k	560k	57.2k	275k	220k	416k
RSD (component)	1.18	0.13	0.42	0.19	0.21	0.16
TOTAL RSD		1.19		0.46		0.26

Lead determinations on splits from the dust audit samples, prepared for the USLADP project, were performed in batches with several batches daily over a two to three day period for each of the samples. A total of about fifty determinations, each determination on a separate split, were performed for each bulk audit sample. An analysis of variance was performed for the categories: values within batches, between batches, within batches for each day, between batches for days, and for all data. Relative standard deviations (RSD) for this work are listed in Table 3. Since the concentration levels for these samples are very different, variances in concentration aren't presented. The RSD values vary little between the categories for each of the samples with the exception of BAL01. The high value, 24%, for the RSD between days, is not significant for the small degrees of freedom since all determinations for splits of that sample were done in two days.

TABLE 3— Standard Deviation summary for dust samples

DUST SAMPLE	LEAD CONC. mg/kg	----OVERALL---- STD DEV.	RSD	---BATCHES--- BETWEEN RSD	WITHIN RSD	-----DAYS---- BETWEEN RSD	WITHIN RSD
BAL01	79	9	11	13	11	24	11
CIN02	253	16	6	7	6	9	6
BAL02	331	21	6	8	6	11	6
BAL03	1480	72	4	5	5	7	5
CIN01	2850	80	2	5	3	7	3
BOS01	17000	868	5	7	5	6	5

The data in Tables 1, 2, and 3 indicate that the total variance for the measurement of lead in the dust audit samples includes larger contributions from the samples than from instrumental sources but not significant contributions between batches or days.

ANALYSIS OF SOIL SAMPLES

During the experimental determination of mean values of lead in soil audit samples and the establishing of satisfactory homogeneity for distribution within project requirements, data for the lead concentration variations of the same three quality control samples were accumulated and are shown in Table 4. The standard reference sample, NIST SRM 1648, was not available at the EMSL-LV laboratory for part of the soil work.

TABLE 4—Variation of quality control sample values during Pb determinations in soils.

DUST SAMPLE RUN	-----Quality Control Samples----- ------LAP5------ AVG	STD	RSD	--NIST 1648-- AVG	STD	RSD	-----LAP9H1A----- AVG	STD	RSD
CINLO	446	6	1.17	-----			18000	271	1.44
BALLO	430	15	3.47	7170	206	2.87	18200	655	3.60
BALHI	446	6	1.17	-----			18000	271	1.44
BOSLO	419	6	1.44	6810	80	1.18	17800	173	0.98
BOSMID	449	24	5.25	-----			17700	495	2.80
CINHI	449	19	4.19	-----			18000	271	1.50
BOSHI	425	10	2.42	7080	186	2.62	19000	115	0.60

Lead determinations on these soil samples were performed in batches of six from each split and for several splits for each bulk soil sample. A total of about fifty determinations were performed for each bulk audit sample. Variances were calculated for values within splits, between splits, for instrument only, and for the total set of samples representing each bulk soil sample. Repetitions for determinations of lead were made on single specimens in order to establish variances for the X-ray instrument.

Lead determinations for the whole group of soil samples were not performed on consecutive laboratory work days as in the case of the dust samples. For any one soil, data were accumulated on the same day or consecutive laboratory work days until analytical work for that soil was completed.

TABLE 5 — RSD summary for soil audit samples.

DUST SAMPLE	LEAD mg/kg	OVERALL RSD RSD	INSTRUMENT RSD	BETWEEN* RSD	WITHIN** RSD
CINLO	303	4.0	1.5	0.7	0.7
BALLO	641	6.2	1.4	7.3	5.6
BALHI	928	4.4	1.3	4.3	4.5
BOSLO	3130	4.2	3.0	4.0	1.3
BOSMID	6090	3.1	2.1	3.0	3.1
CINHI	13800	3.2	0.7	0.5	1.1
BOSHI	15100	4.2	0.4	6.6	3.7

   * Between (splits of bulk soil sample)
   ** Within (values for subsamples of splits)

   Table 5 shows RSDs related to the variances that were studied and indicates that the contribution of the variance due to instrumental measurements is not significant for any sample compared to most of the other variances and to the overall variance. Tests of significance for variance between splits and within splits were performed before project-related distribution of these as audit soil samples and have been reported [2]. There does not appear to be any significant contribution to variance from between sample splits.

   The variance attributed to the overall sample is higher for each of these soil samples than for any of the RC standard soils with similar lead concentration. One known difference between the audit samples and the QC samples and standards is the particle size distribution which may account for the differences in variances for those two groups. The RC reference samples and the QC samples had been pulverized to pass a 200 mesh screen while the audit samples were screened only at 60 mesh. Project samples were usually screened at the 60 mesh level.

   As the particle size distribution increases to larger particles, the sampling needs to be larger in order to get a representative result for the entire bulk sample. In X-ray analysis, self absorption effects will increase with increasing particle size and may affect bias as well as reproducibility. Dust audit or control samples had higher relative amounts of finer particles than did the soils.

SUMMARY

The contributions to variance for the QC samples, during measurements on soil audit samples, was greater than for similar measurements for the same samples during dust analyses. The measurements for the soil audit samples were performed over a longer period with large time gaps between batch analysis periods. The RSD values for the QC samples accompanying the soil audit samples vary considerably between periods.

The larger contribution to audit sample measurement variance for soils compared to that for dusts is indicated to be due to the larger particle sizes in the audit soil samples.

The variance contribution due to the larger particle sizes in audit soil samples could be reduced by pulverizing the sample material to smaller particles. Since pulverizing samples to finer particle sizes involves extra time and costs, the gain in lower variance must be weighed against budget and time constraints. The finer material may be inappropriate to double blind sample applications because of possible recognition by laboratory analysts that it looks different than routine samples.

All XRF data generated at the EMSL-LV laboratory in this study were corrected for variation in the run monitor intensity. The contribution of this to the variance and to bias was found to be negligible. In practice, verification that the monitor values do not exceed certain criteria is necessary to avoid not detecting some instrumental problems that might arise during analysis.

NOTICE

Although the research described in this paper has been funded wholly (or in part) by the United States Environmental Protection Agency, through contract number 68-CO-0049 to the Lockheed Engineering Sciences and Technologies Company, it does not necessarily reflect the views of the agency and no official endorsement should be inferred. Mention of trade names or commercial products does not constitute endorsement or recommendation for use.

REFERENCES

[1]   Boyer, D.M., Hillman, D., Vincent, H.A., "Minimum Sample Size for the Analysis of Lead in Urban Dust by Energy Dispersive X-ray Fluorescence," Pittsburgh Conference, New Orleans, March 9-13, 1992.

[2]   Vincent, H., Newberry,III, W., Hillman,D., Boyer, D., Papp, M., Kohorst, K., "Preparation and Characterization of Quality Assurance Materials for XRF Measurements of Lead in Soil." Sixth Annual Waste Testing and Quality Assurance Symposium, Washington, D.C., July 16-20 1990.

[3]   Massart, D.L., Vandeginste, B.G.M., Deming, S.N., Michotte, Y., and Kaufman, L., Chemometrics: A Textbook, Elsevier, Amsterdam, the Netherlands, 1988.

Gary Dewalt[1], Paul Constant[1], Bruce E. Buxton[2], Steve W. Rust[2], Benjamin
S. Lim[3] and John G. Schwemberger[3]

**SAMPLING AND ANALYSIS OF LEAD IN DUST AND SOIL
FOR THE COMPREHENSIVE ABATEMENT PERFORMANCE STUDY (CAPS)**

REFERENCE: Dewalt, G., Constant, P., Buxton, B. E. , Rust S. W.,
Lim, B. S., and Schwemberger J. G., "Sampling and Analysis of Lead in
Dust and Soil for the Comprehensive Abatement Performance Study
(CAPS)," Lead in Paint, Soil, and Dust: Health Risks, Exposure Studies,
Control Measures, Measurement Methods, and Quality Assurance, ASTM STP
1226, Michael E. Beard and S. D. Allen Iske, Eds., American Society for
Testing and Materials, Philadelphia, 1995.

ABSTRACT: A follow-up study to the U.S Department of Housing and Urban
Development Lead-based Paint Abatement Demonstration Study (HUD
DEMO)[1], the Comprehensive Abatement Performance Study (CAPS or CAP
Study)[2], was performed by the U.S Environmental Protection Agency
(EPA) to investigate the long-term efficacy of the abatement methods
used during the HUD DEMO. This investigation included collection of
approximately 30 dust and soil samples at each of 52 HUD DEMO houses in
Denver. These samples were analyzed for lead content and evaluated by
statistical analysis to address questions related to long-term efficacy
of the abatement methods. This paper describes the sampling and
analysis methods used during the CAP Study. Performance of the methods
as determined by results from Quality Control (QC) samples originating
from the field, laboratory sample preparation, and laboratory
instrumental analysis are discussed. Variability of field sampling is
found to be much higher than variability of laboratory processing.

KEYWORDS: lead, vacuum dust, wipe dust, soil, sampling, analysis

In 1989 the U.S Department of Housing and Urban Development (HUD)
initiated the Lead-based Paint Abatement Demonstration Study (referred
to as the HUD DEMO) in seven urban areas across the United States. A
follow-up study, called the Comprehensive Abatement Performance Study
(CAPS or CAP Study), was performed by the U.S Environmental Protection
Agency (EPA) to investigate the long-term efficacy of the abatement
methods used during the HUD DEMO. This investigation included

[1]Senior Research Chemist and Program Manager, respectively, Midwest
Research Institute, 425 Volker Blvd, Kansas City, MO 64110.

[2]Projects Manager and Research Leader, respectively, Battelle
Memorial Institute, 505 King Ave., Columbus, OH 43201.

[3]Project Task Leaders, EPA Office of Pollution ahd Prevention Toxics,
401 M Street S.W., Washington, DC 20460.

collection of approximately 30 dust and soil samples in and around 52
occupied HUD DEMO houses in Denver, approximately 2 years after the
abatements had been completed. These samples were analyzed for lead
content, and these results were evaluated by statistical analysis to
help address questions related to long-term efficacy of the abatement
methods.

DESCRIPTION OF SAMPLING METHODS

Vacuum dust--Vacuuming was the primary method used for collection
of household dust samples for the CAP Study. Vacuuming methods were
selected, opposed to wipe methods, because of two primary reasons. (1)
Vacuuming methods can collect dust from carpet. Wipe methods do not
have this ability. (2) Vacuuming methods permit the analyst to report
data as lead loading ($\mu g/ft^2$ or $\mu g/cm^2$) and lead concentration ($\mu g/g$).
A cyclone vacuum sampler, shown in Fig. 1, was used for vacuum dust
collection.

The procedure for dust collection consisted of placing an open air
filter cassette (pre-loaded and pre-weighed 37 mm mixed cellulose ester
filter, 0.8 μm and support pad) into the bottom of the cyclone
receptacle followed by vacuuming a defined surface area using an
overlapping back-and-forth and up-and-down sweeping motion over a
selected surface, as diagrammed in Fig. 2. Field personnel were trained
to perform vacuum dust collection at sampling rates of approximately 0.5
ft^2 per minute (0.05 m^2/min). The approximately 1 in. (2.5 cm) diameter
pick-up nozzle was sufficiently large to cover a nominal 1 ft^2 (0.09 m^2)
sampling area within a 2 min time frame. Rapid coverage rates were
considered important to permit collection of a large number of dust
samples in occupied dwellings to minimize inconvenience.

Observations made during field collection indicated that all
visible dust materials within the sampling areas were collected by the
cyclone sampler. Some vacuum samples received at the laboratory were
large (sample weights ranged from 0-14 g each), which confirmed visual
field observations of good collection of surface dust. Heavy weight
samples were observed to contain significant amounts of sand and were
generally collected from areas near or outside of entryway doors.

The amount of dust collected was determined by weighing
conditioned air filter cassettes before and after field collections.
Weight data on filter cassettes were generated in a temperature- and
humidity-controlled environment to minimize weight changes caused by
variations in water content of the sample container. Caps on filter
cassettes were pulled off and equilibration was allowed to proceed for a
minimum of 3 days prior to initiating weighing procedures. The repeated
weighing procedures used to assure weight stability prior to
determination of dust sample weights, included determining weight
differences on each cassette over a 24 h period. Differences less than
±0.002 g were considered stable. Weights used for lead concentration
determinations were obtained from dust samples conditioned at
approximately 23°C and 45% relative humidity to constant weight.

Wipe dust--Wipe samples were used to collect a limited number of
dust samples for use in side-by-side comparisons. The side-by-side wipe-
vacuum dust samples were collected to facilitate comparing CAP Study
results to the HUD DEMO which exclusively employed wipe sampling for
lead in dust. A commercially available baby wipe was used to collect
wipe samples using a repeated overlapping back-and-forth and up-and-down
wiping procedure over a selected surface. Wipes employed for field use
were analyzed for background lead levels prior to field collection. The
brand selected was found to be relatively free from background lead
contamination.

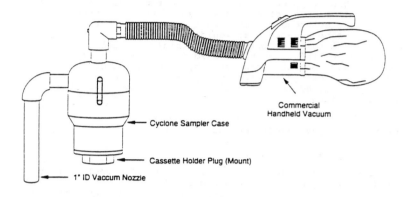

Commercial
Handheld Vacuum

Cyclone Sampler Case

Cassette Holder Plug (Mount)

1" ID Vaccum Nozzle

FIG. 1--Cyclone sampler system.

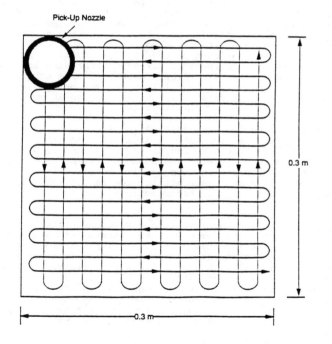

Pick-Up Nozzle

0.3 m

0.3 m

FIG. 2--Vacuum pattern in a 0.09 m² outlied area
showing overlapping passes.

Soil--Soil samples were collected using a coring method. Each sample collected in the field was a composite of 3 sample cores taken within a nominal 1 ft (0.3 m) diameter circle at each sampling location. A coring method, opposed to a scooping method, was use to obtain multiple soil samples of consistent soil depth. A depth of 0.5 in. (1.27 cm) was selected to match what was done in the HUD DEMO and is considered to be a depth that would likely contain lead contamination resulting from human activities. A stainless steel coring tool fitted with a plastic liner insert was used for collection of soil cores. Collection was generally conducted by penetration of the coring tool to a depth of at least 2 in. (5.1 cm). All but the top 0.5 in. (1.27 cm) of soil was removed from the soil core prior to generation of soil sample composites.

DESCRIPTION OF LABORATORY ANALYSIS METHODS

Sample Preparation

Sample preparation procedures for dust and soil samples were carried out using modified versions of EPA SW846 Method 3050 [3], which included use of nitric acid and hydrogen peroxide for sample digestion. Modifications to this standard procedure for each matrix are discussed below.

Vacuum dust--The primary focus of the modifications for the vacuum dust samples was a proportional four fold reduction in reagents and final dilution volume to accommodate an originally anticipated potential small sample size. Many of the samples were digested to a 25 mL final volume to maximize lead detection. Some of the higher weight samples (those higher than 4 g) were digested to a 100 mL final volume consistent with the published procedure. In addition, procedural steps were included to provide specific directions for handling vacuum dust samples contained within air filter cassettes. The entire contents of a given air filter cassette (dust, filter and support pad) were digested for subsequent lead analysis. Data were reported in μg of lead per g of dust and μg per ft^2 (m^2) of sampled area.

Wipe dust--The primary modification for wipe dust samples was an increase in the initial volume of 1:1 nitric acid from 10 mL to 25 mL to provide sufficient reagent volume to cover the entire wipe sample. In addition, procedure steps were included to provide specific directions for handling dust containing wipe samples received from the field in resealable plastic bags. Each entire wipe sample was digested for subsequent lead analysis and reported in μg per ft^2 (m^2) of sampled area.

Soil--The primary modification for soil samples included a sample drying and homogenization procedure to improve method accuracy and precision for the soil sample matrix, and a proportional two fold reduction in reagents and final dilution volume to accommodate a 0.5 g sample size. All soil sample analyses were performed on a dry weight basis and reported in μg of lead per g of soil. The drying and homogenization procedure included rough sieving (U.S. Standard #4), drying at 110°C for 8 h, grinding, fine sieving (U.S. Standard #10), final drying at 110°C for 24 h, and cooling in a desiccator prior to sub-sampling for acid digestion and lead measurement.

Instrumental Analysis

Sample digests for all sample types were analyzed for lead levels by Inductively Coupled Plasma Atomic Emission Spectrometry (ICP-AES) at the 220 nm emission line. Instrumental measurements were performed in

accordance with EPA SW846 method 6010 [3]. Further instrumental
analysis details are discussed in the subsection titled "Instrumental
Analysis Quality Control Samples".

DESCRIPTION OF QUALITY CONTROL SAMPLES

Method performance was assessed during the CAP Study using Quality
Control (QC) samples originating in four different areas: QC samples
originating in the field, reference material samples inserted between
the field and the laboratory, preparation QC samples originating in the
sample preparation laboratory, and instrumental QC samples originating
in the instrumental analysis laboratory. These QC samples are divided
into three classifications for ease of discussion: field QC samples,
sample preparation QC samples (including reference material samples),
and instrumental analysis QC samples.

Field Quality Control Samples

Two types of field QC samples were used during the CAP Study:
field blanks and side-by-side samples.

Field blanks--Field blanks are identical to field samples, except
that no sample is actually collected. Field blanks provide information
on the extent of lead contamination experienced by field samples
resulting from a combination of laboratory processing and field
handling. In addition, field blanks for cassettes provide information
on the sample weight variability resulting from a combination of
laboratory weighing activities and field handling. One field blank for
vacuum dust, and one field blank for soil were collected for each
housing unit in the study. In addition, one field blank for wipe dust
was collected for each housing unit that included collection of wipe
dust samples (i.e. not all housing units in the study included wipe dust
sample collection as part of the study design). An brief description of
the collection and processing of field blanks is given in Table 1.

TABLE 1 -- Descriptions of field blank collection

Sample Type	Collection and Preparation Description
Vacuum Dust	An unused blank cassette is placed into the cyclone vacuum sampler, removed from the sampler and submitted along with other samples for analysis. These field blanks were processed in exactly the same manner as other field samples.
Wipe Dust	An unused wipe is removed from the original bulk wipe container, folded to match wipes carried through the back-and-forth and up-and-down wiping procedure used for actual dust collection, and placed into a sample container for submission along with other samples for analysis. These field blanks were processed in exactly the same manner as other field samples.
Soil	An unused plastic liner is placed into the coring tool, removed from the coring tool, and placed into a sample container for submission along with other samples for analysis. These field blanks were prepared by leaching the empty plastic liners using the same initial acid volumes used for processing field samples prior to completing sample preparation and analysis along with other field samples.

Side-by-side samples--Side-by-side samples are samples that are
collected from adjacent locations. Three types of side-by-side samples
were collected during the study: vacuum-vacuum, soil-soil, and vacuum-
wipe. The first two types were collected to investigate field sampling
variability at a given location. Two pairs of side-by-side vacuum-wipe
samples were collected in 34 of 35 abated houses sampled during the
study. Because one house contained only carpets, no wipe sampling could
be performed. All side-by-side samples for dust were collected on
floors.

Sample Preparation Quality Control Samples

Sample preparation QC samples are used to estimate the precision
and accuracy of sample data through sample preparation and analysis
activities. These samples include method blanks (also called digestion
blanks or reagent blanks), spiked samples, spiked duplicates, and blind
reference materials.

Method blanks--Method blanks are blank samples generated in the
laboratory during sample preparation activities. They are processed in
a manner identical to field samples except that no sample material or
sample medium is present in the container used for sample digestion.
Method blanks provide information on the potential lead contamination
experienced by field samples resulting from laboratory processing in the
absence of field handling. Method blanks were generated at a frequency
of 2 per batch of approximately 40 field samples.

Spiked samples--Spiked samples are samples fortified with known
levels of lead prior to sample preparation activities. Spiked duplicate
samples, which are processed with spiked samples, are replicates of
spiked samples. Unspiked samples, which are processed with spiked
samples, are samples without any lead fortification. Unspiked and
spiked samples are processed in a manner identical to field samples.
Spiked samples provide lead recovery information for use as an
assessment of the accuracy and precision of field sample data through
sample preparation and analysis activities. The unspiked samples are
used to generate native lead levels present in samples to permit lead
recovery calculations. Spiked samples were generated at a frequency of
4 (2 spikes and 2 spiked duplicates) per batch of approximately 40 field
samples.

Use of QC sample data as an assessment of the accuracy and
precision achieved for field sample is partially dependent on the
chemical constituent matching (matrix matching) between the QC sample
and field sample. This is because data generated from a given
analytical processing scheme are generally matrix sensitive. In the
case of soil samples, the matrix matching is very good, because unspiked
and spiked samples were generated from splits of homogenized soil
samples from field sample locations. Therefore, spiked sample data for
soils were expected to closely mimic that of the field samples.
However, blank air filter cassettes and blank wipes were used for
generation of the unspiked and spiked samples for dust, because dust
field samples (vacuum and wipe) could not be split uniformly.
Therefore, the spiked sample QC data for dust samples is possibly less
useful than the spiked sample QC data generated for soils. Regardless
of this limitation, the spiked sample QC data do provide an adequate
measure of the degree of successful execution of the analytical
methodology. Since the methodology (sample preparation and analysis) is
procedurally very similar to methods commonly used and verified
successful for many different types of environmental samples, the spiked
sample QC data for dust samples generated during the CAP Study are still
a useful estimate of precision and accuracy for field samples.

Blind reference material samples-- A Blind reference material sample is a sample containing a known lead quantity that is submitted in a blind manner to the laboratory along with other field samples. Blind reference material samples provide lead recovery information that can be used as an assessment of the accuracy of field sample data as determined by sample preparation and analysis activities. The blind nature of the insertion into the sample processing stream helped provide QC data in a manner that could not be biased by laboratory activities.   Blind reference material samples were generated by placing known quantities of NIST certified standard reference materials (SRMs) into blank filter cassettes (for vacuum dust), blank wipes (for wipe dust) and empty field soil containers (for soils). Blind reference materials were generated at a frequency of 2 (one each of two different materials) per batch of approximately 40 field samples.

The discussion on the use of spiked QC sample data as an assessment of the accuracy achieved for field samples presented applies equally as well to the blind reference materials. As previously discussed, matrix matching is an important determination of usefulness of the accuracy assessment for field samples. In general, reference materials are included in an analysis scheme to help provide higher confidence as to accuracy of field sample data than can be obtained using only spiked samples. Unfortunately, at the time of project initiation, no suitable dust or soil SRMs were available. Two SRMs were chosen as the best readily available approximations to matrix matching to field samples (matching with respect to general matrix components and anticipated lead levels). These are NIST SRM No. 2704 Buffalo River Sediment (lead level = 161 μg/g) and NIST SRM No. 1646 Estuarine Sediment (lead level = 28.2 μg/g). Due to the limits in the matrix match of these to household dust and soils collected in the Denver area, some limits in the usefulness of these data for assessment of the accuracy and precision of field samples are expected. However, these data combined with spiked QC sample data do provide reasonable confidence that analytical methodologies were carried out as planned.

Instrumental Analysis Quality Control Samples

Instrumental analysis QC samples were analyzed along with field samples during instrumental measurement activities to assure adequate instrument performance during lead determinations. These QC samples included daily calibration standards, multiple calibration verification standards, multiple calibration blank samples, and interference check standards. A detailed description, specification, and frequency of use of the instrumental analysis QC standards are shown in Table 2. A summary of the typical sequence order used for instrumental lead measurements is shown in Table 3.

DISCUSSION OF SAMPLING AND ANALYSIS PERFORMANCE RESULTS

Sampling and analysis performance was monitored using lead data obtained from the three classifications of QC samples described above: field QC samples, sample preparation QC samples, and instrumental analysis QC samples. Although the chronological order of creation of these QC classes lists the field samples first, discussion of the performance results in this section is presented in reverse order because of the dependency of the preceding QC classes on later sampling and analysis activities. The performance of the instrumental portion of the analysis activities, which is a measure of the last analysis activity, can be determined separately from field sampling and sample preparation activities. The performance of the sample preparation portion, however, is dependent on the performance of the instrumental analysis and cannot be measured separately from instrumental analysis activities. Lead results from the sample preparation QC samples include

TABLE 2 -- Instrumental QC standards and specifications for ICP-AES

Name	Use	Specification
ICB - Initial Calibration Blank	Used for initial calibration and zeroing instrument response.	Calibration Standard which contains no analyte. Must be measured during calibration and after calibration. Measured value to be less than 10 times the instrumental detection limit.
Calibration Standards	Used to Calibrate instrument. The high standard re-run is used to check for high response roll-over.	Must be matrix-matched to acid content present in sample digests. Must be measured prior to measuring any sample digests. Correlation Coefficient of ≥ 0.995, as measured using linear regression on instrument response(y) versus concentration(x). The highest level Calibration standard must be measured after calibration. The measured value to fall within $\pm 10\%$ of known value.
ICV - Initial Calibration Verification	Used to verify calibration standard levels.	Concentration of analyte to be near mid-range of linear curve which is made from a stock solution having a different manufacturer or manufacturer lot identification than the calibration standards. Must be measured after calibration and before measuring any sample digests. Measured value to fall within $\pm 10\%$ of known value.
ICS - Interference Check Standard	Used to verify accurate analyte response in the presence of possible spectral interferences from other analytes present in samples.	Concentration of lead to be 1 $\mu g/mL$, concentrations of interferant are 150 $\mu g/mL$ of Al, Ca, Fe, and Mg. Must be analyzed at least twice, once before and once after all sample digestates. Measured analyte value to fall within $\pm 20\%$ of known value.
CCV - Continuing Calibration Verification	Used to verify freedom from excessive instrumental drift.	Concentration to be near mid-range of linear curve. Must be analyzed before and after all sample digestates and at a frequency not less than every ten samples. Measured value to fall within $\pm 10\%$ of known value.
CCB - Continuing Calibration Blank	Used to verify blank response and freedom from carryover.	Calibration Standard which contains no analyte. Must be analyzed after each CCV and ICS. Measured value to be less than 10 times the instrumental detection limit.

performance from a combination of the instrumental analysis and sample preparation activities. Likewise, the performance of the field sampling portion of the analysis activities is dependent on sampling, sample preparation, and instrumental analysis activities.

Laboratory Instrumental Analysis Performance

Field samples were analyzed in batches as sample preparation activities on groups of samples were completed. A sample preparation batch is a group of samples with QC all prepared together at the same time. Batch sizes are typically about 50 samples including QC samples. An instrumental analysis batch is a group of samples digests analyzed together in a time period covered by a single instrument calibration as shown in Table 3. Instrumental analysis batches generally included samples from as many as 3 different sample preparation batches. A total of 24 instrumental analysis batches were run during the performance of the CAP Study. All instrumental analysis design specifications described in Table 2 were met for all the 24 instrumental analysis batches.

Instrumental Detection Limits (IDLs) were determined during performance of each analysis batch by analyzing a low-level lead standard a minimum of five times. The average IDL measured during performance of all 24 instrumental analysis batches is 0.037 μg of lead per mL. The lead concentration of the low-level standard used for IDL determination is less than three times the average IDL. This standard was scattered throughout each instrumental analysis run to provide IDL data that were reflective of the entire analysis period.

Calibration blanks, including Initial Calibration Blanks (ICBs) and Continuing Calibration Blanks (CCBs), were analyzed along with field samples to assure adequate instrument performance during lead determinations. Greater than 92% of the calibration blanks are below the average IDL. The maximum lead concentration measured for any instrumental analysis blank is less than two times the average IDL, and the geometric mean is well below the average IDL. These results suggest that field sample results appear to be free from any significant bias caused by carryover.

The estimated central 90% tolerance intervals for percent recoveries for Continuing Calibration Verification Standards (CCVs) and Interference Check Standards (ICSs), summarized in Table 4, were narrow and contained 100% recovery as illustrated in Fig. 3. These data suggest that field samples are free from any significant non-random bias caused by instrumental drift and no commonly encountered spectral interferences.

Laboratory Sample Preparation Performance

All method blank data met data quality objectives of lead levels less than 10 times the IDL. Only one method blank sample result exceeded five times the average IDL. This method blank was one of two in a sample preparation batch that contained only high weight vacuum dust samples. This result, about six times the average IDL, is insignificant compared to the lead levels measured within the batch. A summary of the method blank results are shown in Table 4. These results indicate that no contamination occurred during laboratory processing of the samples.

Spiked sample recovery data are summarized in Table 4 and illustrated in Fig. 3. Recoveries for all but four data points met the data quality objectives of ±30% from the true spiked value. Three of the four points are a result of a spiking error (samples spikes 10 times lower than planned). This error produced measurements approaching the

TABLE 3 -- Summary of typical analysis sequence in an instrumental
analysis batch

Analysis Order	Sample	Sample Description Summary
1	ICB	Calibration Blank used for Instrument Calibration
2-4	low med high	Multi-level Calibration Standards used for Instrument Calibration
5	ICB	Calibration Blank used for Calibration Verification
6	ICV	Check standard used for Calibration Verification
7	high	High level Calibration Standard used for check on calibration curve fit
8	CCB	Calibration Blank used to verify freedom from carryover
9	ICS	Check Standard used to verify freedom from spectral interferences
10	CCB	Calibration Blank used to verify freedom from carryover
11	CCV	Midpoint calibration standard used to verify freedom from instrumental drift
12	CCB	Calibration Blank used to verify freedom from carryover
***** start repeating cycle of samples-Instrumental QC here *****		
13-22	Sample	Sample digestates (maximum of 10 samples)
23-24	CCV CCB	Drift Check Carryover Check
25-34	Sample	Sample digestates (maximum of 10 samples)
35-36	ICS CCB	Interferant Check Carryover Check
37-38	CCV CCB	Drift Check Carryover Check
***** end repeating cycle of samples-QC standards here *****		

IDL and background lead levels in the un-spiked samples. Accurate
determination of the spike recoveries under such conditions is difficult
and is not anticipated to be reflective of performance of field samples.
The other data point (soil sample) is only slightly outside the data
quality objectives (130.9%). Geometric means for all three sample types
are within ±10% of the true spiked value. These data imply that
accuracy for field samples is good and within data quality objectives
for the project.

Performance-control charts for the blind reference material
samples are summarized in Table 4 and illustrated for vacuum, wipe and
soil sample,respectively, in Figures 4, 5, and 6. All recoveries for
NIST SRM No. 2704 met data quality objectives of ±30% from the true
value. However, recoveries for NIST SRM No. 1646 are sporadic. Eight
of the 37 data points are outside data quality objectives.
Investigation into these recovery problems suggested that they were

TABLE 4 -- Summary of results for QC analyses

Quality Control Measure		Parameter Considered	# of Samples[a]	Minimum	Maximum	Geometric Mean	Log Std Deviation	Lower Bound[b]	Upper Bound[c]
Field Blanks	Vacuum	μg/sample	52 (6)	0.344	2.682	0.228	1.059		2.006
	Wipe		34 (1)	2.723	35.445	na[d]	na[d]		na[d]
	Soil		51 (4)	1.198	35.638	0.067	2.387		9.162
Method Blanks	Vacuum	μg/sample	48 (13)	0.468	20.681	0.414	1.135		4.369
	Wipe		6 (1)	2.723	3.975	na[d]	na[d]		na[d]
	Soil		22 (1)	1.276	3.297	na[d]	na[d]		na[d]
Calibration Blanks		μg/mL	431 (33)	0.0004	0.068	0.007	0.956		0.041
Blind References	I	% Recovery	38	0.851	1.231	1.016	0.088	0.841	1.227
	II		37	0.344	1.749	1.109	0.274	0.615	1.999
	III		37	0.229	1.131	0.881	0.316	0.447	1.736
Interferant Check Standards		% Recovery	144	0.997	1.211[e]	1.060	0.035	0.993	1.131
Calibration Verifications		% Recovery	274	0.962	1.058	1.014	0.016	0.986	1.043
Spikes	Vacuum	% Recovery	96	0.930	1.428	1.030	0.068	0.904	1.174
	Wipe		12	0.862	1.000	0.926	0.044	0.820	1.044
	Soil		44	0.733	1.309	0.981	0.098	0.799	1.205
Spiked Duplicates	Vacuum	Ratio	48	1.000	1.094	1.031	0.039		1.068
	Wipe		6	1.001	1.151	1.063	0.080		1.238
	Soil		22	1.001	1.308	1.081	0.109		1.227
Side-by-Sides	Vacuum	Ratio (μg/m²)	52	1.027	40.381	2.334	1.110		6.403
	Vacuum	Ratio (μg/g)	52	1.022	81.101	2.071	1.129		6.605
	Soil	Ratio (μg/g)	51	1.004	4.569	1.296	0.399		1.951

[a] The number of samples measured above the instrumental detection limit (IDL) is enclosed in parentheses.
[b] Represents a lower 95% confidence bound on the 5th percentile.
[c] Represents an upper 95% confidence bound on the 95th percentile.
[d] The statistic could not be calculated due to the large number of results below the IDL.
[e] This value represents an extra ICS analyzed in the middle of an analysis run from an instrument analysis batch containing no field samples (only re-runs of SRM 1646; III). The next highest ICS, 1.182, was also measured in the same analysis batch.

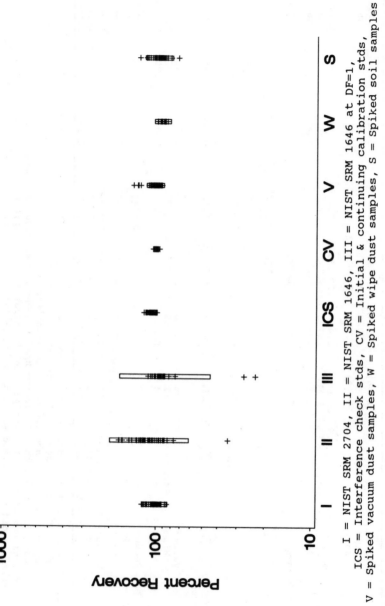

FIG. 3--Individual measurements and central 90% tolerance bounds for percent recovery for selected QC samples. (Tolerance bounds are calculated assuming log-normal data).

I = NIST SRM 2704, II = NIST SRM 1646, III = NIST SRM 1646 at DF=1, ICS = Interference check stds, CV = Initial & continuing calibration stds, V = Spiked vacuum dust samples, W = Spiked wipe dust samples, S = Spiked soil samples

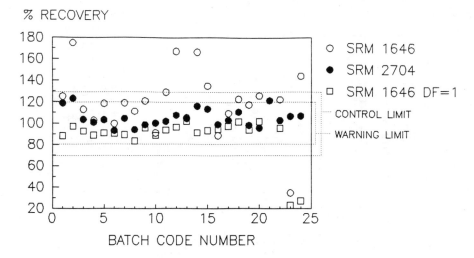

FIG. 4--Performance-control chart of individual blind
reference material recovery data, vacuum dust samples.

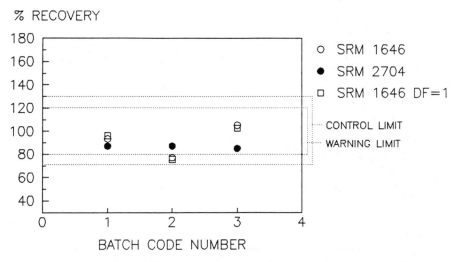

FIG. 5--Performance-control chart of individual blind
reference material recovery data, wipe dust samples.

% RECOVERY

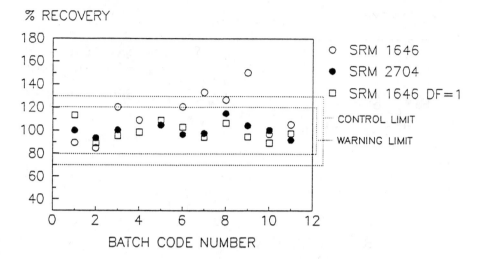

FIG. 6--Performance-control chart of individual blind
reference material recovery data, soil samples.

% ERROR

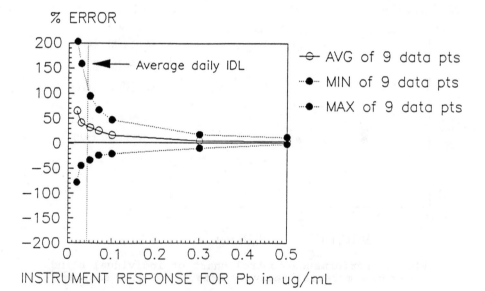

INSTRUMENT RESPONSE FOR Pb in ug/mL

FIG. 7--ICP-AES measurement error near the IDL
for Lead (Pb).

related to corrections for spectral interferences during instrumental analysis measurements.   SRM No. 1646 has a low lead concentration (28.2 $\mu g/g$) combined with high levels of other metals, such as iron.   The iron-to-lead ratio is over 1000 to 1.   To correct for potential iron interferences, the analyst conducting the instrumental measurement efforts must perform serial dilution of the digests to get iron levels within the calibration range of the instrument.   For field samples, extra dilutions were rarely needed.   For the blind SRM No. 1646, extra dilutions were always required.   This extra dilution pushed the measurable lead level down to within a few multiples of the IDL where measurement variance increases relative to higher lead level digests.

A typical example of the increase in instrumental measurement error as lead levels approach the IDL is shown in Fig. 7.   The data in this figure were generated by performing three replicate measurements of each of seven different low-level concentration standards during lead analysis efforts over three non-consecutive days.   Replicate measurements were spread throughout each of the analysis periods to simulate measurements of real field sample digests.   The slightly positive average bias indicated in the figure is suspected to be a result of differences in the true concentrations between the lead stock solution used for calibration and the lead stock solution used for making the low-level concentration standards used for generation of this data.

The extra-dilution theory for explaining the poor recoveries for SRM No. 1646 was confirmed by reanalyzing the original sample digests using an ICP-AES reconfigured eliminate the extra dilution requirement. The reconfiguration was performed to extend the linear range for iron. This permitted measurement of iron at much higher levels, eliminating the need for the extra dilutions.   The results are plotted as the DF=1 (extra dilution factor of 1) data points on the performance control charts.   Using the re-configured instrument, all but two data points for SRM No. 1646 met data quality objectives.   The remaining two points were associated with high weight sample batches that required a sample preparation protocol change as discussed earlier for high weight samples.   The change, which required a four-fold increase in final dilution volume, reduced lead levels beyond that which could be made up by elimination of any extra dilution volumes.   The blind reference material data imply that accuracy for field samples is good and well within data quality objectives for the project.

Field Sampling Performance

Most of the field blank samples generated for each sample type are below the IDL: more than 88% of the vacuum dust samples, more than 95% of the wipe dust samples, and more than 92% of the soil samples.   No field blank result exceeded five times the average IDL.   A summary of the field blank results are presented in Table 4.   These data suggest that no lead contamination occurred during field sampling activities.

Weight data obtained from vacuum dust field blanks show only minor differences between pre-field and post-field container weights (net mean weight gains of 0.0004 g).   Compared to the geometric mean weights of collected samples, which ranged from 0.0892 g for window stools to 1.58 g for exterior entryways, the weight data from field blanks imply that no significant bias related to generation of weight data occurred for field samples.

Results generated for side-by-side vacuum-vacuum and soil-soil samples are summarized in table 4 and illustrated in Fig. 8.   The figure shows the ratio of measured lead values for each pair of side-by-side samples collected for dust and soil in addition to spiked sample replicate data.   The estimated 95% confidence bound at the 95th

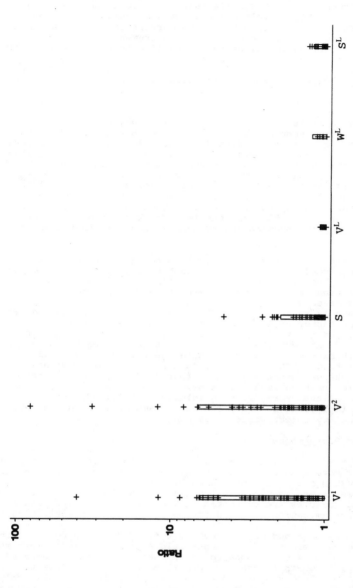

V^1 = vacuum dust samples ($\mu g/m^2$), V^2 = vacuum dust samples ($\mu g/g$), S = soil samples,
V^L = Lab spiked vacuum dust samples, W^L = Lab spiked wipe dust samples, S^L = Lab spiked soil samples

FIG. 8--Individual measurements and the upper 95% tolerance bounds for the ratio of
duplicate samples. (Tolerance bounds are calculated assuming log-normal data).

percentile is portrayed in the figure by the vertical bars. For field collection, side-by-side soil samples exhibit better agreement than dust samples. The figure clearly illustrates that field collection variability is considerably larger than laboratory variability.

Individual data points for side-by-side samples are tabulated in Tables 5 and 6 to stress the real world picture that field sampling variability is generally considered to be much larger than laboratory variability. This reality provides guidance for establishing data quality objectives for the laboratory analysis activities. Care should be exercised to avoid setting control limits on QC samples that are excessively tighter than anticipated variability from field sampling activities. Control limits should be considered excessively tight if either of the following two situations are experienced. First, is significant increases in laboratory costs caused by re-work of samples implied to be out of control. Second, is a censoring of potentially useful sample data that was eliminated as a result of the excessively tight limits. These situations are important in light of the fact that many field samples (including vacuum dust and wipe dust samples) are one-of-a-kind and can not be re-prepared for re-analysis. Field sampling costs are generally high and loss of field sample data as a result of excessively tight laboratory control limits in gross excess of the field sampling variability should be avoided. In this study, the ±30% data quality objectives (recoveries for blind reference materials) for the laboratory analysis efforts appear to be justified with respect to the high variability of the sample collection.

The geometric means of paired floor lead loadings $\mu g/ft^2$ ($\mu g/m^2$) for side-by-side vacuum-wipe samples are plotted in Fig. 9. A solid line, which represents complete agreement between the two sampling methods, is plotted along with the best fit regression line. The large scatter in the plotted points is expected from the field sampling variability previously discussed and illustrated in Fig. 8. A statistical analysis, that assumed that the relationship between vacuum and wipe measurements is log-linear, was performed on the data plotted in Fig. 9. This analysis suggests that on the average, the vacuum lead loadings are 1.4 times larger than matching wipe lead loadings on floors. However, as excepted, the relationship between vacuum and wipe sampling changes for different surface types. A bias toward increased levels of dust collection for vacuum sampling, as measured from lead loading data, occurs with increased roughness of the surface. On the average, the ratio of lead loadings for vacuum to wipe sampling are 0.7 for tile, 1.0 for linoleum, 4.2 for wood, and 12.2 for concrete (the value for concrete was based on a single pair of measurements). The ratios for both wood and concrete are statistically different than 1. However, the ratios for tile (and linoleum) are not.

Arithmetic means of the paired floor lead loadings $\mu g/ft^2$ ($\mu g/m^2$) for side-by-side vacuum-wipe samples are tabulated in Table 7. This data provides additional evidence that field sampling variability can be generally considered to be much larger than laboratory variability. Comparison of relative differences between pairs of wipe samples and pairs of vacuum samples, all collected adjacent to each other, suggest that variability for wipe dust collection, as performed in this study, is slightly lower than variability for vacuum dust collection.

TABLE 5 -- Side by side sample data for vacuum dust samples

	Sample data in $\mu g/m^2$			Sample data in $\mu g/g$	
Sample 1	Sample 2	Relative Difference[a]	Sample 1	Sample 2	Relative Difference[a]
63.29	79.22	-0.22	32.73	269.71	-1.57
238.96	215.49	0.10	99.93	72.79	0.31
13.02	32.29	-0.85	83.43	74.83	0.11
609.78	492.77	0.21	126.36	121.85	0.04
705.68	518.93	0.31	625.56	207.17	1.00
852.07	297.19	0.97	203.24	151.76	0.29
162.75	527.43	-1.06	102.50	216.43	-0.71
5.27	13.89	-0.90	38.07	73.04	-0.63
127.66	124.32	0.03	104.83	121.56	-0.15
11865.60	72604.73	-1.44	444.55	467.57	-0.05
654.66	1743.32	-0.91	172.15	282.75	-0.49
175.02	261.46	-0.40	89.89	64.95	0.32
397.19	365.65	0.08	100.86	73.61	0.31
235.73	195.90	0.18	210.19	158.92	0.28
3441.22	2417.14	0.35	149.77	125.06	0.18
3.66	6.24	-0.52	41.99	1351.31	-1.88
120.88	785.01	-1.47	105.64	181.41	-0.53
13.78	20.34	-0.38	158.21	148.44	0.06
273.08	90.63	1.00	349.90	200.88	0.54
2481.62	6216.27	-0.86	119.78	125.19	-0.04
5165.92	3479.43	0.39	363.88	222.72	0.48
157.48	18.19	1.59	199.06	58.63	1.09
317.64	138.64	0.78	55.13	107.73	-0.65
110.22	32.18	1.10	67.73	95.30	-0.34
9.90	8.72	0.13	369.82	4.56	1.95
255.54	21.42	1.69	106.55	38.85	0.93
17144.22	31253.01	-0.58	12186.30	13567.76	-0.11
24.76	11.73	0.71	78.23	42.38	0.59
3260.71	2083.35	0.44	965.96	372.07	0.89
370.28	324.96	0.13	37.34	35.42	0.05
43.59	132.61	-1.01	11.00	44.15	-1.20
533.78	930.11	-0.54	145.43	128.92	0.12
699.55	1332.14	-0.62	170.21	249.36	-0.38
856.27	21.20	1.90	245.28	200.66	0.20
508.49	334.00	0.41	248.24	62.59	1.19
12.49	17.33	-0.32	94.43	150.21	-0.46
69.97	340.25	-1.32	58.30	390.70	-1.48
2816.70	1175.63	0.82	594.85	322.67	0.59
266.73	677.37	-0.87	115.10	132.71	-0.14
149.19	105.81	0.34	76.63	83.29	-0.08
356.18	623.66	-0.55	44.16	56.54	-0.25
2432.11	3113.25	-0.25	217.68	125.31	0.54
365.65	260.92	0.33	816.65	144.04	1.40
71.69	84.17	-0.16	424.39	566.41	-0.29
4939.02	7368.43	-0.39	609.36	769.94	-0.23
196.12	102.47	0.63	38.40	37.57	0.02
2083.14	634.86	1.07	230.55	388.52	-0.51
178.57	120.23	0.39	64.76	74.74	-0.14
57.16	383.63	-1.48	24.12	96.74	-1.20
56.08	9.90	1.40	854.14	70.58	1.69
125305.37	25461.28	1.32	6217.62	1724.32	1.13
2201.54	11536.54	-1.36	347.13	627.17	-0.57

[a] $\dfrac{(\text{sample 1} - \text{sample 2})}{(\text{sample 1} + \text{sample 2})/2}$

TABLE 6 -- Side by side sample data for soil samples

Sample data in μg/g			Sample data in μg/g		
Sample 1	Sample 2	Relative Difference[a]	Sample 1	Sample 2	Relative Difference[a]
63.23	97.80	-0.43	128.59	137.04	-0.06
278.89	615.88	-0.75	174.50	194.68	-0.11
250.52	222.47	0.12	55.49	56.90	-0.03
106.59	106.18	0.00	150.19	322.87	-0.73
180.72	237.06	-0.27	137.57	132.39	0.04
101.38	87.86	0.14	181.96	208.86	-0.14
46.58	62.36	-0.29	66.56	58.92	0.12
79.42	86.93	-0.09	248.50	401.90	-0.47
38.00	38.29	-0.01	437.66	380.03	0.14
641.01	413.57	0.43	78.99	92.28	-0.16
56.97	116.24	-0.68	310.60	211.16	0.38
151.01	157.18	-0.04	1678.61	654.01	0.88
124.26	117.49	0.06	201.14	208.84	-0.04
181.74	180.89	0.00	66.29	70.36	-0.06
55.22	57.74	-0.04	514.93	459.07	0.11
979.62	773.37	0.24	1068.07	416.89	0.88
8.54	39.02	-1.28	235.15	278.95	-0.17
370.01	454.29	-0.20	259.93	304.16	-0.16
66.62	71.09	-0.06	45.39	42.30	0.07
179.22	186.61	-0.04	58.96	74.12	-0.23
137.13	96.75	0.35	67.18	79.97	-0.17
121.47	129.79	-0.07	339.90	307.04	0.10
161.57	228.79	-0.34	77.29	95.12	-0.21
102.62	104.94	-0.02	159.24	76.66	0.70
200.32	285.35	-0.35	210.37	229.23	-0.09
539.69	602.57	-0.11			

[a] $\dfrac{(\text{sample 1} - \text{sample 2})}{(\text{sample 1} + \text{sample 2})/2}$

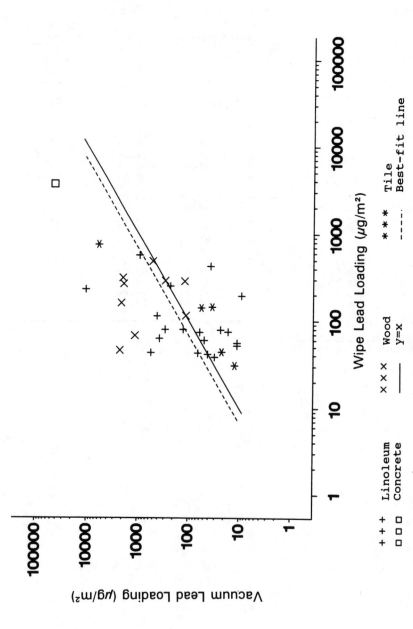

FIG. 9--Vacuum verses wipe comparison: geometric means of side-by-side floor lead loadings (μg/m²) measures. (Est. of vacuum/wipe ratio is 1.42; 90% confidence interval is 0.78, 2.60).

TABLE 7 -- Side by side results for pairs of vacuum-wipe samples

Mean for two Wipe Samples ($\mu g/m^2$)[a]	Relative Difference for two Wipe Samples[b]	Mean for two Vacuum Samples ($\mu g/m^2$)[a]	Relative Difference for two Vacuum Samples[b]	Relative Difference for Wipe-Vacuum Samples[c]
79.01	0.02	340.03	1.06	-1.25
162.70	-0.93	40.74	1.08	1.20
92.62	1.03	175.02	1.37	-0.62
352.25	-0.93	2367.09	-1.10	-1.48
70.50	0.59	1320.84	1.04	-1.80
66.20	0.65	482.12	1.26	-1.52
46.34	-0.36	2284.64	-0.48	-1.92
38.32	0.04	30.89	0.28	0.21
643.09	0.94	1007.23	-0.74	-0.44
286.64	-0.09	151.72	1.21	0.62
54.57	0.60	12.38	-0.89	1.26
78.95	0.20	25.24	-0.76	1.03
41.50	-0.16	42.25	0.28	-0.02
282.93	1.45	9.15	-0.09	1.87
66.20	0.85	53.87	-0.82	0.21
140.47	0.03	86.00	1.51	0.48
116.79	0.46	117.00	0.50	0.00
30.79	-0.10	12.49	0.34	0.85
44.40	0.28	24.00	0.76	0.60
43.33	0.24	659.83	-1.10	-1.75
55.97	-0.15	12.00	0.76	1.29
272.81	-0.78	380.45	1.59	-0.33
75.19	0.22	16.74	-0.19	1.27
798.25	1.59	526.84	-0.33	0.41
84.39	0.97	85.79	1.42	-0.02
230.13	-0.32	12890.27	-1.15	-1.93
464.68	0.79	37.67	0.24	1.70
184.22	1.01	2122.00	0.28	-1.68
749.55	-0.18	6077.79	-0.41	-1.56
44.35	-0.54	72.39	0.86	-0.48
290.30	-0.12	309.84	-0.68	-0.07
119.70	0.70	2218.93	1.96	-1.80
274.37	-0.49	2954.05	-1.54	-1.66

[a] Arithmetic means

[b] $\dfrac{\text{(sample 1 - sample 2)}}{\text{(sample 1 + sample 2)}/2}$

[c] $\dfrac{\text{(mean for wipe samples - mean for vacuum samples)}}{\text{(mean for wipe samples + mean for vacuum samples)}/2}$

REFERENCES

[1]   U.S. Department of Housing and Urban Development, The HUD Lead-
       Based Paint Abatement Demonstration (FHA), Office of Policy
       Development and Research, Washington, DC, 1991.

[2]   Battelle Memorial Institute and Midwest Research Institute, "Draft
       Final Report, Comprehensive Abatement Performance Study", report
       to U.S. EPA Office of Pollution Prevention and Toxics, prepared
       under contract Nos. 68-D2-0139 and 68-D0-0137, 1993.

[3]   U.S. Environmental Protection Agency, Office of Solid Waste, Test
       Methods for Evaluating Solid Waste Physical/Chemical Methods,
       U.S. EPA SW 846, Third Edition, Revision 1, 1987.

Mark L. Demyanek[1], George R. Dunmyre[2] and Gary S. Casuccio[2]

INVESTIGATION OF ADHESIVE LIFT SAMPLING TECHNOLOGY USED FOR THE EVALUATION OF LEAD IN SURFACE DUST

REFERENCE: Demyanek, Mark L., Dunmyre, George R., and Casuccio, Gary S., **"Investigation of Adhesive Lift Sampling Technology Used for the Evaluation of Lead in Surface Dust,"** Lead in Paint, Soil, and Dust: Health Risks, Exposure Studies, Control Measures, Measurement Methods, and Quality Assurance, ASTM STP 1226, Michael E. Beard and S.D. Allen Iske, Eds., American Society for Testing and Materials, Philadelphia, 1995.

ABSTRACT: Environmental and industrial hygiene studies which involve characterization of surface particulate matter frequently require the use of multiple analytical techniques. This paper discusses the application of adhesive lift sampling technology which was developed to permit a surface sample to be collected "in-situ" and analyzed by both bulk and microscopic methods. Lead loading results and microscopy information obtained from adhesive lift, baby wipe and micro-vacuum samples used to collect surface dust from several different surfaces are reported. No attempt was made to statistically compare the results between adhesive lifts, baby wipes and micro-vacuum techniques. An analysis of the variability of lead concentration using side by side adhesive lifts indicate statistically significant differences in the spatial distribution.

KEYWORDS: lead particulate, surface dust, wipe sample, micro-vacuum sample, adhesive lift sampling technology

Environmental and industrial hygiene studies focusing on surface particulate matter often require multiple analytical techniques to obtain important information such as bulk and individual particle composition, morphology, size, relative distribution and matrix associations. Frequently, however, the analytical laboratory technique used for sample analysis is entirely dependent upon the type of sampler employed in the investigation. For example, wipe samples may be very useful for determining the loading (i.e., mass per unit area) of contaminants through chemical analysis, but they are not generally amenable to other techniques, such as microscopy, which could provide additional important information.

The adhesive lift samplers discussed in this paper were developed to collect surface particulates such as lead dust, spores, pollens, asbestos fibers, synthetic vitreous fibers, etc. and to permit sequential, or stratified, laboratory analysis to be performed depending

---

[1] Radian Corporation, 1979 Lakeside Parkway, Suite 800, Tucker, GA 30084.

[2] Manager Analytical Services and Vice President, respectively; RJ Lee Group, Inc., 350 Hochberg Road, Monroeville, PA 15146.

upon particular requirements of the investigation. The samplers, which function similarly to a piece of tape, have one side which is "activated" with a clear glue-like solution. The activated side is then placed face down and pressed onto the surface of interest.   The sampler is peeled from the surface using a motion similar to removing an adhered piece of tape. A typical stratified analytical approach for these samplers might begin with an optical microscope (e.g. stereo scope, polarized light and/or phase contrast) examination followed by various levels of electron microscopy, atomic absorption (AA) or inductively coupled plasma (ICP) emission spectrometry.   One of the important advantages of collecting samples with the adhesive media is to allow for direct preparation and analysis of samples using a variety of analytical techniques.

Previous successful applications of the samplers have involved projects such as:

- cleanliness sampling during/after asbestos abatement projects
- upwind/downwind sampling of fly ash and particulate from industry
- identification of heat altered particles from fires
- clean room evaluations
- determination of particulate on laundered garments
- forensic sampling/gun shot residue (GSR)
- industrial sampling for synthetic vitreous fibers
- sampling during building demolition
- monitoring operations and maintenance activities in buildings
- replicating pores and cracks in materials
- occupied building evaluations for biological agents/allergens
- surface sampling for lead in dust and on paint removal projects

Several lead particulate-specific jobs employing the adhesive sampling and analytical technology have been completed to date.   Data have been obtained from a variety of sources including public and private residential dwellings, commercial facilities and lead-based paint (LBP) abatement projects.[1] Although the adhesive lift samplers are useful for determining lead loadings in dust accumulations, the main advantage of the technology is its amenability to direct sample preparation for microscopic analysis, which is useful in obtaining information on particle morphology, matrix associations, size ranges and distributions. It also permits the sample to be analyzed by multiple analytical techniques.

Listed below are summaries of projects which utilized the adhesive lift technology to assist in the characterization of lead particulate.

U.S. EPA Simulated LBP Removal Project (Evaluation of Pelletized CO_2 Blasting) From Wooden and Metal Doors

The primary purpose of the project was to evaluate the relative effectiveness of pelletized CO_2 blasting of the surfaces and to determine if it was a viable method for LBP removal projects.   This study also involved collecting surface particulate samples after the simulated LBP removal operation from the wooden and metal doors used in the test.[2] Wipe sampling was the primary collection technique employed. Adhesive lift surface samplers were included as part of the overall study and were collected using 25 cm^2 active surface area samplers.   The wipe and adhesive samplers were analyzed by graphite furnace atomic absorption (GFAA) spectrometry to provide an estimate of the lead loading.   Several of the adhesive lifts were also analyzed using computer controlled scanning electron microscopy (CCSEM) to obtain information on lead particle morphology, matrix associations and size ranges.

Lead loadings from the door surfaces using the adhesive lift technology and wipe samples are summarized in Table 1. The lead loadings reported for the adhesive lift samples were consistently lower than the wipe sample results. The difference may have been due to variations in the efficiencies of the sampling methods, the size of the area sampled, variation in the surface's spatial uniformity of particulate lead, or substrate surface texture. The report also noted that the adhesive lift samples were collected immediately after the surfaces were cleaned, whereas the wipes were collected after some (unspecified) time had elapsed. This time delay may have contributed to a greater lead loading of the wipe samples due to additional settling of lead particles in the work area.

TABLE 1--Surface loadings of lead on doors after
pelletized CO_2 blasting GFAA analysis.

Sample #	Door # & Type	Adhesives Pb ($\mu g/cm^2$)	Wipes Pb ($\mu g/cm^2$)	Lead Content in Paint wt. %
1	2A wood	2.59	4.07	0.81
2	1A wood	1.40	5.81	10.70
3	4A wood	0.20	3.98	0.86
4	6A wood	4.10	5.89	3.94
5	3A wood	0.17	0.35	0.07
6	5A metal	0.09	2.51	<0.01
Control	0	0.01	-	-

CCSEM analysis was also performed on several of the samples in an effort to define elemental composition, possible matrix associations and relative sizes of the lead particles. Barium sulfur (BaS)-rich, lead (Pb)-rich, zinc (Zn)-rich and titanium (Ti)-rich particles were detected in significant numbers during the CCSEM analysis. Most of the particles were less than 2.0 μm in diameter. Elemental chemistry spectra and secondary electron images of several of these particles are depicted in Figures 1 and 2.

Figure 1 is a secondary electron image of a Pb-rich particle whereas Figure 2 provides an example of a BaS-rich particle. The particles illustrated in these figures are typical of those detected during the CCSEM analysis. Based on size and elemental chemistry, particles of this nature would be indicative of a LBP source (i.e. pigment).

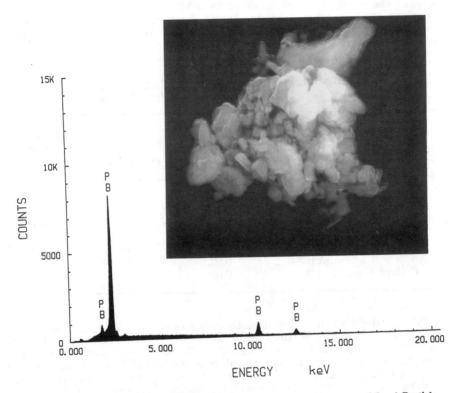

Figure 1. Secondary Electron Image and Elemental Spectrum of Lead Particle

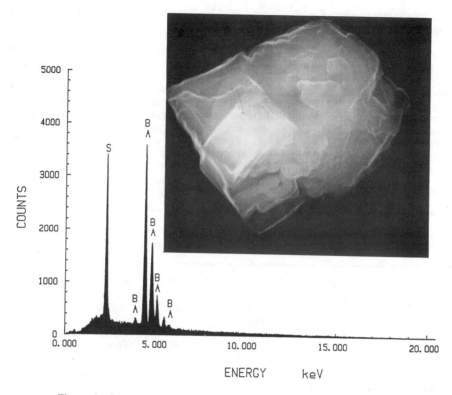

Figure 2. Secondary Electron Image and Elemental Spectrum of BaS-rich Particle

Side-by-Side Comparison of Adhesive Technology With Wipe and Micro-Vacuum Samples in a Public Housing Project

This study was completed during a comprehensive risk assessment in public housing units. The primary application of the adhesive technology in this assessment was to compare relative collection efficiencies for lead with the wipe procedure and, to a lesser degree, the micro-vacuum technique.

In this study, various surfaces were sampled, including wooden floors, linoleum, metal window wells, wooden window sills, carpeting and concrete. These surfaces were noted to be in variable condition, ranging from good to very poor. The majority of adhesive lift samples were collected using 25 cm^2 samplers, however, a number of samples were also collected using the 100 cm^2 samplers (where feasible). Analysis was performed on the adhesive samples using GFAA for total lead concentrations to permit comparisons with the wipe data.

adhesive samples using GFAA for total lead loadings to permit comparisons with the wipe data.

Table 2 summarizes the data obtained from wipe, adhesive lift and micro-vacuum side-by-side sampling of various surfaces. Although the data are limited, samples 1/BR2WW, 2LRF, 3/BR2F and 4LRF show fairly good comparison between the wipe, adhesive and micro-vacuum data. Assuming that the two adhesive lift "recover" samples (5/LRWW and 6/KWW) were effective at removing all of the lead that was remaining on the sampled surface, then it appears that greater than eighty percent of the lead was removed using the wipe procedure. Comparison of the micro-vacuum results with the wipe data for sample 5/LRWW shows variation. The reason for this difference is not clear but again may be due to the surface spatial uniformity of the lead particulate.

TABLE 2--A comparison of wipe, micro-vacuum and adhesive lift sample loadings, Pb (μg/cm^2), from public housing units.

Sample/ Location	Wipe	Adhesive	Micro-Vac.	Surface Substrate
1/BR2WW	0.47	0.30	0.090	Window Well/ Wood
2/LRF	<0.03	0.01	<0.001	Floor/Carpet
3/BR2F	<0.03	0.01	0.030	Mat/Rubber
4/LRF	<0.03	0.01	0.010	Floor/Carpet
5/LRWW	2.77	0.53*	0.500	Window Well/ Wood
6/KWW	6.38	0.56*	3.960	Window Well/ Wood

*Recovery Sample After Wipe

The remainder of the study focused primarily on side-by-side comparisons of the adhesive lift and wipe samples. Table 3 presents data from three representative units of the seventeen total units in which side-by-side sampling was conducted. There is a poor relationship between the sample results. In some instances, the wipe samples reported higher lead loadings, while on other samples the converse occurred. In several cases, the data compare well with the adhesive samplers consistently reporting lower concentrations from the metal track window wells which were noted to be in relatively poor condition. However, the adhesive lift samples from the wooden and concrete surfaces, noted as being in poor condition, generally yielded higher concentrations than the wipes. In summary, the results of the study yielded interesting information in several areas which requires further investigation under better controlled conditions.

TABLE 3--Comparison of loadings, Pb ($\mu g/cm^2$), in surface dust using wipe and adhesive lift sampling* (Public Housing).

Sample/ Location	Wipe	Adhesive	Substrate/ Condition
1/LRWW	2.77	0.53	metal/poor
1/FPL	0.51	1.25	concrete/poor
1/LRF	<0.03	0.002	tile/good
1/BRIF	<0.03	<0.001	tile/good
2/KWS	<0.03	0.03	wood/fair
2/LRWW	2.03	0.86	metal/poor
2/BR2W3	0.26	0.58	wood/poor
2/FPL	0.05	0.02	concrete/fair
3/KWS	<0.03	0.01	wood/poor
3/LRWW	0.29	0.19	metal/poor
3/BR2WW	0.47	0.30	metal/poor

* Excerpts from 89 total samples

Adhesive Lift Sampling Before and After Cleaning a Rifle Range

This study involved the use of the adhesive sampling technology for assessing the relative cleanliness of two areas on a rifle range before and after a cleaning procedure. The adhesive samplers were used to determine lead loadings ($\mu g/cm^2$) by GFAA analysis. This information could then be used to gauge the level of effectiveness of the clean-up procedure as well as possibly provide supplemental information on lead-bearing particles which most likely originated from gun-shot residue (GSR). Results of the two test areas shown in Table 4 indicate the procedures used were effective in reducing lead levels. It is important to note that the purpose of this test was to evaluate effectiveness of the cleaning method rather than comparing results with final clearance criteria on the project.

TABLE 4--Rifle range - lead results for
Type L adhesive strip sampler.

Sample Identification	Area Sampled cm^2	Total Pb μg	Pb $\mu g/cm^2$
Pre - Area A	75.92	1,480	19.50
Post - Area A	73.59	71	0.97
Pre - Area B	77.69	298	3.84
Post - Area B	75.34	177	2.35
Field Blank	100.00	<5*	<0.05*
Sealed Blank	100.00	<5*	<0.05*

*Below Analytical Sensitivity.

STUDY OF ADHESIVE SAMPLING AND ANALYTICAL TECHNOLOGY FOR LEAD IN DUST

Another study was undertaken to further investigate the usefulness of adhesive lift sampling technology in the area of lead dust evaluation. This study, conducted in unoccupied, multi-story public housing units in Baltimore, MD, was primarily designed to investigate the types of data and information which might be obtained by using multiple adhesive sampling strips in areas where dust wipe samples would typically be collected. By collecting samples in this manner, it was possible to compare total lead content and dust load spacial distributions (which could point out "hot spots") within the sampled areas. In addition, through the use of CCSEM, it would also allow for closer examination of lead particle morphology, size ranges and matrix associations.

The adhesive lift samples were collected primarily from wooden floors located in the housing units. Personnel from two research groups were responsible for collection of the adhesive lift samples and their subsequent analysis for total lead. In an effort to compare the adhesive technology with the other sampling methods investigated on the project, the strategy used involved applying four 100 cm^2 adhesive samplers in a square pattern (as indicated by Figure 3) directly adjacent to the other two (929 cm^2) areas used for wipe sampling at each sample location. All of the samples were then analyzed by ICP.

However, at each sample location, an additional 25 cm^2 adhesive sample was collected adjacent to the others. These samples were set aside for optical and electron microscopy analysis. The placement of the 25 cm^2 sampler is also illustrated in Figure 3.

Configuration of Adhesive Samplers

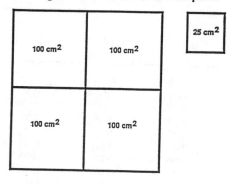

Figure 3. Configuration of 100 cm² and 25cm² Adhesive Samplers

Each of the 100 cm² samplers were analyzed separately to provide data on the variation of lead loadings within the sampling area as well as reporting an average lead loading value for the composite 400 cm² area. Table 5 shows the ICP results from the 100 cm² adhesives, both individual and arithmetic mean, from each sampling location.

TABLE 5--<u>Adhesive lift sample results, Pb ($\mu g/cm^2$).</u>

Sample #	Tape - A	Tape - B	Tape - C	Tape - D	Mean ABCD
1	4.86	4.54	0.08	2.72	3.05
2	IDL	0.07	IDL	IDL	IDL
3	0.07	0.48	0.05	0.35	0.24
4	IDL	2.28	0.55	0.79	0.90
5	IDL	0.07	IDL	IDL	IDL
6	0.05	0.06	0.06	0.06	0.06
7	0.05	0.06	0.05	0.05	0.05
8	0.06	0.06	0.07	0.06	0.06
9	0.10	0.34	0.22	0.10	0.19
10	0.12	0.09	0.17	0.16	0.14
11	0.08	0.07	0.07	0.06	0.07
12	0.06	0.10	0.16	0.31	0.16
13	0.06	0.06	0.05	0.06	0.06
14	0.23	0.15	0.10	0.11	0.15
15	0.06	0.28	7.35	0.08	1.94
16	0.11	0.09	0.08	0.08	0.09
17	0.21	0.10	0.07	0.06	0.11
18	0.09	0.05	0.09	0.05	0.07
19	0.05	0.05	0.05	0.05	0.05

The instrument detection limit (IDL) for the ICP analysis on this study was 0.04 $\mu g/cm^2$. Three control (blank) samples numbers 7, 13, and 19, reported an average value of 0.05 $\mu g/cm^2$. Analysis using GFAA of samplers from the same sample lot number reported an IDL value of 0.002 $\mu g/cm^2$, which was also confirmed independently by a second laboratory. The reason for elevated blank values by ICP has not been conclusively established. Quality control recoveries based on standard reference material (SRM) #2704 spiked samples had an average recovery of 94 percent. The range of recoveries was from 90 to 99 percent.

In general, there is no statistically significant difference in total lead concentration between locations (paired t-test, largest difference B vs. C, p=0.1261). However, considering the individual pairs of locations in a test (Test #1, positions A&B, etc.) and using the smoothed sample variance for each sample location (see ASTM E178) to calculate a pooled variance, there are statistically significant differences between locations within a test. For example, in Test #5, the comparison between positions A and B shows significant differences (paired t-test, p=0.0048).

If all four adhesive measurements from each sample spot (on wooden floors) are treated as replicates, from a statistical standpoint, there were no significant differences (ANOVA, α=0.5) in total lead loadings between floors of units (i.e. upstairs vs. downstairs) or among individual housing units.

Figure 4 provides a graphic illustration of the coefficients of variation for the mean lead loading of the replicate samples.

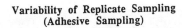

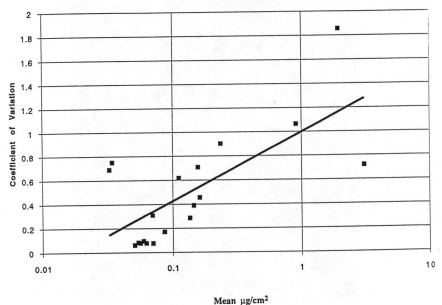

Figure 4. Coefficients of Variation of Replicate Adhesive Lift Samples for Mean Loading, Pb ($\mu g/cm^2$)

Supplemental data was also obtained on individual lead-bearing particles through stereo-optical, polarized light (PLM), manual scanning electron microscopy (SEM) and CCSEM analysis of the 25 cm² adhesive samples which were collected adjacent to the four 100 cm² adhesives. The stereo-optical and PLM analyses were very effective in the identification of various particle types. Figure 5 is an example of a particle observed during the low power stereo optical analysis.

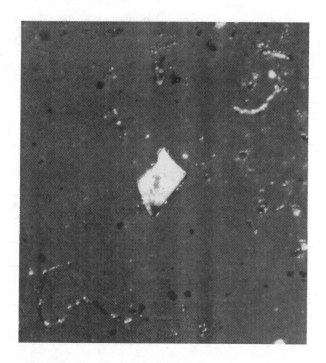

**Figure 5. Low-power Stereo Photograph of
Paint Chip (70X)**

The SEM and CCSEM analysis of the samples yielded substantial information relative to the morphology, chemical composition, matrix associations and sizes of lead-bearing particles. The SEM micrographs indicate that the majority of lead-containing particles are bound in matrices, presumably paint chips. Many of the lead-bearing particles were also agglomerated into clusters. Where it was possible to distinguish individual lead particles, the majority of them were approximately 1.0 µm or less in diameter.

Figures 6 through 11 provide examples of the types of particle information available through the use of SEM in conjunction with the adhesive samplers. Figure 6 shows a low magnification (200X) secondary electron image of a large feature of interest. Also included in this figure is a high magnification (10,000X) secondary electron image of a section of this particle. Note what appears to be a cubic shaped particle in the center of the image.

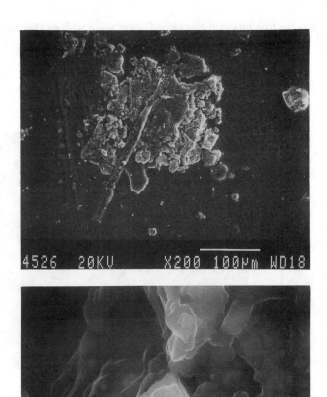

Figure 6.   Secondary Electron Images at Low and High
Magnification of Lead-bearing Feature

A backscattered electron image of this same feature along with its elemental spectrum is provided in Figure 7. As can be seen, the bright feature is composed of lead.

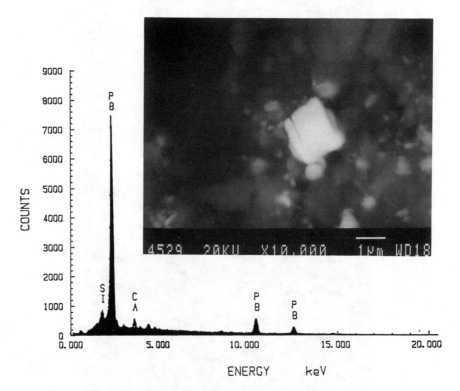

Figure 7.   Backscattered Electron Image and Elemental Spectrum of Lead-bearing Particle

This particle is brighter than the surrounding features because the backscattered electron signal is proportional to the atomic number of the element. High atomic number particles such as zinc, cadmium and lead appear brighter than low atomic number particles such as carbon, aluminum and silicon.

Figure 8 is a secondary electron image of a large particle which is composed primarily of carbon.

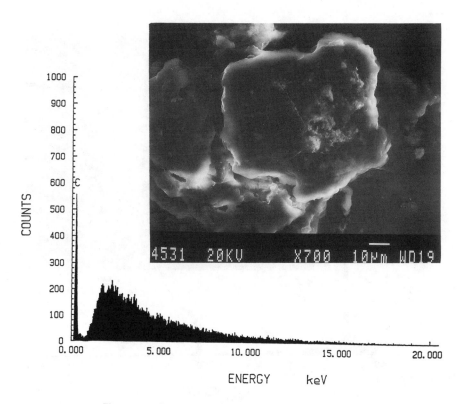

Figure 8.   Secondary Electron Image and Elemental Spectrum of Carbon-rich Particle

Figure 9 is a backscattered electron image of the same particle. Note the bright features clustered within the particle. The elemental spectrum indicates that the bright features are lead. As can be seen in this figure, the backscattered electron signal is very useful for the detection of lead and provides for the examination of low concentrations of lead in the SEM in an efficient manner.

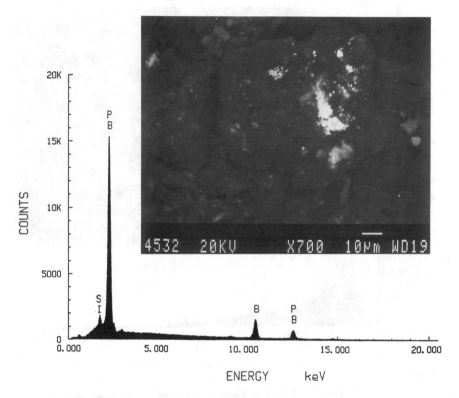

Figure 9.   Backscattered Electron Image and Elemental Spectrum of "Bright" Lead Features

An example of an individual lead-bearing particle approximately 1 μm in size is provided in Figure 10. CCSEM analysis of this sample indicated that the lead was concentrated in two sizes. The majority of the lead-bearing particles were less than 15 μm.

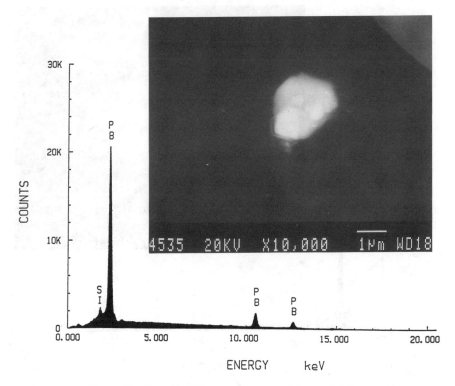

Figure 10. Secondary Electron Image and Elemental Spectrum of Individual Lead Particle

However, lead-bearing particles between 30 and 150 µm were also detected. An example of one of the large lead-bearing particles is observed during the CCSEM analysis illustrated in Figure 11.

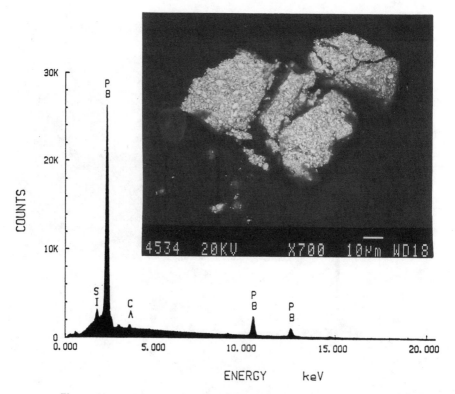

Figure 11. **Backscattered Electron Image and Elemental Spectrum of Larger Lead Particle Detected During CCSEM Analysis**

SUMMARY AND CONCLUSIONS

Based on the information and data generated in studies discussed in this paper using adhesive sampling technology and stratified analytical approach, it is apparent that this technology holds promise for lead particle collection, identification, measurement and surface loading indexing. As an alternative to historically employed sampling procedures such as wipe or micro-vacuum sampling, adhesive technology may be a cost-effective tool, which not only provides surface concentration index data, but also may yield ancillary information on individual particles. Information of this nature may enable practitioners to understand more about sources of particulate contaminants. Furthermore, data of this nature may provide information relevant to the bio-availability of the particles.

Although the side-by-side sample data are still undergoing review, the recently completed study of public housing units in Baltimore, MD indicates that there are spatial distribution differences, even within one square foot sampling areas, which may be indicative of relatively small "hot spots" of lead-bearing dust. This may be an important issue to consider in conducting lead surveys in facilities and in designing or carrying out lead clean-up projects.

The next step in the continuing process of refining the adhesive sampling and analytical technology and understanding the data generated through its use is to carefully evaluate the side-by-side data comparing the devices with the other available sampling methods and to continue building the library of information available on lead-bearing particles using manual SEM, CCSEM and other analytical approaches.

REFERENCES

[1]   Casuccio, G., et.al; Characterization and Identification of Lead-Rich Particles: A First Step in Source Apportionment., presented at the American Chemical Society National Meeting; Washington, DC. 1992.

[2]   Kominsky, J.R., et. al.; Pelletized Carbon Dioxide as a Fluidized Agent for Paint Removal: A Demonstration; Unpublished report prepared for the United States Environmental Protection Agency, Risk Reduction Engineering Laboratory; Cincinnati, OH. 1992. U.S. EPA contract No. 68-CØ-ØØØ3.

Yaacov Mamane[1], Robert D. Willis[2], Robert K. Stevens[3], and John L. Miller[4]

SCANNING ELECTRON MICROSCOPY/X-RAY FLUORESCENCE CHARACTERIZATION OF LEAD-RICH POST-ABATEMENT DUST

REFERENCE: Mamane, Y., Willis, R. D., Stevens, R. K., and Miller, J. L., "Scanning Electron Microscopy/X-ray Fluorescence Characterization of Lead-rich Post-Abatement Dust," Lead in Paint, Soil and Dust: Health Risks, Exposure Studies, Control Measures, Measurement Methods, and Quality Assurance, ASTM STP 1226, Michael E. Beard and S. D. Allen Iske, Eds., American Society for Testing and Materials, Philadelphia, 1995.

ABSTRACT: Scanning electron microscopy (SEM) and laboratory X-ray fluorescence (XRF) were used to characterize post-abatement dust collected with a HEPA filter. Three size fractions of resuspended dust (0-150 μm, 2.5-15 μm, and <2.5 μm) were collected on teflon filters and analyzed by energy-dispersive XRF. Automated SEM was used to determine the size, morphology, and chemistry of individual particles from 0.2 μm to greater than 250 μm. Minerals associated with construction materials, paint fillers, and soil were the dominant species in all size fractions. Lead-rich particles were found in all sizes and could be grouped into three categories: lead-only (includes lead oxide and lead carbonate), mixed lead/minerals, and automotive lead. Isolated lead oxide or lead carbonate particles derived from paint pigments were the dominant form of the lead-bearing particles in the size fraction <15 μm.

KEYWORDS: lead, dust, scanning electron microscopy, X-ray fluorescence, post-abatement, paint

Knowledge of the sources, size-distribution, and lead content of lead-bearing particles is critical to assessing risk and controlling environmental lead exposure. Much information can be learned from field samples by combining bulk analytical techniques with microanalysis of individual particles. This paper discusses results of a preliminary effort to characterize a lead-rich post-abatement dust sample using a combination of laboratory X-ray Fluorescence (XRF) for bulk analysis and manual and computer-controlled Scanning Electron Microscopy (CCSEM)

[1]Associate Professor, Environmental Engineering Department, Technion, Haifa 32000, Israel.

[2]Research Scientist, ManTech Environmental, Research Triangle Park, NC 27709.

[3]Chief, Source Apportionment Research Branch, U.S. Environmental Protection Agency, Research Triangle Park, NC 27711.

[4]Senior Consultant, US EPA, Research Triangle Park, NC 27711.

coupled with energy-dispersive X-ray microanalysis (EDX) for individual particle analysis. XRF provides rapid, quantitative, multielement analysis thus providing an "elemental context" for lead measurements and enabling interelement relationships to be investigated. Scanning Electron Microscopy is an excellent complement to the XRF technique. Recent papers [1,2,3,4] demonstrate the power of CCSEM in apportioning sources of environmental lead based on size, morphology, and composition of individual particles.

Major objectives in the present study were to determine if lead concentrations varied as a function of particle size and to identify sources for the lead-bearing particles.

EXPERIMENTAL METHOD

Sample Description

The sample used in this study, designated as dust D-5, was prepared for the Atmospheric Research and Exposure Assessment Laboratory of the U.S. Environmental Protection Agency. The sample was developed for the purpose of establishing protocols and evaluating methods for the analysis of lead-contaminated dust. Details of the dust collection, sample preparation, and bulk analysis of the dust are given by Williams et al.[5]. The sample consisted of lead-rich dust collected with a HEPA filtered vacuum system during the abatement clean-up process in several homes which had lead-based paint removed or encapsulated. The majority of the dust particles were therefore expected to be products of abatement activities. The bulk lead concentration in D-5 was previously determined to be 4550 $\mu g/g$ of dust based on a round-robin analysis of the sample by atomic absorption (AA) and inductively-coupled plasma (ICP) techniques.

Sample Preparation

Samples were prepared for both XRF and SEM analysis by aerosolizing sieved fractions of the dust and collecting the dust on teflon or polycarbonate membrane filters. Similar procedures for preparing XRF and SEM samples were used by Batterman et al.[6] in characterizing soils and street dust. The parent D-5 material had been sieved at 60 mesh to remove particles >250 μm. Prior to resuspension the dust was manually sieved a second time by the authors into two size fractions: 150-250 μm and below 150 μm. Figure 1 shows the particle resuspension chamber. The dust sample was introduced from the top of the chamber. The chamber was designed such that particles smaller than about 30 μm aerodynamic diameter were suspended in the chamber by air forced through the glass frit at the base. It is possible that the original size distribution of the D-5 dust was altered due to mass fractionation in the resuspension process, but such effects were beyond the scope of this study; some preferential loss of smaller particles for example might be expected due to electrostatic forces between particles and the system walls.

A Versatile Air Pollution Sampler (VAPS) [7,8] was connected to the glass resuspension chamber via a PM-15 inlet operating at 32 lpm. The purpose of the VAPS was to generate XRF and SEM samples in different size fractions. Particles entering the inlet impinged on a virtual impactor with a cut-point of 2.5 μm, were partitioned into a coarse fraction (2.5 to 15 μm, aerodynamic diameter) and two fine fractions (<2.5 μm), and were collected on pre-weighed 47mm teflon filters. To avoid making large corrections for X-ray attenuation, dust loadings for XRF samples were limited to less than 200 $\mu g\ cm^{-2}$. Thus, the quantity of dust collected on each filter ranged between 0.1 mg and 2 mg.

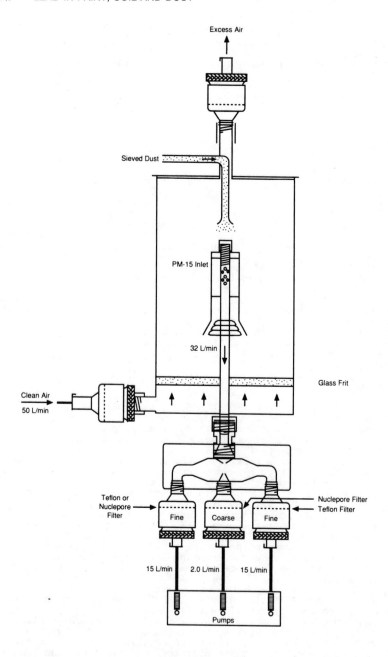

FIGURE 1--Schematic diagram of the dust resuspension chamber. Dust particles injected from the top of the chamber were size-selected using a Versatile Air Pollution Sampler (VAPS) and collected on filters for analysis by XRF and SEM/EDX.

XRF Analysis

Nine aliquots of the fine sieved material were resuspended and analyzed by energy-dispersive XRF using a spectrometer custom built by Lawrence Berkeley Laboratory for the Source Apportionment Research Branch (SARB) of the EPA [9]. The XRF spectrometer employs a pulsed tungsten X-ray tube to sequentially excite four secondary fluorescer targets (Ti, Co, Mo, and Sm) in order to optimize detection sensitivity across the periodic table. The tube operates at a constant power of 24 W and a maximum voltage of 68 kV (Sm fluorescer). The system was specifically designed for analyzing aerosol samples collected on membrane filters and measures ng/cm^2 concentrations for elements heavier than magnesium. Determination of elemental mass densities is accomplished by a least-squares fit by assuming that the observed spectra can be expressed as a linear combination of pure element spectra. Once the elemental masses per unit area are determined, they are corrected for attenuation of X-rays by the sample itself and for X-ray line interferences between elements. Additional details are provided by Drane et al. [10] and Dzubay et al. [11]. Calibration of the spectrometer was independently determined for each of 39 elements using vacuum-deposited metal film standards (Micromatter Co., Deer Harbor, WA) and/or polymer film standards containing known concentrations of metals [12]. Standards of both types were used in establishing the system's lead calibration which utilizes the lead L and M X-ray lines. In addition, QC standards including a polymer film containing Fe and Pb and NIST glass-film SRM #1833 containing certified lead were measured before and after the sample analyses to validate each analytical run.

The nine samples are summarized in Table 1 below and include four fine fractions, three coarse fractions, and two "total" fractions.

TABLE 1--Post-abatement dust samples analyzed by XRF and SEM.

Sample ID	Size, μm	Analysis
F1	0 - 2.5 [1]	XRF
F2	0 - 2.5 [1]	XRF
F3	0 - 2.5 [1]	XRF
F4	0 - 2.5 [1]	XRF
C2	2.5 - 15 [1]	XRF
C3	2.5 - 15 [1]	XRF
C4	2.5 - 15 [1]	XRF
T1	0 - 150 [1]	XRF
T2	0 - 150 [1]	XRF
F5	0.2 - 4 [2]	CCSEM
C5	1.5 - 15 [2]	CCSEM
FS1	5 - 50 [2]	CCSEM
CS1	40 - 350 [2]	CCSEM

Notes: 1) Aerodynamic diameter.
2) Geometric diameter.

"Total" fractions were collected by removing the PM-15 inlet and replacing the VAPS with a single filter holder operating with a flow of 25 lpm; these samples in principle included particles ranging in size from zero up to the maximum particle size (nominally 150 μm) of the fine sieved dust. "Total" filters were not expected to represent proportionately the <150 μm size distribution of the D-5 dust both because the resuspension chamber was designed only to aerosolize particles less than 30 μm and because the larger particles have a higher probability of settling directly into the sampling inlet. Therefore, data obtained from "total" samples was interpreted only in terms of the differences between "total" and fine or coarse samples.

Filter tare weights were measured after allowing the filters to equilibrate for at least 12 hours in a temperature and humidity-controlled room. After sampling, the loaded filter was again equilibrated in the balance room for at least 12 hours before weighing.

Four additional samples were prepared for automated SEM analysis. Samples F5 and C5 (Table 1) were made with resuspended dust as described above but collected on polycarbonate filters for improved SEM imaging. Samples FS1 and CS1 were prepared by manually sprinkling fine sieved dust (<150 μm) and coarse sieved dust (150-250 μm) respectively directly onto carbon planchets for SEM analysis. No attempt was made to preserve the original size distribution of the dust. The particle sizes given in Table 1 for the four SEM samples are the effective diameter criteria used by the SEM to search for particles in the automated mode.

SEM samples were analyzed by computer-controlled SEM/EDX at R.J. Lee Group, Inc. (Monroeville, PA). The study utilized a JEOL JSM-840 SEM and a Tracor Northern TN-5500 EDX system, both interfaced to the Zeppelin operating system (R.J. Lee Group, Inc.) which permits collection and storage of digital images and spectra on optical disk. Analytical conditions were as follows: 20 kV accelerating potential, 15 mm working distance, 0° stage tilt, minimum X-ray acquisition time of 12 s (longer for imaged particles), and magnifications ranging between 25X and 1000X determined by the size fraction being analyzed. Analyses were carried out in both secondary electron (SE) and backscattered electron (BSE) modes. Particles were automatically sized by SEM and analyzed by EDX. Images of particles containing high-Z elements (Bromine and heavier) were automatically collected and stored on optical disk for off-line review. The resulting particle data and image files were processed and interpreted at the EPA using the Zeppelin Microimaging System developed for interpreting CCSEM data off-line. The software initially sorts particles based on the four dominant elements in the X-ray spectra. These particle data were reviewed and particles were then classified into a reduced number of particle classes (Tables 3 and 4) through the use of user-defined rules. Data for each sample were summarized in the following tables:

1. Number of features in each particle class, percentages, and average particle geometric diameter.
2. Size, area and mass distribution of features by average diameter and particle class. (A density is assigned to each particle based on its elemental composition).
3. Average elemental composition of the particle classes provided in the first table.
4. Mass and number distribution by aerodynamic diameter.

RESULTS

XRF Analysis

Elemental concentrations (ng/cm2) measured by XRF for the nine resuspended dust samples listed in Table 1 were converted to μg/g concentrations using the measured area and deposited mass for each filter. During preparation of the samples it was found that a substantial fraction of the deposited dust, especially on heavily loaded coarse and total filters, could be shaken off during handling of the filter. Mass losses occurring after the loaded filter was weighed and before XRF analysis would cause concentrations to be underestimated as well as bias the size distribution. In order to put bounds on the measured concentrations, all teflon filters were weighed again after XRF analysis to determine sample losses due to handling.

Results of the individual XRF analyses are shown in Table 2 as well as averages and relative variability values (sample standard deviation divided by the mean value) for each size fraction. The relative variability in the XRF data is contributed primarily by sample mass losses especially in the coarse and total fractions, and is approximately 20%, 25%, and 40% for fine, coarse, and total fraction results respectively. Abundances have been corrected for mass loss assuming that two-thirds of any mass losses due to handling occurred prior to analysis. If larger fractions of sample were lost from the coarse and total filters, their elemental concentrations would be underestimated in Table 2. Thus, the apparent increase in elemental concentrations with decreasing particle size may be artificial.

Average abundances for selected elements are shown in Figure 2. High concentrations of aluminum, silicon, sulfur, potassium, calcium, titanium, iron, zinc, and lead were detected in all three size fractions of D-5.

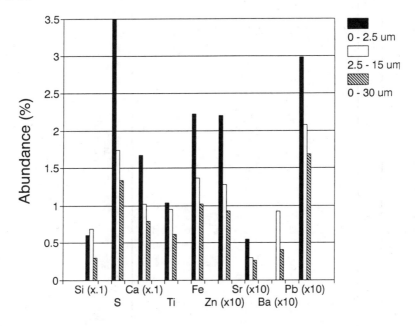

FIGURE 2--Average elemental abundances measured by XRF in three size fractions of post-abatement dust. The apparent increase in concentration with decreasing particle size may be an artifact associated with uncertainties in the sample masses.

Not surprisingly, calcium had the highest elemental concentration in the post-abatement dust: calcium carbonate is the major constituent of cement, while gypsum ($CaSO_4$) is a major constituent of plaster and wallboard, and is frequently used as a filler in paints. Some of the aluminum, silicon, and potassium is probably associated with soil-derived dust or street dust. SEM analysis of individual particles suggests that aluminosilicates may also be associated with paint as

TABLE 2--XRF abundances (per cent) in post-abatement dust samples.

Sample	Al	Si	S	K	Ca	Ti	Mn	Fe	Cu	Zn	Sr	Ba	Pb
F1	1.00	5.14	3.04	0.40	13.21	0.89	0.070	1.98	0.037	0.184	0.033	nd	0.253
F2	2.97	7.20	4.19	0.63	20.14	1.15	0.089	2.59	0.047	0.308	0.066	nd	0.348
F3	1.39	5.29	3.26	0.53	15.33	1.00	0.070	2.02	nd	0.192	0.052	nd	0.299
F4	nd	6.60	3.51	0.61	18.03	1.11	0.080	2.31	nd	0.197	0.066	nd	0.293
Avg	1.79	6.06	3.50	0.54	16.68	1.04	0.077	2.23	0.042	0.22	0.054	nd	0.298
% Var	58	17	14	19	18	11	12	13	17	27	29		13
C2	0.97	5.98	1.64	0.34	9.96	0.94	0.032	1.15	0.009	0.108	0.025	0.09	0.163
C3	1.84	8.50	2.22	0.47	12.30	1.13	0.047	1.77	0.017	0.158	0.039	0.11	0.277
C4	1.49	6.18	1.34	0.34	8.42	0.78	0.026	1.18	0.015	0.117	0.024	0.08	0.183
Avg	1.43	6.89	1.73	0.38	10.23	0.95	0.035	1.36	0.014	0.128	0.029	0.09	0.208
% Var	31	20	26	20	19	18	30	26	32	21	29	14	29
T1	0.84	2.93	1.33	0.25	7.92	0.61	0.028	1.02	0.009	0.093	0.026	0.04	0.168
T2	1.57	5.95	2.27	0.46	13.55	1.08	0.045	1.90	0.019	0.170	0.042	nd	0.307
Avg	1.21	4.44	1.80	0.36	10.74	0.85	0.037	1.46	0.014	0.13	0.034	0.04	0.238
% Var	43	48	37	42	37	39	33	43	51	41	33	...	41

1. Results assume that two-thirds of the mass lost by each sample occurred prior to analysis.
2. nd = not detected at the 3-sigma quantitation limit.
3. % Var = sample standard deviation divided by the mean value, expressed as a percent.

paint fillers. Kaolinite and talc for example are common fillers in
paints. Sulfur, titanium, iron, zinc, strontium, barium, and lead are
all commonly found in paint pigments.

The lead concentration in the fine fraction samples is estimated
to be 2980 µg/g assuming that two-thirds of the observed mass losses
occurred prior to XRF analysis. Even if all the mass losses are assumed
to occur prior to analysis, the average fine fraction lead concentration
would only increase to 3200 µg/g. This is considerably less than the
bulk concentration of 4550 µg/g determined by AAS and ICP and adopted as
the consensus value. This may represent a true difference between the
lead concentration in the bulk dust and in the fine fraction, or there
may be additional sources of error in the XRF analysis (e.g., matrix
effects) which have not been accounted for. The above result is however
similar to the bulk concentration of 2485 µg/g determined by XRF in the
round-robin analysis of D-5.

SEM Analysis

Table 3 summarizes CCSEM results obtained on samples F5, C5, and
FS1 in the SE mode. (Sample CS1 was analyzed only in the BSE mode).
The results show similarity in the composition of the three size
fractions. As expected, minerals associated with construction materials
and paint fillers dominate the three size fractions. The titanium-rich
particles are probably fragments of paint chips. Examination of
individual particles showed that the titanium was generally accompanied
by aluminum silicate and calcium or gypsum. Iron-rich particles in
general were also rich in calcium, silicon, and sulfur. Lead-rich
particles were those for which the lead L and M X-rays comprised more
than 15% of the total X-ray counts. (Lead was considered to be present
in a particle if the lead L and M X-ray lines were present after
correcting for possible overlaps from sulfur, molybdenum, and arsenic.
Peak overlaps (e.g., Pb $M_{\alpha,\beta}$ and S $K_{\alpha,\beta}$) were deconvoluted by examining
the relationships of the primary to secondary peaks for selected
elements and comparing to elemental standards [13]).

TABLE 3--CCSEM analysis of D-5 samples (SE mode).

Sample	F5	C5	FS1
#Particles	385	500	232
Size, µm	0.2-4[1]	1.5-15[1]	5-50[1]
Particle Class	Percent by number		
Carbonates	39	36	42
Gypsum	26	22	9
Alum-Silicate	19	24	19
Quartz	7	10	19
Ti-rich	5	4	7
Fe-rich	3	3	4
Pb-rich	1[2]	0.5[2]	0.4

Notes: 1) Average geometric diameter.
        2) Based on CCSEM analysis in Backscatter mode.

Fine and coarse fraction samples were also analyzed by CCSEM
operating in the BSE mode. The intensity of the BSE signal increases
with atomic number. By setting a threshold on the BSE signal one can

exclude particles of lower average atomic number from automated searches and thereby enhance the efficiency of searches for particles rich in heavy elements such as iron, copper, zinc, barium, and lead. The BSE threshold was adjusted while examining several iron-rich features in the line-scan mode such that particles with average atomic number less than iron would not be detected. In this mode, 100 fine and 161.5 coarse fields of view were scanned, equivalent to analysis of a population of 9600 and 18800 particles respectively. A total of 216 fine and 300 coarse heavy element-rich particles were found in the BSE search. The results are summarized in Table 4. Examination of x-ray spectra revealed that the majority of these particles were iron-rich, or lead-rich, or barium or zinc-rich particles possibly associated with paint materials. (Barium was almost always accompanied by sulfur indicative of barium sulfate pigment). The detection of a few gypsum, calcium carbonate, and titanium-rich particles is not unexpected because the BSE threshold is not absolutely sharp.

TABLE 4--CCSEM analysis of D-5 samples   (BSE mode).

Sample	F5	C5
#Particles	216	300
Size, μm	0.2-4[1]	1.5-15[1]
Particle Class	Percent by number	
Pb-rich	45.8	26.0
Fe-rich	34.3	62.7
S-Ba	13.4	2.0
Gypsum	1.8	2.0
Zn-rich	1.4	1.3
Ti-rich	0.9	1.3
Carbonates	0.5	2.7
Other	1.4	2.0

Notes: 1) Average geometric diameter.

The concentrations of lead-rich particles in the fine and coarse fractions were respectively around 1 and 0.5 particles per field of view at a magnification of 1000X. Their average sizes were 0.8 μm and 2.5 μm respectively. Table 5 shows an estimate of the lead concentration in the fine and coarse fractions based on the the BSE and SE data. The results agree well with the XRF results for the same size fractions.

TABLE 5--CCSEM-based estimate of Pb concentrations in Fine and Coarse fractions.

Fraction	A #Particles per field [1]	B Avg. size (μm)	C Density (g/cm³)	Relative Loading (AxB³xC)
Fine Pb	0.99	0.8	5	2.53
Fine Total	96.25	1.6	2.7	1064
Coarse Pb	0.48	2.5	5	37.7
Coarse Total	116.28	3.6	2.7	14650

Notes: 1) Magnification = 1000X.
Estimated Pb in Fine fraction = 2.53/1064 = 2380 μg/g.
Estimated Pb in Coarse fraction = 37.7/14650 = 2570 μg/g.

Fine sieved dust sprinkled by hand onto a carbon planchet was analyzed in the size range of 5 to 50 μm and the results are as follows: 232 particles were found in 34 fields at magnification of 300X. In the SEM backscatter mode only one 7.6 μm lead-rich particle was found in 35 fields of view representing an estimated concentration of 2400 ppm as calculated above. Time limitations precluded an extended search of more fields in order to obtain better statistics for this size range.

Lead-bearing particles--The speciation of lead particles was one of the objectives of this study. Off-line examination of the morphologies and X-ray spectra of the lead-rich particles identified three major groups of particulate lead:

1. **Lead Only Particles**--This group includes particles comprised only of elemental lead, or lead in the form of lead oxide or lead carbonate. Many of the particles in this group displayed the cubic or hexagonal morphology characteristic of basic carbonate of white lead, the pigment commonly used in leaded paints. This was the most abundant class of lead-rich particles found in the fine and coarse fractions of D-5. Manual SEM showed the presence of these particles down to 0.25 μm. The hexagonal morphology easily distinguishes these particles from combustion-generated lead-only particles which typically appear as chain aggregates. Figure 3 shows a typical lead carbonate particle.

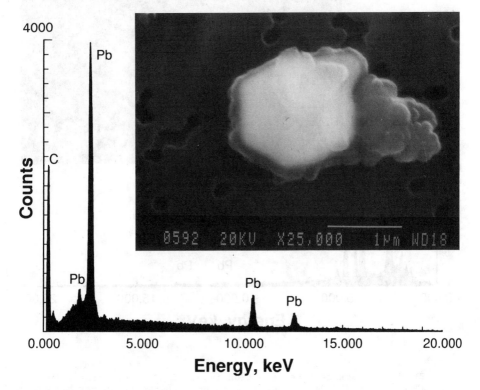

FIGURE 3--Scanning electron micrograph and X-ray spectrum of a lead carbonate particle in D-5. The hexagonal symmetry is characteristic of basic white lead carbonate commonly used in paint pigments.

2. **Mixed Lead/Minerals**--Minerals enriched in lead, apparently as lead oxide or lead carbonate particles attached to gypsum, calcite, or aluminosilicate surfaces were found in all size ranges in the samples analyzed. These are probably fragments of gypsum wallboard or other construction materials that had been painted with leaded paint. Figures 4 and 5 are photomicrographs of paint chips rich in lead.

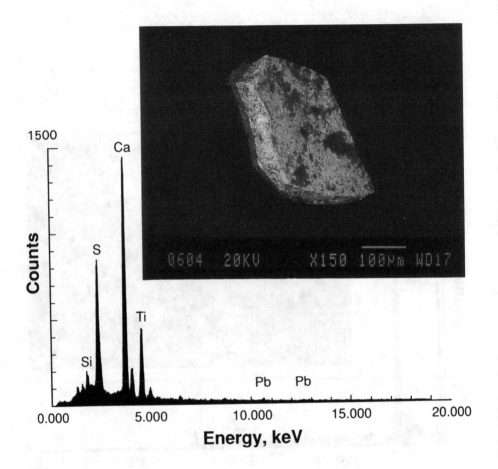

FIGURE 4--Backscattered electron image of a leaded paint chip approximately 200x300 µm. Areas rich in heavy elements appear bright in the BSE mode. X-ray analysis of the bright areas showed high lead concentrations. The X-ray spectrum above was collected from an area adjacent to the lead-rich region and indicates calcium and sulfur (probably as gypsum), titanium, and aluminum silicate.

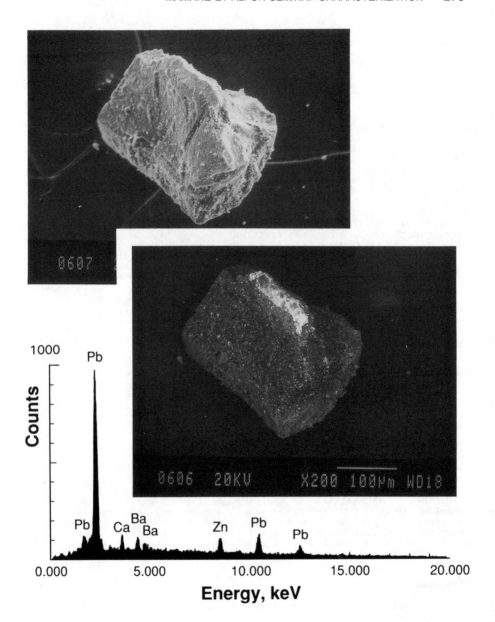

FIGURE 5--Secondary Electron (top) and Backscattered Electron (bottom) images of a leaded paint chip. The bright ridge in the BSE image was rich in lead, zinc, barium, and calcium as shown in the X-ray spectrum. Analysis of areas adjacent to the lead-rich region showed gypsum, titanium, and aluminum silicate.

3. **Automotive Lead**--Because the D-5 dust sample was comprised of post-abatement dust, the contribution from street dust was expected to be small. Nevertheless, several particles containing both lead and bromine and possibly associated with automotive emissions were found in D-5. These particles were all smaller than three microns. Unfortunately, no high-resolution images of these particles were acquired.

DISCUSSION AND CONCLUSIONS

The primary objective of this limited study was to characterize post-abatement dust using a combination of laboratory XRF for bulk analysis of size-selected fractions, and SEM/EDX for analysis of individual particles, especially lead-rich particles. The results confirmed the expected dominance of construction-related and paint-derived (pigment and mineral filler) particulates in the post-abatement dust. Approximately 1% of the 9600 fine-fraction particles (0.2-4 μm) and 0.4% of the 18800 coarse particles (1.5-15 μm) analyzed by CCSEM were lead-rich. In both size fractions the majority of these particles were isolated lead oxide or lead carbonate particles derived from paint pigments. In the coarse fraction a larger fraction of the lead appeared as lead carbonate particles attached to other minerals or as mixed lead/mineral particles.

One of the goals in this study was to determine how lead concentrations vary with particle size. DeVoe at NIST has recently measured lead concentrations in sieved fractions of lead-rich dusts and found the highest lead concentrations in particles less than 50 μm [14]. This finding is consistent with the high concentration of lead oxide or lead carbonate particles observed by CCSEM in the size fraction below 15 μm. Quantitative differences, if any, in the lead content of D-5 in the fine, coarse, and total size fractions analyzed by XRF were unfortunately obscured by the large uncertainties in the mass deposited on the XRF samples. Also, because of probable mass fractionation effects associated with the particle redeposition process, the size distribution of the analyzed samples cannot be assumed to be representative of the original dust.

Problems which limited the present study should be minimized in future studies with the recent acquisition of a new XRF spectrometer by the Source Apportionment Research Branch. The new system will enable quantitative, multielement analyses on bulk dust samples without restriction to particle size, thus eliminating the need for resuspension. The ability to analyze larger samples will minimize the potential for non-representative sampling which may have contributed to uncertainty in the XRF data. Additional computer-controlled SEM/EDX analysis of samples collected from fluidized bed resuspensions should further enhance our ability to characterize and determine the sources of lead particles in the environment.

ACKNOWLEDGEMENTS

The assistance of Mr. Bradley Henderson and Mr. Gary Casuccio of R.J. Lee Group, Inc. in the CCSEM analysis, and Mr. Robert Kellogg of ManTech Environmental Technology Inc. in the XRF analyses is gratefully acknowledged. The authors also express gratitude to Ms. Karen Blume for her assistance and many helpful suggestions during the course of the project.

DISCLAIMER

The information in this document has been funded in part by the U.S. Environmental Protection Agency under contract (#68-D9-0131) to Acurex and contract (#68-D0-0106) to ManTech Environmental Technology, Inc. It has been subject to Agency review and approved for publication. Mention of trade names or commercial products does not constitute endorsement or recommendation for use.

REFERENCES

[1]   Casuccio, G. S., Demyanek, M. L., Dunmyre, G. R.,Henderson,B.C., and Stewart, I. M., "Characterization and Identification of Lead-Rich Particles: A First Step in Source Apportionment," Proceedings of the 204th Symposium of the American Chemical Society, Washington DC, August 23-28, 1992, in press.

[2]   Vander Wood, T. B. and Brown, R. S., "The Application of Automated Scanning Electron Microscopy/Energy Dispersive X-ray Spectrometry to the Identification of Sources of Lead-Rich Particles in Soil and Dust," Environmental Choices Technical Supplement, July/August 1992, pp. 26-32.

[3]   Hunt, A., Johnson, D. L., Watt, J. M., and Thornton, I., "Characterizing the Sources of Particulate Lead in House Dust by Automated Scanning Electron Microscopy," Environmental Science and Technology, Vol. 26, No. 8, 1992, pp. 1513-1523.

[4]   Johnson, D. L. and Hunt, A., "Speciation of Lead in Urban Soils by Computer Assisted SEM/EDX - Method Development and Early Results," Proceedings of the 1993 Boulder Conference on Lead in Paint, Soil, and Dust, Boulder CO, July 25-29, 1993, this publication.

[5]   Williams, E. E., Binstock, D. A., Estes, E. D., Neefus, J. D., Meyers, L. E., and Gutknecht, W. F., "Preparation and Evaluation of Lead-Containing Paint and Dust Method Evaluation Materials," Proceedings of the American Chemical Society Symposium on Lead Poisoning in Children: Exposure, Abatement and Program Issues, Washington DC, August 24-25, 1992, in press.

[6]   Batterman, S. A., Dzubay, T. G., and Baumgardner, R. E., "Development of Crustal Profiles For Receptor Modeling," Atmospheric Environment, Vol. 22, No. 9, 1988, pp. 1821-1828.

[7]   Cofer, W. R. III, Stevens, R. K., Winstead, E. L., Pinto, J. P., Sebacher, D. I., Abdulraheem, M. Y., Al-Sahafi, M., Mazurek, M. A., Rasmussen, R. A., Cahoon, D. R., and Levine, J. S., "Kuwaiti Oil Fires: Compositions and Source Smoke," Journal Of Geophysical Research, Vol. 97, 1992, pp. 14521-14525.

[8]   Stevens, R. K., Pinto, J., Conner, T. L., Willis, R., Rasmussen, R. A., Mamane, Y., Casuccio, G., Benes, I., Lenicek, J., Subrt, P., Novak, J., and Santroch, J., "Czech Air Toxics Study (CATS): Project Summary," Proceedings of the 86th Annual Meeting of the Air and Waste Management Association, Denver CO, June 13-18, 1993, in press.

[9]   Dzubay, T. G., Stevens, R. K., Lewis, C. W., Hern, D. H., Courtney, W. J., Tesch, J. W., and Mason, M. A., "Visibility and Aerosol Composition in Houston, Texas," Environmental Science and Technology, Vol. 16, 1982, p. 514.

[10]   Drane, E. A., Rickel, D. G., Courtney, W. J., and Dzubay, T. G.,
"Computer Code For Analysing X-Ray Fluorescence Spectra of
Airborne Particulate Matter," Advances in X-ray Analysis, Vol. 23,
1980, p.149.

[11]   Dzubay, T. G. and Nelson, R. O., "Self-Absorption Corrections for
X-ray Fluorescence Analysis of Aerosols," Advances in X-ray
Analysis, Vol. 18, 1975, p.619.

[12]   Dzubay, T.G., Morosoff, N., Whitaker, G. L., Yasuda, H., Bazan,
F., Bennett, R., Cooper, J., Courtney, W. J., Frazier, C. A.,
Gatti, R. C., Germani, M., Gordon, G., Hanamura, S., Kellogg, R.
B., Rhodes, J. R., and Schindler, J. S., "Polymer Film Standards
for X-ray Fluorescence Spectrometers," Journal of Trace and
Microprobe Techniques, Vol. 5, 1987, p.327.

[13]   Gary Casuccio, R. J. Lee Group, Inc., private communication.

[14]   Jim DeVoe, private communication.

David L. Johnson[1] and Andrew Hunt[2]

ANALYSIS OF LEAD IN URBAN SOILS BY COMPUTER ASSISTED SEM/EDX--METHOD
DEVELOPMENT AND EARLY RESULTS

REFERENCE: Johnson, D. L., and Hunt, A., **"Analysis of Lead in Urban
Soils by Computer Assisted SEM/EDX--Method Development and Early Re-
sults,"** Lead in Paint, Soil and Dust: Health Risks, Exposure Studies,
Control Measures, Measurement Methods, and Quality Assurance, ASTM STP
1226, Michael E. Beard and S. D. Allen Iske, Eds., American Society for
Testing and Materials, Philadelphia,1995.

ABSTRACT: Particulate lead in urban soils from Syracuse, NY, was
characterized by computer assisted scanning electron microscopy (SEM)
and X-ray energy spectroscopy (EDX). Samples collected from the
building line of houses built prior to 1940 showed bulk lead values of
870 to 5350 $\mu g/g$, the origin of which is suspected to have been from
lead-based paints. In contrast to previous analyses of household dusts,
only a small fraction of the particulate lead could be identified with
potential input materials; most of the lead is strongly associated with
the iron and manganese phases in the soils. Estimates of the amount of
soil bulk lead amenable to SEM characterization ranged from 20 to 115%
with lower values being associated with lower soil pH. The results
suggest that soil lead derived from paint undergoes a relatively rapid
transformation and redistribution with consequent loss of its
potentially distinctive individual particle identity.

KEYWORDS: scanning electron microscopy, image analysis, urban soils,
particulate lead, speciation, lead paint, redistribution

Numerous studies, conducted worldwide, indicate that lead contamination of urban soils is an ubiquitous contemporary phenomenon. The
physical/chemical form of lead in such soils bears a fundamental relationship to studies of human exposure and risk assessment, bioavailability, transport and recontamination, and the development of potential
remediation strategies. Chaney, et al. [1] summarize the four general
approaches to lead speciation studies as: 1) use of X-ray diffraction

[1]Faculty of Chemistry, SUNY College of Environmental Science and
Forestry, Syracuse, NY, 13210.

[2]Department of Pathology, SUNY Health Science Center,
Syracuse, NY, 13210.

for crystalline lead compounds, 2) determination of compounds controlling lead solubility in soil solutions, 3) use of sequential extraction
reagents in comparison with known compounds, and 4) addition of lead
compounds to soils to follow their potential transformations to other
lead species. In this paper, we present initial results from
application of a fifth approach--automated individual particle analysis
(IPA) based on scanning electron microscopy (SEM) and X-ray energy
spectroscopy (EDX). This technique can provide information on the size,
shape, and elemental composition (X-ray spectral data) of statistically
significant numbers of particles in a time efficient manner.

The IPA methodology has been used extensively in the UK as part of
a comprehensive study of lead contamination in environmental dusts [2].
Hunt, et al. [3,4] have presented the technique for, and the results of,
particulate lead source apportionment in household dusts based on this
analytical procedure. It also provided a critical interpretive
capability in the Port Pirie, South Australia, environmental lead
contamination study [5]. Used in conjunction with traditional bulk
chemical analysis methods, IPA has great potential for improving our
understanding of the sources, fate, and transport characteristics of
particulate lead in urban soils.

The soils discussed in this report were collected within, or near,
the city of Syracuse, NY. For comparison, the NIST standard reference
material (SRM) 2710, Montana soil, is included. Background soil lead
levels in the city, collected at 0-10 cm depth in open spaces away from
buildings, are generally less than 150 $\mu g/g$ [6]. The surface loading
may be higher than this value, but diluted by mixing with the whole of
the 0-10 cm column. Four of the five ambient soil analyses presented
here are from surface layers (0-3 cm) taken at the building line of
houses built prior to 1940; particulate lead may have derived from
lead-based paint. Furthermore, these preliminary results are limited to
the soil particle size fraction generally less than about 30 μm in area
equivalent diameter. Nevertheless, the findings have a general
applicability to urban soil lead enrichment in temperate North America.

BACKGROUND AND METHODS

The Syracuse soils are largely derived from glacial till
(Orthents), though one soil from Manlius, NY, is classified as Mohawk
(silty loam)--soil 1521. The first two or three digits of the soil
identification number refer to the City of Syracuse or Onondaga County
census tract number. Samples were collected from the top 0-3 cm of the
soil column using a stainless steel spoon. Specimens were oven dried at
70°C, and sieved through 2 mm aluminum mesh to remove extraneous matter.

For SEM preparation, 1.0 g of soil and 200 ml of deionized water
were placed in a 250 ml flask and subjected to ultra-sound agitation for
15 min. Clay particles are probably not completely disaggregated by
this treatment, but the procedure minimizes the occurrence of
adventitious lead particle/soil particle associations and improves the
accuracy of the individual particle enumeration and characterization
process. After allowing the samples to sit undisturbed for 10 min.,

aliquots of the suspension (the SUS fraction) were removed with a
pipette. A few drops of the SUS fraction were diluted with deionized
water and filtered through 25 mm diameter, 0.4 μm pore size
polycarbonate membrane filters. These were affixed to 25 mm graphite
disks with carbon paint and coated with carbon (20-30 nm thick) in a
high vacuum evaporator prior to the SEM analysis. The optimum mass
loading is about 20 to 30 μg per cm^2 to provide a monolayer of features
separated from each other by sufficient distance to minimize stray X-ray
"contamination" from adjacent particle fluorescence. Note that the 10
min. settling time employed effectively eliminates inorganic particles
larger than about 30 μm from the SUS fraction. However, the resultant
preparations are much more reproducible in the automated SEM analyses,
and decrease the variability of computed bulk lead described below.

The individual particle characterizations were carried out using
an ETEC Autoscan SEM interfaced with a LeMont Scientific DA-10 Image
Analysis system and a KEVEX 7500 X-ray Spectrometer (30 mm^2 detector).
A complete description of the procedure can be found elsewhere [7]. In
this study, a magnification of 400X, a 30 kV accelerating potential, 25
mm working distance, 0° stage tilt, and a live-time X-ray acquisition
time of 5 sec were used. The feature search point density (with the
digital scan generator) was adjusted to locate particles as small as
0.2 μm in area equivalent diameter. Detailed examination of specific
features was carried out manually on a Hitachi S520 SEM operating in
tandem with a PGT IMIX Microanalysis System.

During automated X-ray data acquisition, 25 elemental regions of
interest (ROI) and 63 background regions for net X-ray relative intensity computations were delineated within the X-ray energy spectrum. Final
window widths and efficiency factor adjustments were made after the
analysis of NBS (NIST) SRM 1633 (fly ash) and USGS standard BCR-1. Lead
X-rays were measured using the Lα line (10.36-10.70 keV), correcting for
arsenic. The lead overlap with the sulfur Kα line was corrected using a
lead oxide (PbO) standard so that in its analysis, less than 1% of the
net X-ray relative intensity was reported as sulfur. This conservative
correction resulted in a slight underestimate for sulfur in lead sulfate
particles--about 35% sulfur and 65% lead. Other overlap pairs, such as
sodium/zinc, were corrected in similar fashion. The lead X-ray relative
intensity efficiency factor was adjusted by analysis of lead containing
brass (3% lead) and leaded glass (15.5% lead).

For an element to be reported as "present", the integrated number
of X-ray counts per channel within the ROI was compared to the counts
per channel in the designated background regions. If the counts per
channel in the ROI did not exceed those in the background regions by a
user specified amount, the elemental "presence" was set to zero. Decreasing this background factor has the effect of lowering the detection
limit for an individual element at the expense of increasing the probability of "false hits". Using a dataset of lead-free elemental standard
particles (about 1000) and 1200 lead-free suspended sediment particles
from a drinking water supply tributary stream, the background factor was
decreased until no more than 1 "false positive" occurrence of a lead
containing feature (<0.05%) was observed. With a factor of 1.25 times
the square root of the background counts per channel, the effective

detection limit for lead in an individual particle was about 0.7% for net X-ray relative intensity. Some fraction of lead in a given soil may be widely dispersed on many particles by adsorption or ion exchange; for an individual particle, it may be present below the IPA detection limit. In such cases, the resolution of IPA for physicochemical speciation of lead is reduced, and it is natural to ask "what fraction of lead in the prepared specimen is described by IPA characterization"? Following on from the work of Johnson, et al. [8], the SEM accountable lead (SAL) was defined as the fraction of individual particle mass contributed by lead--the lead X-ray relative intensity times the estimated feature volume. This was weighted by the proportional increase in specific gravity of PbO (8.0/2.5) or lead carbonate (6.14/2.5), compared to an assumed average specific gravity of 2.5 for all features, in accordance with the percentage of particle X-rays emitted by lead. The computation was summed over all features analyzed and compared to the bulk lead measured in the SUS fraction.

To test the SAL computations, a reference soil (AR45) was pre- pared. A 40 g portion of soil 4501 and a 60 g portion of soil 4502 were mixed with 500 ml of deionized water and subjected to ultra-sound agita- tion for 30 min. The suspension was then stirred and into it was poured 50 ml of a suspension containing 1.0 g of reagent grade PbO previously dispersed with ultra sound agitation. The PbO was finely divided, dominated by particles in the 1 to 3 μm diameter size range. The mix- ture was stirred for a further 30 min. and then oven dried overnight at 110° C to remove water. The reference material was then ground and passed through an 821 μm Nylon mesh, discarding the larger fraction.

Bulk acid-soluble lead concentrations were determined by inductively coupled plasma (ICP) with a SPECTRO Analytical Instruments model FMA-03 spectrometer. Typically, 1.0 g of soil was stirred with 50 ml of 2 N nitric acid for one hour at room temperature and then filtered through Whatman #1 for ICP runs. The NIST SRM 2710 was subjected to a more vigorous attack using 1:1 nitric acid followed by 1:1 hydrochloric acid [9], as were soils R39A, 4502, and 4501 for comparison with the simple 2 N nitric acid attack.

RESULTS AND DISCUSSION

Bulk Properties

The major element composition of the soil matrix was quite similar for the suite of samples described here. The SEM image analysis program computes a summary which approximates the bulk chemistry of the specimen by summing over all features, weighted by estimated feature volume and total net X-ray counts. The results (TABLE 1) are comparable to elemental analyses expressed as "oxides". With urban samples, it is frequently difficult to know whether the specimens represent the original "in-place" soils of the region, or were transported from some other location to be used as fill. However, the composition summaries do not indicate that any particular sample was unusual in comparison to the others. The last two columns (of TABLE 1) show the IPA summary results for the NIST SRM 2710 converted to elemental weight along with

the NIST certified values.   Reasonable agreement was obtained between
the IPA computations and the actual bulk concentrations.

TABLE 1--Approximate soil matrix elemental composition.

Element	1521	R39A	4501	4502	4301	2710	SRM 2710 % wt as the element IPA	NIST
Na	0.1	2.5	0.3	0.2	0.3	1.0	0.8	1.1
Mg	1.6	1.1	4.0	6.2	2.9	0.8	0.5	0.9
Al	11.7	7.3	7.6	6.5	13.9	13.2	7.0	6.4
Si	70.4	67.3	72.4	68.8	64.4	70.8	32.9	29.0
P	0.3	0.5	...	<.1	0.4	...	...	0.1
S	0.3	0.3	0.1	0.1	0.1	0.1	<.1	0.2
Cl	0.2	0.6	0.1	0.2	0.3	0.2	0.2	...
K	2.7	2.3	3.7	2.2	3.8	2.4	2.0	2.1
Ca	2.7	6.8	5.0	8.7	3.4	3.4	2.4	1.3
Ti	0.8	3.0	1.3	0.6	1.9	0.2	0.1	0.3
Mn	0.2	0.2	<.1	<.1	0.1	1.7	1.3	1.0
Fe	8.0	7.9	5.1	6.0	7.8	5.1	3.6	3.4

The column group headers over the numeric columns read: "Percent by weight as the oxide in soils:" (spanning 1521, R39A, 4501, 4502, 4301, 2710).

    While the background soil lead concentrations in Syracuse are low,
the "close and old" soils collected for IPA showed bulk lead values from
870 μg/g to over 5300 μg/g (TABLE 2).   Within the analytical uncertainty
of $\pm$ 5% for replicates, the simple 2 N nitric acid attack released the
same amount of lead as the more vigorous, heated nitric/hydrochloric
attack.   Note that the entry of 5532 μg/g for SRM 2710 is the certified
value.   Preliminary analysis of this material gave a value of 5260 $\pm$ 330
μg/g (1 σ), and little if any change in lead content was observed for
the SUS fraction.   The low lead soil, 4301, is included for comparison.
After analysis of over 2800 features, only 23 were identified as
lead-bearing, making further characterization time inefficient.

    For the other samples, the frequency of occurrence of lead
containing features ranged from 2.17% for soil 4501, to 15.6% for soil
1521.   The Syracuse soils show roughly a 2.5% frequency of occurrence
for lead bearing features for each 1000 μg/g increment in bulk lead
concentration.   This rule of thumb was used in estimating the time
required for analysis.   However, there is a wide range of particle size
distribution in these soils, as shown by the fraction of mass in the SUS
preparation (Table 2).   The enrichment of lead in the SUS fraction does
not show a simple relationship to the SUS mass.

    For each sample characterized by IPA (except 4301), the size
distribution of particles in the SUS fraction was compared with that of
the subset for lead containing features only (FIG. 1).   The results are
shown as the relative frequency distribution of the particle volume
after log transformation.   Soil 4501 and SRM 2710 show nearly identical

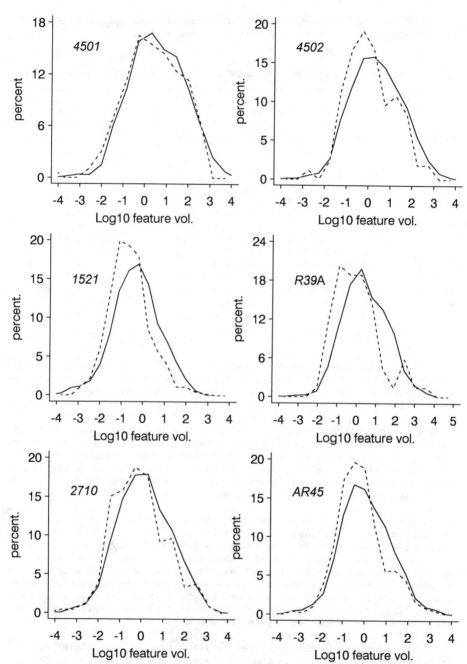

Fig. 1--Particle volume frequency distributions for all (——) and Pb-bearing (- - -) particles analysed by SEM in soil samples 4501, 4502, 1521, R39A, 2710 and AR45.

soil matrix particle and lead particle volume distributions. At the
other extreme, soils R39A and 1521 exhibit a distinct tendency for the
lead to be distributed in a smaller particle volume range.
Interestingly, these latter two soils are also those with the highest pH
values (TABLE 2), and, as discussed below, they have the highest
percentage of particulate lead identified as discrete lead metal, lead
oxide or lead carbonate grains. The result for soil AR45 is consistent
with the distributions for soils 4501 and 4502 separately, but a greater
shift for lead towards smaller particle volumes was expected judging
from the material added.

TABLE 2--Comparative bulk properties of test soils.

| Property | Soils | | | | | SRM | Ref. |
	1521	R39A	4501	4502	4301	2710	AR45
Features, n	2930	4308	5059	3267	2819	2163	2433
Pb hits, n	457	114	110	167	23	239	764
pH	7.8	7.7	6.7	7.2	7.3	5.1	...
Bulk Pb, $\mu g/g$	5350	1260	870	1980	40	5532	10700
SUS mass frac.	0.18	0.14	0.24	0.25	0.13	0.39	0.24
SUS Pb, $\mu g/g$	10360	2100	2270	3140	120	5130	26700
SAL (O), %	164	104	27	72	55	122	103
SAL (CO_3), %	115	79	20	52	48	96	78

Physicochemical Speciation of Lead

    For classifying the particulate lead features in these soils, the
approach   used by Hunt, et al. [3,4] in the examination of household
dusts was adopted. Each particle from the IPA characterizations can be
considered as an object vector with 27 elements (observation variables);
these are the relative net X-ray intensity for 25 chemical elements,
width/length ratio, and either the total net X-ray counts or the feature
area--the latter two variables are not completely independent. The
subset of all object vectors from soils 4501, 4502, R39A, 1521 and SRM
2710 which contained lead (n=1087), were subjected to a divisive
hierarchical clustering [3] based on the shapes of the normal quantile
plots for the X-ray relative intensity variables only. Where distinct
changes in slope, or gaps in the distributions were evident in the
normal quantile plot, the data were subset and the process repeated on
each of the smaller populations. This was done in SAS using Proc Rank.

    Some variables were not useful as cluster division parameters;
either because they were observed so infrequently (cobalt, nickel,
arsenic, mercury, selenium, bromine) or they were widely distributed in
almost all particles and showed little departure from linearity in the
cumulative probability plots. Silicon and (generally) aluminum fall
into the latter category. Thus, the cluster dendrogram groups (FIG. 2)
should be considered largely as silicate or alumino-silicate type

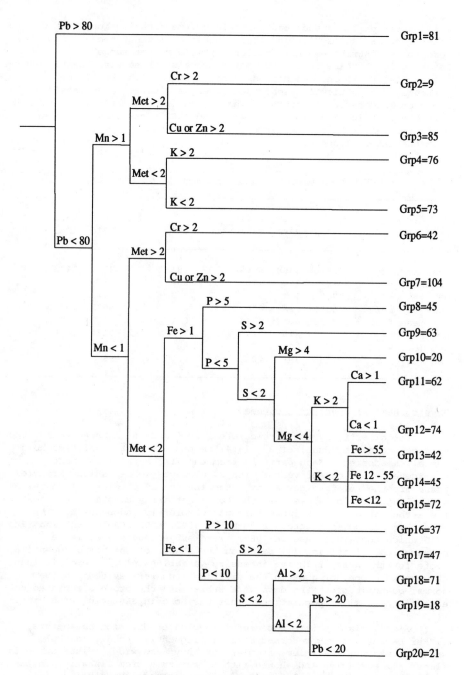

FIG. 2--Normal quantile clustering dendrogram for 1087
lead containing soil particles.

materials, associated with detectable amounts of lead, but subdivided by the minor element occurrences as indicated.

The cluster dendrogram (FIG. 2) shows that 75% of the lead bearing features in this data set are associated with silicon or alumino-silicate particles containing iron and/or manganese in the soil matrix. This is consistent with previous observations [10, 11], but here confirmed on an individual particle basis. Only 7.5% were "high Pb" (X-ray relative intensities > 80%), features taken to be PbO or lead carbonate (PbCO$_3$). Of the remaining 17.5%, about 8% have high associations with either phosphorus or sulfur (groups 16 and 17), while the remainder are variously low iron and low manganese, silicon or alumino-silicate rich (groups 18 - 20). The strong association with sulfur is considerably less frequent than that found by Olson and Skogerboe [12], though some sulfur is found in many groups. Calcium is substantially present in all of the low iron/manganese groups-- particularly in the high phosphorus group (16). Met (FIG. 2) refers to the metals chromium or copper or zinc.

This clustering of lead/elemental associations in soils is dramatically different from what has been found in household dusts [13]. In such passive chemical environments, particulate lead species are much more readily identified as being similar to their potential source materials when judged by chemical element composition. In the urban soils examined here, the matrix elements of lead containing particles substantially resemble those of the soil matrix within which they are found. One hypothesis for such differences might be transformation and redistribution reactions in the more chemically active environment of soils as compared with house dusts.

Some significant differences are evident among the individual soils after each has been classified according to the group definitions shown in (FIG. 2). The percentage distribution of lead bearing features in each dendrogram group for the four Syracuse soils are compared in TABLE 3. These are summarized in two blocks: the "Class B" soils R39A and 1521, and the "Class A" soils 4501 and 4502. The particulate lead analyses for SRM 2710 are shown in the fifth column. In the right most column is the average, non-lead containing soil particle distribution for the Syracuse soils; they have been sorted by the same dendrogram cluster group criteria. For reference to the following discussion, certain group numbers (TABLE 3) are identified as Class A or Class B.

When compared as the percentage of lead bearing features distributed in the 20 groups (TABLE 3), the "Class A" soils 4501 and 4502 show more than twice as many features in the manganese groups (4,5) and in the iron groups (10,12) than do the slightly more alkaline "Class B" soils 1521 and R39A. The reverse trend is observed for the high lead group (1), the high phosphorus and sulfur groups (16,17) and the aluminum group (18). When averaged by the two pairs of samples and summed over the Class A groups versus the Class B groups, the differences are more than 3 fold; soils 1521 and R39A have 38.1% of lead features in the Class B groups and 11.3% in the Class A groups, while soils 4501 and 4502 have 12.2% of features in the Class B groups and 37.5% of features in the Class A groups.

TABLE 3--<u>Percent distribution of particulate Pb features in dendrogram groups by sample.</u>

Group	Soil Class B		Soil Class A		SRM	Non-Pb Syr. Soil
	1521	R39A	4501	4502	2710	Avg.
1 B	10.7	13.9	5.9	4.9	0.8	0.0
2	1.0	0.0	0.9	0.0	0.4	0.0
3	3.4	3.2	11.6	4.3	19.4	0.2
4 A	2.0	2.4	19.4	12.8	8.5	1.3
5 A	4.0	1.6	4.8	9.1	14.2	0.6
6	6.0	3.2	2.9	1.2	0.4	0.4
7	8.6	9.0	8.8	7.3	12.5	5.3
8	2.4	5.6	1.9	2.4	1.2	0.8
9	5.4	2.4	2.9	3.6	10.7	2.3
10 A	0.7	1.6	1.9	6.7	0.8	10.8
11	6.9	2.4	5.9	11.5	0.8	10.9
12 A	6.2	4.0	12.6	7.9	5.6	20.4
13	2.8	5.6	3.8	8.5	1.2	3.1
14	3.4	3.2	2.9	4.3	6.9	4.1
15	8.0	2.4	1.9	9.7	5.6	13.9
16 B	6.0	6.5	1.0	0.0	0.4	0.4
17 B	5.8	8.2	1.0	0.0	3.9	1.4
18 B	9.5	8.2	4.8	2.4	3.9	3.2
19	2.0	2.4	1.0	1.2	1.2	0.0
20	0.9	5.7	3.8	2.4	0.8	20.9

When the particulate lead classification criteria (FIG. 2) were applied to the average, non-lead bearing Syracuse soil particles, the results are shown in column 6 of TABLE 3. More than 3/4 of the observations fell into 5 categories (10A, 11, 12A, 15, 20). In the other 15 defined particle types, soil particles containing lead occurred more frequently than those of the same type without lead. To quantify this "enrichment", or frequency of occurrence, of lead with chemically defined particle types, the dendrogram cluster criteria were adapted to create 10 generic particle classes. The IPA results for each particle were sorted by element percentages of total net X-ray count, where:

        group = Sulfur if Pb<75%, Ti<15%, Mn<1%, P<10%, and S>10%, or
        group = Phosphorus if Pb<75%, Ti<15%, Mn<1%, P>10%, or
        group = Manganese if Pb<75%, Ti<15%, Mn>1%, or
        group = Calcium if Pb<75%, Ti<15%, Ca>20%, or
        group = High Fe if Pb<75%, Ti<15%, Fe>55%, or
        group = Medium Fe if Pb<75%, Ti<15%, Fe>12%, Fe<55%, or
        group = Low Fe if Pb<75%, Ti<15%, Fe>1%, Fe<12%, or
        group = Titanium if Pb<75%, Ti>15%, or
        group = Silicon if Pb<75%, Si>10%, or
        group = High Pb if Pb>75%.

Each group was sub-divided according to whether Pb X-rays were greater than 0.7% or less than 0.7%. This classification scheme is a linear (top to bottom), "first fit" algorithm. Note that element X-ray relative intensities not included in the criteria may take on any value.

"Frequency of occurrence enrichments" (FOE) were computed from this classification scheme, dividing the fraction of lead containing particles in each class by the total fractional abundance of lead bearing particles in a particular sample (TABLE 2). These summaries (TABLES 4 and 5), tabulated by particle size, illustrate whether a generic lead/soil particle matrix association occurs more frequently (values > 1.0) or less frequently (values < 1.0) than the occurrence of

TABLE 4--<u>Particulate Pb frequency enrichment by size and type for the Class A soils 4501 and 4502.</u>

Type	Size, μm <1.5	<3.0	<6.0	<12	<24	>24	Percent by Type
Sulfur	2.1	-	10.0	-	-		1.1
Phosphorus	2.7	7.8	3.0	+			4.7
Manganese	13.7	8.1	12.1	5.2	10.0		30.0
Calcium	0.6	0.5	0.5	0.2	0.8	-	4.3
High Fe	1.4	1.4	4.5	2.3	-		9.0
Medium Fe	1.3	0.8	0.5	1.3	0.3	-	19.1
Low Fe	1.1	0.6	0.2	0.4	0.8	-	16.6
Titanium	0.5	0.6	1.4	-	-		3.2
Silicon	0.5	0.2	0.5	-	-	-	5.4
High Pb	+	+	+				6.5
Percent by Size	40.0	27.9	21.7	7.6	3.1		

TABLE 5--<u>Particulate Pb frequency enrichment by size and type for the Class B soils 1521 and R39A.</u>

Type	Size, μm <1.5	<3.0	<6.0	<12	<24	>24	Percent by Type
Sulfur	5.5	2.8	5.6	-			8.0
Phosphorus	4.8	5.8	1.6	4.2	5.6	-	16.1
Manganese	4.5	6.0	10.0	8.4	9.0	-	10.0
Calcium	0.2	0.2	0.1	-	-	+	1.3
High Fe	0.6	0.7	0.5	1.1			3.6
Medium Fe	1.0	0.3	0.1	-	-	-	9.3
Low Fe	1.6	0.3	0.3	0.4	0.6	-	20.6
Titanium	0.4	0.4	-	1.6	-	-	1.9
Silicon	1.5	0.2	-	-	-	-	12.1
High Pb	+	+	+	+			17.0
Percent by Size	71.2	19.9	6.2	1.9	0.6	0.2	

that individual particle type which doesn't contain any lead. A purely random association would show an average FOE value of 1.0. TABLE entries of "+" means only lead containing particle types, and an entry of "-" indicates the absence of lead containing features.

Again, important differences are observed for these two soil groupings. For the Class A soils, not only are there more particles in the iron and manganese groups (Percent by Type in TABLES 4 and 5), but the frequency enrichments for lead bearing particles within those groups are higher as well. The reverse is true for the phosphorus and sulfur categories. For both soil groups, the associations with the calcium and the silicon particle categories are significantly lower than 1.0, indicating a less than random distribution. For soils 4501 and 4502, the titanium frequency enrichment shows an increasing trend with larger particle sizes; this may be related to the degradation of lead-based paint chips. The differences in particulate lead size distribution (FIG. 1) are very clearly evident in the frequency enrichment tables.

SEM Accountable Lead Estimates

The estimates of SAL (TABLE 2) vary considerably, but it is impor-tant to attempt such calculations in order to have some idea of whether the IPA characterizations can be extrapolated to all particles on the specimen preparation. Note that SAL does not account for fractionation in the sample mounting procedure; it is an estimate of the amount of lead in the specimen detected during the individual particle analysis. A propagation of error treatment indicates that the uncertainties in this estimate should be in the range of ± 15% (1 σ), but the two major unknowns not included in that estimate are the actual molecular or crystalline form of occurrence of the lead, and the probability that the calculation is distorted by inaccuracies in the measured lead-containing particle volume distribution. Further work is necessary to address these aspects. However, certain fundamental concepts are clear: 1) the SEM specimen(s) and the aliquots subjected to bulk chemical analysis must come from the same sample preparation, and 2) SAL estimates signif-icantly greater than 100% suggest either inaccurate preparations or substantial violations of assumptions inherent in the calculation.

The SAL estimates (TABLE 2) are presented for two different forms of occurrence. Clearly, in the case of soil AR45, the estimate should be based on the oxide form; there is good agreement between the computed bulk lead and that measured in the SUS fraction. For soil 1521, the carbonate form seems most applicable. The sample was taken from the soil of a house more than 100 years old (judging by architecture and construction), and white lead ($PbCO_3$) could easily have been a major component. The oxide calculation gave the best fit for the other soils. For the Syracuse soils, SAL was highest for the Class B group, with extremely poor accountability for soil 4501 (either calculation form). SRM 2710 gave intermediate results.

Particulate Lead Redistribution Phenomena

While the SAL estimates for the soil amended with PbO (AR45) indicated complete accountability, within experimental error, the frequency enrichment results for IPA (TABLE 6) showed that substantial

phase redistribution had occurred during its preparation. Not unexpect-
edly, addition of the PbO particles raised the number of lead containing
features from about 3% to over 31%. If the PbO particles had remained
"intact", the frequency enrichments for the combined soils 4501 and 4502
(TABLE 4) should all have showed values lower by a factor of ten because
the FOE values were normalized to the overall number of lead bearing
particles in the sample analysis. Instead, a distribution very much
akin to the unamended soil was observed. Harrison, *et al.* [10] noted a
similar effect in their bulk phase selective extraction procedures when
soil was amended with particulate lead sulfate. While PbO has a low
solubility (about 20 $\mu g/g$), the results suggest that some rapid
repartitioning had taken place. Only about 60% of the SAL could be
identified with PbO; the rest was associated with the manganese and iron
alumino-silicate particle types, and to some extent, with the phosphorus
type particles. Careful visual inspection of soil AR45 in the SEM
failed to identify any aggregate features of soil particles associated
with small particles of PbO.

TABLE 6--<u>Particulate Pb frequency enrichment type size and type for
amended soil AR45, lead oxide addition.</u>

| Type | Size, μm | | | | | | Percent by type |
	<1.5	<3.0	<6.0	<12	<24	>24	
Sulfur	1.2	0.5	0.5				1.3
Phosphorus	1.4	2.3	+	1.1			2.2
Manganese	2.0	1.7	2.1	2.1			3.7
Calcium	-	0.2	0.2	0.2	1.6	-	0.9
High Fe	1.1	1.7	2.7	+	+		6.3
Medium Fe	1.1	0.7	1.0	1.3	0.6		20.7
Low Fe	1.0	0.6	0.4	0.9	2.1		19.5
Titanium	0.2	0.1	0.4	-			0.7
Silicon	1.6	0.5	0.2	0.1	-		13.5
High Pb	2.9	2.4	1.3	1.6			31.3
Percent by Size	55.6	25.5	11.5	6.2	1.0	0.1	

That such redistribution phenomena could occur rapidly was demonstrated by use of the low lead soil 4301 which was incubated for two
hours with 1000 $\mu g/ml$ of soluble lead added as the nitrate (1.0 g of
soil with 100 ml of solution). While the initial number of lead
containing features in this soil was about 0.8% of all particles
analyzed, it was greater than 40% after the two hour contact time. The
frequency enrichment (TABLE 7) was not different from an additional
sample taken after 24 hours, showing that lead was quickly associated
with the iron phases in the soil. Apparently, the cation exchange
capacity of the soil was exceeded by this treatment, since the superna-
tant fluid was completely clear after settling overnight. This was not
observed in un-amended soil suspensions. Similar uptake and frequency

enrichment results for this soil (4301) were obtained with 10 minute contact time of aqueous lead at roughly the 1000 μg/g level, and for 12 hour contact times at an aqueous lead concentration as low as 10 μg/g.

The zero point of charge for manganese oxides is at a lower pH than that for iron hydroxide and manganese oxides exhibit even stronger adsorptive properties than does iron. SRM 2710 has a higher manganese content than the study soils (TABLE 1) and shows a strong association with lead (TABLE 3). The Class A soils show a strong frequency enrichment for the manganese particle type, and their adsorption "sites" may be saturated as the soils have a low manganese concentration. This would explain the lower manganese particle type frequency enrichments in the amended soil AR45 (TABLE 6) compared to the Class A soils prior to amendment (TABLE 4). In the aqueous lead incubation experiment with soil 4301 (TABLE 7), the numbers of manganese type particles are too few to adequately calculate frequency enrichments.

TABLE 7--Particulate Pb frequency enrichment by size and type for soil 4301, 2 hour contact with 1000 μg/g Pb^{2+}.

| Type | Size, μm | | | | | | Percent by Type |
	<1.5	<3.0	<6.0	<12	<24	>24	
Sulfur	1.2	+					1.3
Phosphorus	1.2	1.2					0.9
Manganese	+	-	-	+			1.8
Calcium	-	0.2	-	0.6	-		2.2
High Fe	0.5	-					0.4
Medium Fe	1.5	1.1	1.5	0.9	1.9		26.5
Low Fe	1.3	1.0	1.4	1.8	1.2	-	58.4
Titanium	1.1	-	-	1.2			2.7
Silicon	0.6	0.3	0.2	-	-		4.0
High Pb	-	-	+				0.9
Percent by Size	33.6	22.4	23.2	16.6	4.0		

The dissolution of particulate lead and its redistribution among other soil phases explains many observations. Indeed, there is evidence of particle dissolution in the Syracuse soils in the form of pitted (FIG. 3a) and etched grains (FIG. 3b). Where progress towards equilibrium is more advanced, as perhaps in the case of soil 4501, low SEM accountable lead values could result from adsorption to iron and manganese phases at levels below the IPA detection limit. Since iron seems to be present in a majority of soil particles, the particulate lead which can be measured by IPA resembles the soil matrix material. The particulate lead size distribution in such a case would appear like that of the parent soil (FIG. 2). If lead is strongly associated with the organic matter in soils [14], the process would have to be very selective in order for the frequency enrichments (TABLES 4-7) to show such pronounced differences between soil particle types. In soils where the redistribution process has not progressed so far, as perhaps for soils 1521 and R39A, more of the original particulate lead input can be identified. This would lead to higher SAL values, more distinctive patterns of lead containing particle types, and a size distribution for soil lead particles more nearly approximating the original material.

This hypothesis would predict that even lead particle species with limited solubility, such as the oxides, sulfates, or carbonates, might not be substantially detected in temperate soils where lower pH values could lead to particulate lead dissolution . Furthermore, if the parent soils contained even modest amounts of iron or manganese phases, lead would be concentrated in the surface layers [15]. More arid or (perhaps) alkaline soils would likely show a higher probability of particulate lead existing in the physical/chemical form characteristic of its origin. Further characterizations of soils discussed here, to measure organic matter content, cation exchange capacity, and the bulk lead fractions associated with selective extractants is currently underway.

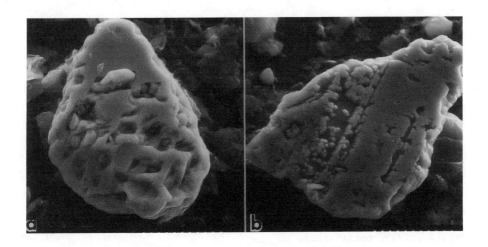

FIG 3.--SEM micrographs of pitted (a) and surface etched (b) Pb grains
     from soil 1521. Bar markers equal to 6 μm.

SUMMARY

Individual particle analysis shows great potential for the study of particulate lead speciation in contaminated soils. In certain re-spects, its resolution is far greater than that achievable from selec-tive extraction, bulk chemical analysis techniques. When combined with such approaches, the kinetics of particulate lead diagenetic processes in soils would seem amenable to characterization. Where particulate lead inputs have retained their original identities, the method may be useful for source attribution.

For the limited suite of samples examined here, the soil lead generally does not resemble its (suspected) source material. Because these soils are an active chemical environment, the lead appears to have been substantially repartitioned. This likely takes place on different time scales depending on the chemical conditions in the soils. The proportion of lead in soils which is SEM accountable will be determined by the type of soil, the quantity and rate of lead input, and the nature and extent of repartitioning which has occurred.

ACKNOWLEDGEMENTS

We thank Amel Himed for technical assistance, and Drs A. Davies, D.J.A. Davies and J.A. Abraham for reviewing the manuscript This research was supported by U. S. Environmental Protection Agency contract # 2D3110NAEX.

REFERENCES

[1]   Chaney, R. L., Mielke, H. W., and Sterrett, S. B., "Speciation, Mobility, and Bioavailability of Soil Lead," Lead in Soil: Issues and Guidelines, B. E. Davies and B. G. Wixson, Eds., Science Reviews Limited, Northwood, 1988, pp 105-129.

[2]   Thornton, I., Watt, J. M., Davies, D. J. A., Hunt, A., Cotter-Howells, J., and Johnson, D. L., "Lead Contamination of UK Dusts and Soils and Implications for Childhood Exposure: An Overview of the Work of the Environmental Geochemistry Research Group, Imperial College, London, UK, 1981-1992," Environmental Geochemistry and Health, (in press).

[3]   Hunt, A., Johnson, D. L., Thornton, I., and Watt, J. M., "Characterizing the Sources of Particulate Lead in Housedust by Automated Scanning Electron Microscopy," Environmental Science and Technology, Vol. 26, 1992, pp1513-1523.

[4]   Hunt, A., Johnson, D. L., and Thornton, I., "Descriptive Apportionment of Lead in Housedust by Automated SEM," Water, Air, and Soil Pollution, Vol. 57-58, 1991, pp69-77.

[5]   Body, P. E., Inglis, G. R., and Mulcahy, D. E., Lead Contamination in Port Pirie, South Australia, SADEP report No. 101, South Australia Department of Environment and Planning, 1988, ISBN 0 7243 9021 9.

[6]   McNaughton, S. J., 1993, personal communication.

[7]   Johnson, D. L., "SAX Characterization of Particulate Inclusions in Biological Tissue," Scanning Electron Microscopy/1983/III, 1983, pp1211-1228.

[8]   Johnson, D. L., McIntyre, B. L., Fortmann, R., Stevens, R. K., and Hanna, R. B., "Chemical Element Comparison of Individual Particle Analysis and Bulk Chemical Analysis," Scanning Electron Microscopy/1981/I, , 1981, pp469-476.

[9]   Francek, M. A., "Soil Lead Levels in a Small Town Environment: a Case Study from Mt. Pleasant, Michigan," Environmental Pollution, Vol. 8, 1991, pp251-257.

[10]   Harrison, R. M., Laxen, D. P. H., and Wilson, S. J., "Chemical Association of Lead, Copper and Zinc in Street Dusts and Roadside Soils," Environmental Science and Technology, Vol. 15, 1981, pp1378-1383.

[11]   Scokart, P. O., Meeus-Verdinne, K., and De Borger, K., "Speciation of Heavy Metals in Polluted Soils by Sequential Extraction and ICP Spectrometry," International Journal of Environmental Analytical Chemistry, Vol. 29, 1987, pp305-315.

[12]   Olson, K. W. and Skogerboe, R. K., "Identification of Soil Lead Compounds from Automotive Sources," Environmental Science and Technology, Vol. 9, 1975, pp227-230.

[13]   Hunt, A., Johnson, D. L., Thornton, I., and Watt, J. M., "Apportioning the Sources of Pb in Housedusts in the London Borough of Richmond, London," Science of the Total Environment, Vol. 138, 1993, pp183-206.

[14   Zimdahl, R. L., and Skogerboe, R. K., "Behavior of Lead in Soil," Environmental Science and Technology, Vol. 11, 1977, pp1202-1207.

[15]   Ward, N. I., Brooks, R. R., and Roberts, E., "Heavy-Metal Pollution from Automotive Emissions and its Effect on Roadside Soils and Pasture Species in New Zealand," Environmental Science and Technology, Vol. 11, 1977, pp917-920.

Quality Assurance

Robert L. Watters, Jr.[1] and James R. DeVoe[2]

COMPARABILITY AND TRACEABILITY OF CHEMICAL MEASUREMENTS

REFERENCE: Watters, R. L., Jr., and DeVoe, J. R., "Comparability and Traceability of Chemical Measurements Related to Lead in the Environment," Lead in Paint, Soil, and Dust: Health Risks, Exposure Studies, Control Measures, Measurement Methods, and Quality Assurance, ASTM STP 1226, Michael E. Beard and S. D. Allen Iske, Eds., American Society for Testing and Materials, Philadelphia, 1995.

ABSTRACT

The accurate chemical determination of lead in the body or in the environment is a critical factor in assessing human exposure limits and in identifying sites where remediation is required. To compare and evaluate data from laboratory studies or to determine when and where expensive abatement procedures must be employed, chemical analysis data must be tied to an accepted system of measurement accuracy.

The need for comparability and traceability of chemical analysis data is becoming recognized world-wide. Efforts are now underway by the International Committee for Weights and Measures (CIPM) through its laboratory, the International Bureau of Weights and Measures (BIPM) to link chemical measurements to the International System of Units (SI) at the highest levels of national systems of measurement. As the U.S. member of the CIPM, the National Institute of Standards and Technology (NIST) is responsible for providing the link between chemical measurements in the U.S. and the SI units of the kilogram and the mole. NIST provides this traceability for measurements through a highly leveraged system of key Standard Reference Materials (SRMs) and primary methods. The design, development, and application of these SRMs and primary methods for use in secondary reference material and reference methods development will be described. In addition, the role that SRMs and primary methods are intended to play in ensuring traceability to the national system of measurement will be outlined.

KEYWORDS: accreditation, measurement comparability, measurement traceability, quality assurance, reference materials

INTRODUCTION

The need for improved quality in chemical measurements spans both the public and private sector in the United States. Accurate chemical measurements are the key to avoiding costly site remediation, effectively monitoring the progress of cleanup, and reliably determining

---

[1]Supervisory Research Chemist, Inorganic Analytical Research Division, Chemical Science and Technology Laboratory, National Institute of Standards and Technology, Gaithersburg, MD 20899.

[2]Chief, Inorganic Analytical Research Division, Chemical Science and Technology Laboratory, National Institute of Standards and Technology, Gaithersburg, MD 20899.

when the site is safe for re-use. Industrial competitiveness in the U.S. is the driving force behind attention to quality assurance. Improved quality of chemical measurements leads to better manufacturing process control, more efficient specification and use of feedstocks, reduction of chemical waste production, and improved after-sales support. Industry must also deal with the same site-assessment issues facing DOD, EPA and DOE, which requires high-quality chemical measurements. NIST's mission is to provide an accurate measurement base *via* the transfer of chemical measurement technology, particularly through Standard Reference Materials (SRMs).

Accurate chemical measurements are of concern on an international scale. The identification of trends in the state of the biosphere and the evaluation of the effects of toxic species in the environment are only possible on the basis of reliable chemical measurement data. A significant proportion of industrial production and international trade is dependent on analytical chemical measurement.' Export of environmental technologies relies on buyer-seller agreements on specifications and verified performance through chemical measurement. The uncertainty in the validity of many of these measurements means that there is considerable measurement repetition, particularly on the part of private industry. The expense incurred wastes dollars and impedes industrial competitiveness. Consequently, there are increasing demands for high quality measurements in chemistry.

PHYSICAL MEASUREMENT TRACEABILITY

International uniformity and accuracy in *physical* measurement can be ensured through the agency of the national standards laboratories working with the International Bureau of Weights and Measures (BIPM) under the authority given to it through the International Committee for Weights and Measures (CIPM) [1]. The BIPM maintains the standards which serve as the basis for the International System of Units (SI) and develops the means for the national metrology laboratories to realize a common accuracy base for measurements based on the SI. These means are comprised of transfer standards whose accuracy is *traceable* to each of the basic SI units defined by the primary standards maintained by the BIPM. Thus, the uniformity or comparability of physical measurements made at each of the national metrology laboratories is ensured through its traceability link with the BIPM. The accuracy base for physical measurement is extended throughout national measurement systems by transfer standards traceable to the national metrology laboratories. This hierarchy of traceable standards ensures worldwide uniformity in these physical measurements, and is accepted without question as being essential for the progress of advanced technology. The National Institute of Standards and Technology (NIST) serves as the U.S. member of the CIPM and is the traceability link between the BIPM and the U.S. national system of physical measurement. In conjunction with the efforts to maintain the SI units, the International Organization for Standardization (ISO) provides written procedural standards and guides to establish worldwide conventions on the practice of measurement, the use of terminology, and the treatment of data.

Some examples of the physical measurement traceability chain are shown in Figure 1. The BIPM and NIST work together to establish a link based on the primary SI units. In these examples, the standard volt and the standard kilogram provide both instrument manufacturers and end users with calibrated equipment and measurements through standards linked to NIST and ultimately to the BIPM. Buyers and sellers participating in such a system are ensured of comparability in these physical measurements because traceability to primary standards provides the common accuracy base.

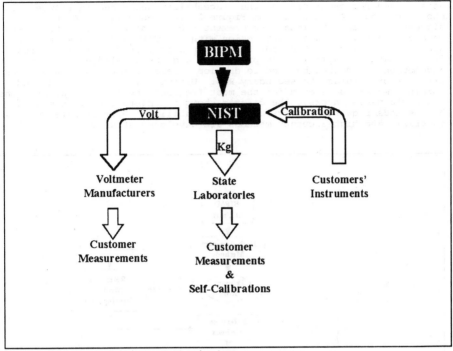

Figure 1.   Traceability of Physical Measurements.

CHEMICAL MEASUREMENT TRACEABILITY

Traceability to the SI units should be applicable to *chemical* as well as physical measurements, and it was at the request of the chemical community expressed through the International Union of Pure and Applied Chemistry (IUPAC), among others, that the mole was made one of the base units of the SI [2]. The term *chemical measurement* refers to the determination of chemical composition in terms of analyte mass per unit sample mass. Such a measurement is directly traceable to the mole and the SI kilogram when it is based on gravimetric data for species of known atomic or molecular weight. The NIST membership in the CIPM, links all NIST traceable chemical measurements to the worldwide system. Transfer of traceability, and therefore accuracy, to a wider set of chemical measurement applications is afforded through the use of a hierarchy of surrogate reference standards of certified chemical composition. The top of such a hierarchy of surrogate standards is a NIST Standard Reference Material (SRM). To achieve agreement or comparability among chemical measurements, national and international networks of reference materials must be traceable to the SI units. Traceability enables quantitative statements of analyte values and their uncertainties to be made and ensures the stability of reference values with time.

Systems of traceability for chemical measurements are not as well established as are those in place for physical measurements. A more generalized representation of the traceability described in Figure 1 is shown in Figure 2 (adapted from Figure 2, reference [3]). At the highest level in a National Measurement System, high-accuracy transfer methods are developed in conjunction with the BIPM and used with appropriate transfer standards to develop a primary reference material for the National System. The primary RM and the knowledge gained in its development, can then be used to develop reference methods to aid in the transfer of accuracy to secondary RMs. Ultimately, field methods and working RMs are developed for the most frequent level of QC calibrations and performance checks. The diagram shows the hierarchy of standards and methods required for systems of traceability. Primary reference materials and high-accuracy methods are developed at NIST.

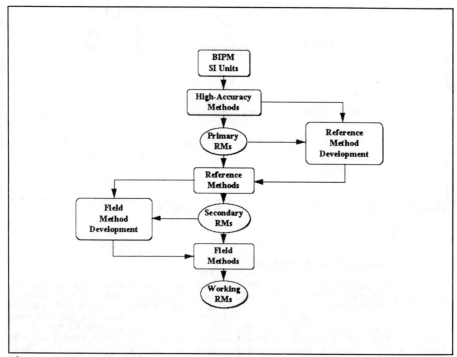

Figure 2. Relationships of traceability system components.

For chemical measurements, NIST produces and certifies SRMs using various combinations of definitive and independent methods of chemical analysis [4-6]. For the most part, SRMs intended for use in chemical analysis fall into one of two categories: 1) solids, gases or simple solutions of pure materials to be used for calibration, and 2) compositional materials of a natural chemical matrix to be used as analysis control samples. Certification of constituents may be based on high-accuracy analyses to determine the best estimate of their total concentration. In some cases, however, the concentration of an analyte can only be defined in the context of a recoverable amount which depends entirely on how the constituent is extracted from the matrix (eg. the analysis of polychlorinated biphenyls or organically bound heavy metals in soil). SRMs certified in this manner are intended to be used with primary methods whose results are understood to rely on the context and

execution of the prescribed extraction procedure. Such methods may also
be prescribed by environmental regulation or may be required to expedite
the sample treatment step where high throughput is essential. It is
apparent, therefore, that traceability depends on both the use of
reference materials and the incorporation of appropriate primary
methods.

The development of accurate chemical analysis methodology is one
of the main goals of NIST's chemical research program. The publication
of this methodology in the open literature is one of the principal means
of transferring this technology. When coupled with good quality
assurance programs and quality control procedures, accuracy can be
transferred to our customers' laboratory analyses. But our experience
with this mode of technology transfer has shown that details critical to
the success of the method can be operator dependent and/or difficult to
describe. Consequently, personal contact is often needed to determine
which part of the methodology has not been communicated effectively.
Efforts toward automating the entire chemical measurement process will
eventually ensure the complete transfer of accurate analysis methods,
but totally automated systems will not be a reality for some time. Even
when automation is realized, the links shown in Figure 2 among the
primary RMs, secondary RMs and reference methods need to be maintained
to ensure traceable chemical measurements.

Effective traceability systems often need more than just methods
and standards. Examples of a few measurement programs are described
below, and the additional elements of feedback and measurement quality
assurance found in these traceability systems are apparent.

Asbestos Measurements

NIST designed and continues to administer a program for
Proficiency Testing (PT) as part of the response to a Congressional
Mandate to accredit asbestos analysis laboratories. Reference methods
for the qualitative and quantitative analysis of asbestos in bulk
building materials were developed and their reliability was determined.
NIST originally served as the primary reference laboratory for the
characterization of the PT materials, but recently this role has been
passed on to a secondary reference laboratory. NIST is now playing an
oversight quality assurance role. Currently, the secondary reference
laboratory performs a series of analyses on PT materials and reports to
NIST. NIST also analyzes a small subset of the same materials and
compares its results to those of the reference laboratory. These data
comprise the reference values against which round-robin data from the
participating laboratories are compared. Acceptable ranges are
determined using a combination of the statistical intervals determined
on the reference results and the consensus values determined by the
laboratories.

The PT program typically involves both qualitative and
quantitative analysis, using a variety of reference methods developed by
NIST including polarized light microscopy (PLM), analytical electron
microscopy, x-ray diffraction, thermal gravimetry, differential thermal
analysis, and infrared spectrometry. NIST has also developed a suite of
nine materials packaged in SRMs 1866, 1867, and 1868 (about to be
released) especially for the PLM laboratories.

Gas Measurements

NIST produces a number of primary standard gas mixtures, prepared
by primary methods and validated for stability. SRM gas mixtures are
certified for a specified period of time and are distributed to end

users and secondary gas mixture producers. SRMs are also used to certify producers' gas mixtures for use in an EPA measurement program. These Certified Reference Materials (CRMs) must be a close match in composition to an existing suite of SRMs. The certification process involves collaboration among NIST, the producer, and a designated reference laboratory.

A new NIST program has been developed in collaboration with the EPA and secondary standard gas mixture producers to replace the CRM program and to fill gaps in the range of SRMs available for establishing traceability for gas producers' secondary reference materials. NIST will now provide certification measurements on samples of a producers' lot of a gas mixture. Such a mixture must be similar to an existing suite of SRM gas mixtures so that either direct comparison or interpolation measurements can be used to assign a certified value for a given analyte. The process is started with a proposal from an agency or gas producer. NIST will work with the requester to develop acceptance criteria and the necessary prototype testing program. Once the gas producer has completed the feasibility testing, the resulting data will be evaluated by NIST. If the design criteria are met, NIST will analyze a sampling of the production lot and provide certification data for that lot. Once certified as a NIST Traceable Reference Material (NTRM), samples from this lot may be distributed to end users by the producer as traceable reference materials.

For producers' gas mixtures whose analyte types or concentrations are outside of any existing SRMs, NIST has instituted a new Research Gas Mixture (RGM) program. Once a RGM project is proposed and agreed upon, a gas mixture or series of mixtures can be provided to NIST for evaluation. NIST will develop and test the primary standards necessary to determine the RGM analytes. It is expected that the uncertainty limits for RGM certification will be relatively wider than related NTRMs. Stability testing at NIST will be required before the RGM is released to the gas producer with certified values. The batch of certified RGMs can then be returned to NIST for re-assessment of stability and possible re-certification. RGMs will normally have prescribed limits as to their use, but may lead to the development of a matching suite of SRMs and NTRMs.

In either of these two programs, NIST and the requester work closely together on the design of the mixtures, the production methods, the mode of certification and the allowable usage of NTRMs and RGMs.

Radioactivity Measurements

NIST provides standards and measurement quality assurance in several areas related to ionizing radiation measurement. These programs support laboratory accreditation activities for the calibration of various instruments including medical x-ray equipment, personal dosimetry devices and field survey instruments. Accrediting bodies working with NIST include federal, state and private sector organizations. Each of the programs involves the development of primary and transfer standards by NIST. The transfer standards are used by secondary reference laboratories to perform their own calibrations. These data are provided to NIST, which evaluates a secondary laboratory's performance and issues a report to the laboratory and to the relevant accrediting body. Performance measures are related not only to the actual calibration values, but also to their uncertainties. Site visits by NIST and accrediting body personnel are also used to evaluate performance and to resolve any problems. In certain cases NIST develops specialized calibration transfer standards and software to ensure that a specific step in a secondary reference calibration is performed properly.

Spectrometric Solution Standards

To ensure accuracy in the calibration step of inorganic analytical methods using atomic absorption and inductively coupled plasma emission and mass spectrometry, NIST produces single and multielement solutions of inorganic elements. These SRMs are certified for total content of each element based on one of three primary methods: 1) the purity and weight of metal dissolved and diluted in a calibrated volume, 2) a titrimetric comparison between a solution of the metal and the SRM solution made from a compound, or 3) a gravimetric assay of the SRM solution. The choice of primary method depends on the availability of pure metal starting material and/or the degree to which a compound is of a single stoichiometry.

There are a number of producers of similar calibration materials, some claiming traceability to NIST. Our experience, and that of others, suggests that the substantiation of traceability claims could be improved by consultation with NIST and the use of the SRM spectrometric solutions for comparison analyses either by the producers or perhaps by NIST. Some producers have indicated an interest in establishing closer links with NIST, and these possibilities are under consideration.

The Lead Program

The EPA has established a National Lead Laboratory Accreditation Program(NLLAP). This Program is open to any qualifying laboratory accrediting organization that can meet the EPA requirements. Guidelines for operation of these accrediting organizations have been established [7], and the EPA has established specific requirements [8]. The laboratory accreditation will involve a systems audit of accredited laboratory and in addition, each laboratory must pass a series of periodic proficiency tests. This proficiency testing program requires that the accredited laboratory measure correctly the concentration of lead in real samples such as soil, paint and house dust. The most active program is being conducted by the American Industrial Hygiene Association in cooperation with the National Institute of Occupational Safety and Health.

The performance evaluation materials(secondary reference materials) are being produced by the Research Triangle Institute. The materials are checked for homogeneity before sending to the participating laboratories. The results of the test are compared with a consensus value that is obtained from a set of selected reference laboratories. The program uses NIST SRMs where available to verify the accuracy of the proficiency samples. At the present time NIST provides consultation on the process, but is not directly involved in the evaluation of the test materials which would constitute a more direct link of traceability to NIST.

APPROACHES FOR EXPANDING CHEMICAL MEASUREMENT TRACEABILITY

It is evident from Figure 2 and the measurement program examples above that reference materials lie at the heart of any traceability system. Without reference materials, neither primary nor secondary reference methods could be developed and verified. Furthermore, to ensure that any method yields results that are at least stable over time, a homogeneous reference material must be analyzed. Two possible scenarios for developing traceable reference materials are 1) establishing traceability between NIST and secondary reference material producers and 2) cooperative reference material development between NIST and an organization responsible for a particular measurement program.

The establishment of traceability for a secondary reference material producer would most likely be linked to a particular measurement need. Such a program might originate with a regulatory agency like the EPA, HUD, NIOSH or one of the State environmental agencies, or it might be initiated to support the DOE or DOD. In any case, NIST would work with the relevant agency to establish the criteria for RM production required by the measurement program. These criteria would then become the elements of a traceability program between NIST and a secondary RM producer.

NIST's experience in producing SRMs has shown that there are basic issues common to most RM development. The first issue is to establish the specific criteria for the secondary RM. Specifications as to chemical matrix and form, intended use, analyte target values and the degree of material homogeneity are among the principal components of RM design. The next major issue is to decide on a development design which includes sample collection methods, processing of the material, acceptance testing, packaging, final homogeneity assessment, the determination of the reference values and provisions for stability testing. Once these design parameters are determined, a traceability program might call for the secondary RM producer to furnish acceptance and characterization data to NIST for evaluation. Finally, the traceability program might call for NIST to perform site visits and/or periodically acquire samples of a secondary RM for analysis in its own laboratory.

The second scenario involving only NIST and the relevant measurement program agency would contain essentially the same elements. In this case, however, NIST is more directly involved in actually carrying out the development steps. NIST might work directly with either an agency's own laboratory, or a key contractor laboratory to perform the sampling, processing, and characterization of the material. In some instances this may be a preferred mode for RM production. The first scenario, however, has the benefit of more effective leveraging NIST resources as well as promoting private sector business.

Whatever scenario or combination of scenarios is adopted, procedures to monitor measurement quality assurance (MQA) must be in place. Documentation, the use of in-house controls, proper training, adherence to measurement procedures and participation in measurement intercomparison studies are among the MQA items which should be in evidence. MQA programs are required by regulation for some federal and state contractors and NIST believes that when MQA programs supplement the use of primary standards and methods, a particularly effective form of traceability is achieved [9].

LABORATORY ACCREDITATION

The various modes of traceability of chemical measurements and secondary RM development described above provide a research and measurement chain which can be effectively used in a laboratory accreditation program for secondary RM producers. NIST can provide the necessary guidance to accrediting institutions on how to evaluate the traceability chain with regard to actual adherence to a prescribed method and the use of an SRM. Where a hierarchy of methods, materials, contractors and sub-contractors are used, NIST can work with accrediting bodies to establish an effective system of traceability evaluation for the whole chain. In some of the examples above, NIST traceability and accreditation are combined in a single program administered by NIST's National Voluntary Accreditation Program (NVLAP). Other agency and private sector accrediting institutions could also cooperate with NIST to incorporate traceability into their programs.

INTERNATIONAL IMPLICATIONS

Traceability to national physical measurement standards has resulted in universal acceptance of such measurements around the world. Similar systems for chemical measurements are being established by various international bodies, with the same goal of world-wide acceptance. The CIPM has established a Working Group for Metrology in Chemistry with representatives from the national chemical metrology laboratories of 16 countries and IUPAC, and is chaired by Dr. John Lyons of NIST. This working group is exploring the concept of traceability to the kilogram and the mole and comparability of chemical measurements at the highest levels of national systems of chemical measurement. Interlaboratory studies using primary reference materials and definitive methods for the analysis of inorganic elements in solution and simple gas mixtures are now underway. The chemical metrology laboratories in Europe have formed the organization EURACHEM to explore the ways in which traceability can be extended down to the working levels of European Community chemical measurements. EURACHEM activities include proficiency testing, laboratory accreditation, and reference materials. The European organization responsible for traceability in physical measurements, EUROMET has recently formed a working group on "Amount of Substance" to explore what role it should play in chemical measurement traceability. In 1993, 45 delegates from laboratories around the world participated in a workshop to explore the means by which traceability in analytical chemistry can be establish. This group formed the Cooperation on International Traceability in Analytical Chemistry (CITAC) for facilitating interactions on traceability, harmonizing analytical quality practice, providing a guide on the quality requirements for the production of reference materials and preparing a directory of world-wide chemical metrology programs. There are also a number of long-standing organizations like the International Standards Organization (ISO), IUPAC, the Association of Official Analytical Chemists (AOAC), and the Office of International Legal Metrology (OIML) which have activities related to harmonization of chemical standards.

CONCLUSION

For most chemical measurement programs in the U.S., traceability to NIST is indirect at best. Some of the best systems of traceability involve both the use of SRMs and measurement quality assurance programs. It is clear that the trend is toward more traceability within the national measurement system and the realization of world-wide acceptance of traceable measurements.

REFERENCES

[1]   Metric Convention, May 20, 1985, Paris.

[2]   Approved by the Ninth General Council on Weights and Measures (CGPM), 1948, Paris.

[3]   Rasberry, Stanley D., "The Role of NBS SRMs in Quality Assurance," ASQC Quality Congress Transactions, 1983, Boston, pp. 343-348.

[4]   Cali, J. Paul and Stanley, Connie L., "Measurement Compatibility and Standard Reference Materials," Annual Reviews of Materials Science, Volume 5, 1975, pp. 329-343.

[5]   Epstein, Michael S., "The Independent Method Concept for Certifying Chemical-composition Reference Materials," Spectrochim. Acta, Volume 46B, No. 12, 1991, pp. 1583-1591.

[6]   Moody, John R. and Epstein, Michael S., "Definitive Measurement
       Methods," Spectrochim. Acta, Vol. 46B, No. 12, 1991, pp. 1571-
       1575.

[7]   Laboratory Accreditation Program Guidelines: Measurement of Lead
       in Paint, Dust, and Soil Prepared by Task Group on Methods and
       Standards of the Federal Interagency Lead-based Paint Task Force;
       distributed by U. S. Environmental Protection Agency, Exposure
       Evaluation Division, TS-798, Office of Pollution Prevention and
       Toxics, March 1992

[8]   Announcement of Program appears in Federal Register Volume 58, No.
       136 July 19,1993.

[9]   Belanger, Brian C., "Traceability: An Evolving Concept," ASTM
       Standardization News, Volume 8, No. 1, 1980, pp. 22-28.

Eldert C. Hartwig, Jr.[1]

COMPONENTS OF A QUALITY ASSURANCE PROGRAM FOR ANALYTICAL
LABORATORIES

REFERENCE: Hartwig, Jr., E. C., "Components of a Quality
Assurance Program for Analytical Laboratories", Lead in
Paint, Soil and Dust: Health Risks, Exposure Studies,
Control Measures, Measurement Methods, and Quality
Assurance, ASTM STP 1226, Michael E. Beard and S. D. Allen
Iske, Eds., American Society for Testing and Materials,
Philadelphia, 1995.

ABSTRACT: The goal of any legitimate analytical laboratory
is to produce, within its resources, the highest quality of
analytical data possible that is accurate, precise,
reproducible, defensible, and documented. How can the
laboratory owner and the data user of that laboratory be
assured that the results are as reported? While there is no
absolute guarantee that data generated by a particular
laboratory are without error, a good quality assurance
program can minimize error and assure the highest quality
data.

This presentation defines quality assurance and quality
control; distinguishes between external and internal quality
control; describes the elements of each, including the
specimen sampling, storage, packaging, acceptance/rejection
criteria, records, personnel, equipment testing, including
methods and standards, proficiency testing and reporting,
and discusses the interrelationship of the elements.

KEYWORDS: Laboratory Quality Assurance, Laboratory Quality
Control, Elements of QA, Elements of QC

    Thank you for the opportunity to share with you this
morning a few remarks on the components of a quality
assurance program for analytical laboratories. This

---

[1]Chief, Office of Laboratory Services, Department of
Health and Rehabilitative Services, State of Florida, P. O.
Box 210, Jacksonville, FL 32231

presentation is not intended to be all inclusive but rather to give a flavor of what one might expect from an accrediting body for a Quality Assurance Program.

My experience has been with blood lead analyses and very little with other matrices, but these principles of quality assurance apply to any analytical laboratory.

The goal of an analytical laboratory is to produce the highest quality of analytical data within its resources that are accurate, precise, reproducible, defensible and documented. But what can one do to assure oneself that the results obtained are, indeed, quality data? Controlling the variables and recognizing when an analytical system is out of control lends considerable credibility to results. One can do this if one has a well established quality assurance and quality control program.

DEFINITIONS

Quality control (QC) is defined as that specific measure taken to assure accuracy and precision at each step of the analytical process to produce a high quality analytical result. Quality assurance (QA) is a written program encompassing and detailing the aggregate of quality control measures taken to assure the quality of an analytical result, from the taking of the sample/specimen to the reporting of the result to the submitter or data user and the necessary follow-up.

While I will be in the context of QA, I will focus on typical QC consideration.

For purpose of this presentation, I am defining the span of control as either external or internal. The factors of external QC are those elements over which the laboratory has little or no control, i.e., what happens to the specimen before it gets to the laboratory. Internal QC includes those elements over which one has direct control, i.e., while the sample is in the laboratory.

EXTERNAL QUALITY CONTROL

External QC factors (Fig. 1) include sampling, storing of specimens, packaging/shipping, acceptance criteria and report follow-up. About the only influence the laboratory has on these external factors is education through consultation, procedural guides, or rejection of samples.

Sampling
Storing
Packaging/Shipping
Acceptance Criteria
Report Follow-Up

FIG. 1--External Quality Control.

We often hear that data quality is no better than the specimen. If it is a poor sample, the results will be poor no matter how good the analytical control. Yet, this is the one area over which the laboratory has the least control unless the laboratory collects its own samples.

There are no real standards in lead sampling except for blood (Fig. 2). Factors influencing the quality of the specimen and the reliability of the results are such things as labeling, type of sample, site preparation, or collection detail and collection devices.

The minimum information on the sample container label are the name of the patient for blood lead or the site or location of the sample collected and the date and time of collection. The request form gives greater demographic detail. In any case, the sample label must match the identification on the test request form.

Is the sample for screening or confirmation for blood; a recheck for water or an initial sample? Is it single or composite? Is it whole or capillary blood, paint, water, dirt, plant material, etc.? The type of sample determines the method of analysis.

Because the action level for blood lead is so low, 10 ug/dl, and the volume is so small, external contamination can be a major problem, therefore, cleansing the skin before blood extraction is critical. In the case of a soil sample, is the area of sampling 12 in^2, 16 in^2, or 24 in^2, and what is the depth? Is it one inch of surface soil or 4 inches? If paint, was the surface wiped to remove dust to assure one is measuring just paint? Is the sample from 6 in^2, 12 in^2, etc.? Is it from brick, wood, etc.? If water, is it the first out of the faucet or after flushing 10 minutes? Is it from the hot or cold tap? All of these impact on the quality of the sample and directly affect data calculations, results, and reproducibility.

Was the sample collected by capillary or vacutainer? Was there a preservative and what was the preservative, EDTA or heparin? Is the swab cotton, cellulose acetate, kim wipe or some other material (the absorption and dissolution are different)? Was the container glass or plastic? Were preservatives present and what were they? This yields information as to the integrity and quality of the sample.

LABELING

    o Name patient, site, location
    o Date collected, time
    o Request form

TYPE OF SAMPLE

    o Screening, confirmation
    o Single, composite
    o Whole blood, capillary blood, paint, water, dirt, soil, plant material

SITE PREPARATION

    o Cleansing skin for blood withdrawal
    o Soil - area, depth, sand, clay, gravel, wet, dry
    o Paint - clean surface, area(size), brick, wood, plastic
    o Water - 1st take, flush 5 minutes, cold, hot faucet

COLLECTION DEVICES

    o Capillary or vacutainer, preservative EDTA, heparin
    o Swab: cotton, other material
    o Container: glass, plastic, preservatives

FIG. 2--External QC: Sampling.

One of the best ways to get a submitter's attention is to reject the specimen or qualify the result (Fig. 3). Listed are the criteria for which a sample must be rejected. If a blood specimen is frozen, exposed to light (photolysis), clotted or hemolyzed, it was improperly preserved or collected. The same is true if the HNO_3 preservative has been discarded from the water sample bottle or not added.. Insufficient volume, time frame for analysis has expired upon sample receipt, wrong container (glass instead of plastic or vice versa) or a leaky/broken container should all be rejected. If the sample labels do not match the field submission form or there are bubbles in

a volatile organic carbon sample on which one does headspace
analysis, then these should be rejected as well.

      o   Improperly preserved
      o   Improperly collected
      o   Expired on receipt
      o   Wrong container
      o   Leaky/broken container
      o   Improper documentation
          Sample labels
          Field submission
      o   Bubbles in VOC sample

FIG. 3--Rejection Criteria.

The submitter must be instructed on how to collect and
preserve a proper sample. Assume that the collector does
not know how to collect a proper sample. The submitter must
be told the rejection/acceptance criteria ahead of time.

Alternatively, the reported results should have
disclaimers, i.e., "Results may not be reliable because the
sample was received in an improper container" etc. Your
laboratory's integrity, reputation, and ethics are at stake.

INTERNAL QUALITY ASSURANCE

Now, lets turn to those components over which the
laboratory does have control (Fig. 4).

An internal QA plan addresses elements such as
personnel, equipment, the specimen, testing (methods,
standards, controls), proficiency testing (P.T.), QC
records, and reporting. The QA plan must address each of
these in detail in writing.

```
Personnel
Equipment
Specimen
Testing  -  methods, standards, controls
Proficiency testing
Quality control records
Reporting
```

FIG. 4--Internal Quality Assurance.

     Some of what I share with you may not be strictly
required in a QA plan but are required by OSHA, especially
that regarding safety.

Personnel

     The plan must include personnel qualification (Fig. 5).
Are the technical staff qualified to do the job and what are
those qualifications? Has the analyst had hands-on
operational experience and have troubleshooting knowledge of
the equipment? Does the analyst understand the principle of
the instrument operation and analysis? Can the analyst
follow the method unassisted and is he/she familiar with all
the details of the method?


```
Education
Training
Experience
Familiarization

     o  Instrumentation
     o  Technology
     o  Methodology

Continuing education
```

FIG. 5--Internal QC: Personnel.

     There must be an in-house familiarization or
orientation and training before the analyst is turned loose.
There must be documented, continuing education and training
through workshops, seminars, meetings, short courses, etc.

Equipment

The equipment must be addressed in the QA plan (Fig. 6). If lead-free glassware makes a difference, it should be mentioned and how to assure that it is, indeed, lead-free. Is the equipment appropriate for the method? One does not use a hematofluormeter to measure blood lead for an action level of 10 ug/dl when this instrument is only sensitive above 25 ug/dl. Are voltage regulations and surge suppressors required? What is the preventive maintenance schedule? Instrument servicing and date of the service must be documented on a maintenance record.

Lead free glassware
Appropriate for test
Voltage regulators
Surge suppressors
Preventive maintenance schedule
Maintenance record

FIG. 6--Internal QA: Equipment.

Specimens

How specimens are handled needs to be indicated (Fig. 7). What are the receiving and storage requirements if the analyst cannot analyze the specimens immediately (i.e., refrigerated, frozen, left at room temperature)? Where in the analysis can one delay or hold without impacting the results?

Receiving/storage
Accessioning
Acceptance criteria

o Tube ID
o Match request slip
o Appropriate sample for request
o < 7 Days post collection
o Not broken/no leakage
o Non clotted
o Non hemolyzed

FIG. 7--Internal QC: Specimens.

How is the accessioning done? The plan should explain the numbering system. All specimens/samples are to be accessioned, including the rejected ones, with an indication as to why the rejection.

Acceptance and rejection criteria already mentioned are to be detailed in addressing the handling of specimens.

Testing Methods--In Fig. 8 are listed the assorted instruments that may be used in blood lead testing; but whether a soil, paint, or water sample, the procedure manual for the methodology must indicate the instruments to be used, their principle of operation, detection limits, standardization, etc. You will recognize that blood lead instrumentation vary as to principle of operation, sensitivity levels, procedures, and automation.

Zn protoporphyrin (ZPP) [Hematofluorometry]

Erythrocyte protoporphyrin (EP or FEP) [fluorometric extraction procedure]

Anodic stripping voltometry (ASV)

Atomic adsorption spectroscopy (AAS)

Graphite furnace AAS

Inductively coupled argon plasma - isotope dilution mass spectroscopy (ICP-IDMS)

FIG. 8--Internal QC: Testing - Methods.

The procedure manual must outline the method in detail indicating the purpose of the procedure, the principle of the method, the equipment, the supplies required with detail of reagent description and preparation, a schedule of standards and controls and how they are generated. Standards, controls, spikes, etc. to be used with examples of calculations are to be noted. Other information such as limits of methods, normal values, action levels, data interpretation, and extensive bibliography are required as well.

Standards--In the QA plan, the standards (Fig. 9) must
be defined and specified indicating their purpose and
source.. These are for calibrating the instrument and
establishing reference and calibration curves. The
frequency of use should be defined depending on instrument
stability and the range of standards including the levels to
be used. Standards establish linearity and accuracy of the
instrument over the range to be analyzed against known
primary standards or ones directly traceable to standard
reference materials.

Purpose: To calibrate instrument

Source: Standard reference material (SRM)

    o National Institute Standards and
       Technology (NIST)
       SRM 3121 Aqueous
       SRM 955A Lead in blood (bovine)
    o Centers for Disease Control and
       Prevention (CDC)
    o Range QCM 5-100 ug/dl (3 levels)

Use: Establish reference curves

    o Frequency
    o Range: Low (2-8 ug/dl)
           Medium (20-30 ug/dl)
           High (35-50 ug/dl)
    o To establish linearity and accuracy
       of instrument

FIG 9--Internal QC: Testing - Standards (Blood Lead).

Controls--The control samples (Fig. 10) must be
detailed as well in the QA plan. The purpose of controls is
to check the method for accuracy, precision, and
sensitivity. Specified must be the source and this is
variable depending on the analyte and matrix. It may be
CDC, vendors, or manufacturers. Former proficiency test
samples, repeat samples, or round robin samples may be used,
but these are not the best and must really be checked out.
Controls should be matrix-specific, if possible, whether
blood, water, soil, paint, etc. Frequency and replication
cannot be ignored. Controls are to bracket the analytical
range and should include low, medium, and high levels as
well as reagent, diluent, and field blanks throughout a run.

Purpose: To check methods for accuracy,
            precision, sensitivity

Source

    o   CDC quality control material (QCM)
        Blood lead laboratory reference
        system (BLLRS)
    o   Vendors
    o   Proficiency testing samples
    o   Repeat samples

Matrix

    o   Human blood
    o   Bovine blood
    o   Goat blood

Frequency   -   every run, spaced throughout
Replication -   dependent upon sensitivity of
                method
Range   -   bracket analytical range
            low, medium, high, reagent/diluent
            blanks
Levy Jennings chart   -   each control

FIG. 10--Internal QC: Testing - Controls (Blood Lead).

Each control level should have a Levy-Jennings chart
[1] reference. In Fig. 11 is depicted a typical Levy-
Jennings QA chart of a mid-range blood lead level control of
34 ug/dl ranging from 32 to 36 ug/dl (2 S.D.).

The Levy-Jennings QC chart is generated by performing
20 consecutive daily analyses on each control level,
plotting the results on a graph, then determine the two
standard deviation (S.D.) limits. If a data point falls
outside the two S.D. limit, then there is an error somewhere
requiring documented investigation. The error may be
pipetting, dilution, sample preparation, sample injection,
method sensitivity, bad standards or controls, alignment,
contamination, etc.

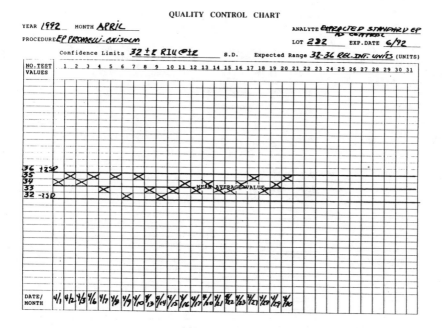

FIG. 11--Quality Control Chart.

The controls should be placed at the beginning and throughout each run as illustrated in Fig. 12 on a whole blood lead analysis worksheet. We do 400-600 blood leads a day and use the automated graphite furnace atomic adsorption instrument. Position 1, 2 and 3 are the low, medium, and high level blood lead controls. These are placed throughout the run as well-positions 12, 22, and 36 in this 36 well run. Runs should also include the appropriate reagent and field blanks.

WHOLE BLOOD LEAD ANALYSIS

Worksheet = _1007_   Date _4-2-92_   Control Lot #_5760l/6o2/6o3_
Instrument _5100 ZEEMAN_   Blank _TX-100_   Exp. Date _30APR 95_
Analyzed by _KM_   Cal. 1_P590- 8.9_   Control-Low_u 5760l_
Approved by _DM_   Cal. 2_P390- 31.0_   Control-Med_2 5760L_
Date Apprvd _4-8-92_   Cal. 3_P490- 57.3_   Control-High_3 57603_
                           BLLRS Pools 390/493/590 R2   _0.99999_

40-- Blank   39--Cal.1   38--Cal.2   37--Cal.3

Pos. #   Specimen #   Lead Result   --QC--   Remarks

01   Control-Low _L1_ _(4.6-6.8)_   _____   _____
02   Control-medium_L2_ _(20.8.28.6)_   _____   _____
03   Control-high _L3_ _(38.9-52.7)_   _____   _____
04   _____   _____   _____   _____
05   _____   _____   _____   _____
06   _____   _____   _____   _____
07   _____   _____   _____   _____
08   _____   _____   _____   _____
09   _____   _____   _____   _____
10   _____   _____   _____
11   _____   _____   _____
12   CDC-Low _Pb17_   _____   _____   _____
13   _____   _____   _____   _____
14   _____   _____   _____   _____
15   _____   _____   _____   _____
16   _____   _____   _____   _____
17   _____   _____   _____   _____
18   _____   _____   _____   _____
19   _____   _____   _____   _____
20   _____   _____   _____   _____
21   _____   _____   _____
22   CDC-medium_Pb11_ _____   _____   _____
23   _____   _____   _____   _____
24   _____   _____   _____   _____
25   _____   _____   _____   _____
26   _____   _____   _____   _____
27   _____   _____   _____   _____
28   _____   _____   _____   _____
29   _____   _____   _____   _____
30   _____   _____   _____   _____
31   _____   _____   _____   _____
32   _____   _____   _____   _____
33   _____   _____   _____   _____
34   _____   _____   _____   _____
35   _____   _____   _____
36   Control-High_Pb20_ _____ _____   _____

FIG. 12--Whole Blood Lead Analysis.

Proficiency Testing--The QA document should address
proficiency testing, the purpose of which is for external
evaluation and to compare the performance of one's
laboratory with that of others (Fig. 13). This can be done
by blind or double blind methods. The blind method is the
analysis of a proficiency test specimen, the value of which
is unknown to the analyst and he/she knows that it is a test

sample of unknown value. This tests the analytical accuracy and precision of one's laboratory's analytical capabilities. The double blind test specimen is one of unknown value that is introduced into the system before it gets to one's laboratory and the analytical staff does not know it is an unknown. This measures the proficiency of the entire system process.

Purpose

1. External evaluation of test system
2. Compare performance with other labs
3. Required by certifying agencies

    o Health Care Financing
       Administration (HCFA), Clinical
       Laboratory Improvement Act, 1988
       (CLIA '88)
    o OSHA

FIG. 13--Internal QC: Proficiency Testing.

Certifying and regulatory agencies require that a laboratory participate in proficiency testing obtained from the certifying body itself or by subscription to one approved by the certifying or regulatory agency. Examples of certifying agencies may be the Health Care Financing Administration (HCFA), OSHA, a state, or a private group such as the American Industrial Hygiene Association (AIHA).

The frequency (Fig. 14), usually two-three times per year, is set by the accrediting or regulatory agency or by laboratory management as to the number of cycles per year and the number of samples in each cycle. The passing grade is also set by the regulatory body or management. The source may be from EPA, EPA contractor, NIST, vendors/manufacturers, state, or College of American Pathologists (CAP).

Frequency
    3-4 cycles/year
    3-5 samples each cycle

Passing
    o CAP/OSHA
       6 ug/dl under 40 ug/dl
       15% over 40 ug/dl
    o CDC/Wisconsin/New York
       4 ug/dl under 40 ug/dl
       10% over 40 ug/dl

FIG. 14--Internal QC: Proficiency Testing (Blood Lead).

Reporting--Policies regarding result reporting should be detailed in the QA document (Fig. 15). The reporting form should indicate the result initialed by the analyst, date reported, normal values, interpretation, recollection schedule, if necessary, with detailed collection instructions. There should be some statement as to the quality of the results or confidence limits. Some states or official agencies may require copies of results in addition to the user or submitter, particularly if the results exceed some trigger level or may have health implications. If follow-up is necessary, maintain a tickler file to remind one to send a follow-up letter reminding the submitter or data user to submit follow-up samples.

Reporting

        o   Result
        o   Date reported
        o   Normal values
        o   Interpretations
        o   Recollection schedule
        o   Collection instructions
        o   User/official agency

Follow-Up

        o   Tickler file
        o   Letter

FIG. 15--External QC - Reporting/Follow-Up.

Records--In summary (Fig. 16), the QA plan document must detail personnel policies such as the requirement for immunizations and safety training, the dates received and verified by the employee's signature. Each instrument must have a preventive maintenance schedule and repair records with documentation as to what was done and when. Specimen handling procedures must be described including the accessioning system and acceptance criteria and sample collection instruction sheets. Testing procedures must include methods, standards, controls, and other information regarding biomedical waste disposal and safety. How is the analyst to dispose of waste; where does it go; who picks it up; and when and who is the external vendor that disposes of it? Safety precautions including the type of protection the analyst must use, i.e., gloves, safety glasses, face shields, hoods, etc.; who inspects the hoods, how often; and where the material safety data sheets are kept should all be addressed in the QA plan. Details of proficiency testing include from whom the PT samples are obtained, frequency, address, phone number, who is to review the PT results, etc.

The Quality Assurance Plan

Personnel Policies

Equipment - Preventive maintenance and repair
            records

Specimens - Acceptance criteria

Testing

    o   Methods - manuals, references,
        procedures
    o   Standards - what, where obtained,
        frequency, volume
    o   Controls - what, where, frequency of
        use, out of control, what done
    o   Other - Waste disposal: where,
                  who, when pick-up
    o   - Safety: what, when, who to
                  contact, immunizations,
                  MSDS

Proficiency Testing - who, frequency, where
                      obtained, record review

Frequency of Review, Signature

FIG. 16--Internal Quality Control - Records.

.   The QA plan, itself, as a whole must be reviewed periodically by management or the QA officer to assure it is continually pertinent to the operation.

CONCLUSION

No QA/QC plan or accreditation program will guarantee quality data, but a good comprehensive QA plan that is rigorously followed will help a laboratory to produce the highest quality of analytical data within its resources that are accurate, precise, reproducible, defensible, and documented.

REFERENCES

[1]   Henry, J. B., _Clinical and Diagnosis Managment by Laboratory Methods_, W. B. Saunders, Philadelphia, 1991.

David A. Binstock[1], Eva D. Estes[1], John D. Neefus[1], Emily E. Williams[1], William F. Gutknecht[1], Sharon L. Harper[2], and Michael E. Beard[2]

PREPARATION AND EVALUATION OF LEAD-CONTAMINATED DUST METHOD EVALUATION MATERIALS

REFERENCE: Binstock, D. A., Estes, E. D., Neefus, J. D., Williams, E. E., Gutknecht, W. F., Harper, S. L., and Beard, M. E., **"Preparation and Evaluation of Lead-contaminated Dust Method Evaluation Materials,"** Lead in Paint, Soil and Dust: Health Risks, Exposure Studies, Control Measures, Measurement Methods and Quality Assurance, ASTM STP 1226, Michael E. Beard and S. D. Allen Iske, Eds., American Society for Testing and Materials, Philadelphia, 1995.

ABSTRACT: A greater understanding of the health effects associated with exposure to environmental lead has resulted in an increased emphasis on risk assessment and abatement programs by Federal, state, and local governmental agencies. As programs for sampling and analysis of lead grow, and an environmental lead laboratory accreditation program begins, the need for method evaluation materials (MEMs) for lead in dust has become critical. To meet this need, distinct dust MEMs were prepared from dusts collected from private and commercial dwellings, from paint-abatement sites and from street sweepings. Processing included sterilization, sieving, mixing and finally further sieving to remove fine debris such as hair. The bulk materials prepared were analyzed to confirm homogeneity. Portions of these bulk materials were also loaded onto wipes to be used as dust wipe method evaluation materials. Through both a round-robin evaluation, and use in the American Industrial Hygiene Association Environmental Lead Proficiency Analytical Testing (ELPAT) program, the bulk dust materials were found to be acceptably homogeneous (i.e., precision better than 10%).

DISCLAIMER: This research was performed by Research Triangle Institute under EPA Contract 68-D1-0009, and therefore was wholly funded by the U.S. Environmental Protection Agency. This document, however, does not necessarily reflect the views of the Agency; official endorsement should not be inferred.

KEYWORDS: lead, dust, method evaluation materials, dust wipes, homogeneity

[1]   Research Triangle Institute, Research Triangle Park, North Carolina 27709
[2]   Atmospheric Research and Exposure Assessment Laboratory, U.S. Environmental Protection Agency, Research Triangle Park, North Carolina 27711

INTRODUCTION

The adverse health effects resulting from exposure of young children to environmental lead has received increasing attention in recent years. Studies have shown that chronic exposure even to low levels of lead can result in impairment of the central nervous system, mental retardation, and behavioral disorders [1-2]. Although young children are at the greatest risk, adults may suffer harmful effects as well [3].

The major sources of exposure to lead in housing units are paint, dust, and soil, with dust implicated as the most common route of exposure for young children [4]. Concentrations of lead in dust must be determined accurately and reliably if a comprehensive approach to reducing lead exposure is to be established. Lead levels in dust are currently measured in the laboratory by atomic absorption spectrometry (AAS) or inductively coupled argon plasma emission spectrometry (ICP). To evaluate laboratory performance and ensure good laboratory practice, reliable reference materials must be employed for AAS/ICP analyses. This paper describes the preparation and validation of such reference materials for lead in dust.

The objective of this work was to prepare dust method evaluation materials (MEMs) to support environmental lead studies where MEMs meet target values for concentration and homogeneity. The target values for concentration reflected established regulatory levels and real-world concentrations, while the target for homogeneity reflected the AAS/ICP quality control requirements [5].

Although preparation of synthetic dust and use of real-world dusts were both considered for preparation of the reference materials, real-world dusts were selected because this material would provide the analytical challenges typically encountered in the analytical laboratory.

The approach to preparation of dust MEMs involved collection, sterilization, material processing, and concentration verification.

EQUIPMENT

Rotary Blender (Model T2C Turbula Blender, Glen Mills, Inc., Maywood, NJ)

Ro-Tap Sieve Shaker (Fisher Scientific, Pittsburgh, PA)

No. 10 Sieve, stainless steel (2 mm mesh) (Fischer Scientific, Pittsburgh, PA)

No. 60 Sieve, stainless steel (250 μm mesh) (Fischer Scientific, Pittsburgh, PA)

Carpco Sample Splitters, Models 55-32-6 and 55-16-3 (Carpco, Inc., 4120 Haines Street, Jacksonville, FL)

Mettler AJ100, AT400 Electronic top loading balance (Mettler Instruments Corp., P. O. Box 71, Highstown, NJ 08520)

PROTOCOL

Material Selection Criteria

Materials for preparation of dust MEMs were selected to meet criteria relevant to regulatory levels and ranges of lead concentrations found in typical field and laboratory analyses. Clearance requirements during post abatement as required by the U.S. Department of Housing and Urban Development (HUD) range from 200 μg Pb/ft² for floors to 800 μg

Pb/ft^2 for window wells (Table 1) [6]. Lead in dust levels typically range from 5 to 1000 μg for wipe samples collected in public and private housing (Table 2) [5].

TABLE 1--Lead-in-dust levels relevant to abatement clearance.

HUD	200 μg/ft^2	floors
HUD	500 μg/ft^2	window sills
HUD	800 μg/ft^2	window wells

[1]

TABLE 2--Lead-in-dust levels typical of those found for field and laboratory analysis.

Matrix	Concentration	Rationale
Dust (bulk)	50 μg/g	Typical low level found in real-world samples
	500 μg/g	Typical low level of CDC[a] protective range
	10,000 μg/g	Typical high level found in real-world samples
Dust (wipes)	5 μg	Typical low level found on hand wipes
	50 μg - 1,000 μg	Range of values commonly encountered in real-world samples

[a]Centers for Disease Control, Atlanta Georgia [5]

Collection of Material

Dust for the preparation of MEMs was collected from a variety of sources. Dwelling dust was collected in vacuum bags from local homeowners, cleaning services, and hotels. Dust from HEPA-Vac systems used in post-abatement cleaning of dwellings and other buildings was collected from abatement contractors. Street dust was obtained from street sweepers. Each batch of dust was documented as to the source, type (dwelling, post-abatement, or street), and other pertinent information such as the age of the dwelling.

Sterilization of Dust

When enough bags of dust had been collected to fill 2 to 3 boxes 24"x24"x24", they were sent for sterilization by gamma-irradiation (Neutron Products Inc., Dickerson, MD). The samples were irradiated for 12 hours, receiving a minimum total dose of 2.5 Mrads. Upon completion, the boxes of source dust material (sterilized, though not radioactive) were returned to Research Triangle Institute (RTI) for storage.

Screening Analysis

The approximate lead concentration of each sample collected was first determined by means of a screening sample. A representative grab sample of sterilized dust was taken by pulling or scooping several small amounts of raw dust from different locations in each sample bag or container. Care was taken to include portions of the fine dust usually found at the bottom of each bag or container. Enough material was removed to fill a 12 in. diameter, No. 10 sieve. A No. 60 sieve was placed immediately below the No. 10 sieve. The pan on the bottom completed the stack. This stack was then placed on a Ro-Tap sieve shaker. The Ro-Tap was operated for 30 minutes. The fraction consisting of materials less than or equal to 250 μm (No. 60 sieve fraction) was collected and placed in a labelled 1,000 mL Nalgene container. The container was hand-tumbled and two 0.100 g samples were taken from different locations in the container. The two samples were extracted using a HNO_3/HCl microwave extraction procedure and analyzed by inductively coupled plasma emission spectrometry (ICP) [7]. If the average of the two analyses indicated a lead concentration in the range of interest, preparation of the remainder of the raw bulk dust was performed as described below. Otherwise the material was returned to the repository for possible use at a later date.

Preparation of Bulk Material

Sieving--The unsieved remainder of each sterilized dust was placed in portions on the Ro-Tap Sieve Shaker apparatus and sieved as described above until processing of the sample was complete. The material passing through the No. 60 sieve was placed in the labelled 1000-mL Nalgene container along with the previously sieved grab sample. Some portion of hair in the original raw dust passed through the 250 μm sieve. This hair was removed by hand and also by pouring the sieved dust through a screen having 2 mm openings several times.

Mixing--It is desirable to prepare at least 200 g of a method evaluation material from a single source of dust. This may not be possible, however, due to lack of a material of the appropriate concentration or there may not be enough material in any one sample to total 200 g. In such cases, mixing dust from two or more sources to achieve an adequate weight at a specific concentration will be necessary. If blending is required, it is performed on the material passing through the No. 60 sieve. The following steps must be followed to determine the proper mix to achieve 200 g of the target concentration.

a.   The inventory is searched to determine the source dusts available in the range of the target concentration. To ensure homogeneity of the product, the ratio of the concentration of the source materials to be mixed should not exceed 2:1.

b.   The portions of the dusts to be mixed are calculated as follows:

Let W   = target total weight (e.g., 200 g for dust)

A   = concentration of component A

B   = concentration of component B

W_A* = available weight of component A

W_B* = available weight of component B

C   = target concentration

w_a = weight of A to be used in blend

w_b = weight of B to be used in blend

Note: C must satisfy: A<C<B or A>C>B

$$CW = Aw_A + Bw_B \qquad (1)$$

$$W = w_A + w_B \qquad (2)$$

$$W(C - A) = w_B(B - A) \qquad (3)$$

$$w_b = \frac{W(C - A)}{B - A} \qquad (4)$$

$$w_a = \frac{W(C - B)}{A - B} = W - w_B \qquad (5)$$

Solutions for w_A and w_B are not feasible if the calculated w_A or w_B are greater than $W_A{}^*$ or $W_B{}^*$ respectively. In either case, an additional source of materials of appropriate concentration will be necessary.

The appropriate amounts of each material are weighed out on a balance to ±0.01 g and placed in a 1000-mL Nalgene container. Careful records are kept in a laboratory notebook of the amounts of each source material that are combined to make the final mix. This blending process is repeated until the total weight of the blended source reference material totals at least 200 grams.

Final Mixing and Homogenization--Each method evaluation material sieved was placed into a Turbula Rotary Mixer for 30 minutes, and then stored again in the labelled 1000-mL Nalgene container.

Preparation of Dust Wipes for ELPAT

The American Industrial Hygiene Association (AIHA) Environmental Lead Proficiency Analytical Testing (ELPAT) program involves sending four bulk paint, four bulk soil, and four dust-spiked wipes to participating laboratories on a quarterly basis. To prepare each wipe, a 0.100 g portion of dust was carefully removed from the bulk container and transferred to a 9 cm Whatman No. 40 filter paper. The filter, serving as the wipe, was folded and placed in a 20 mL plastic vial. To prevent growth of mold, each loaded filter was treated with 0.5 mL of a 3% hydrogen peroxide solution (ACS Reagent grade).

Verification of Concentration

Five representative samples of approximately 1 g each were taken from each prepared bulk MEM material using a Carpco mechanical sampler. A 0.100 g aliquot was removed from each of the five samples. Each aliquot was then analyzed using microwave extraction and measurement by ICP [7]. Specification goals were that the concentration be within 30% of the target concentration set for the material, and that the relative standard deviation of the analysis results not exceed 10%. Being within ±30% of the target concentration was adequate because the range of samples received in the laboratory covers approximately three orders of magnitude, that is 50 µg/g to 10,000 µg/g. If specifications were not met, the material was sieved and blended again, and then reanalyzed. If the material still did not meet specifications, another MEM material was prepared.

The spiked wipe samples for the ELPAT program were subjected to a final verification analysis prior to being submitted to the participating laboratories. These samples were analyzed by RTI using the microwave and ICP methods [7] and by the National Institute of Standards and Technology using NIOSH Method 7300, a hotplate digestion with a 4:1 (v/v) nitric acid: perchloric acid mixture. Measurement was by ICP [8].

DUST MEM EVALUATION

The MEM materials were evaluated in an EPA-sponsored round robin, [9] and are being further evaluated through their use in the AIHA ELPAT program [8].

EPA Round Robin Study

In the round-robin study, two dust MEM materials of different concentration were analyzed in duplicate by 33 laboratories to test the preparation protocol and homogeneity of the method evaluation materials [9]. Five analytical methods were employed with a number of laboratories analyzing by more than one method.

A statistical analysis was performed to determine the relative standard deviations for samples of these materials as a measure of material homogeneity. These values are presented in Table 3. Only one case (Low Dust, HP/ICP) was determined to have a significant difference between samples (8.9%). In all other cases, the sample-to-sample differences were <0.1% (8 out of 10 cases) and not significant relative to the uncertainties of the analytical methods themselves [9].

The high results noted with measurement by AAS are thought to be due to lack of background correction by participating laboratories while the low XRF results are thought to be due to lack of both suitable calibration standards and a common standard operating procedure.

ELPAT Program

Final verification results for Round No. 001 (sample sent out 11/30/92) appear in Table 4. Fifteen wipe samples were analyzed by RTI and ten were analyzed by the National Institute for Occupational Safety and Health (NIOSH). The maximum acceptable relative standard deviation as set by the AIHA for any one concentration level is 10%. The relative standard deviation values ranged from 4.9 to 8.1% for RTI and 3.2 to 6.2% for NIOSH.

Summary statistics for 22 reference laboratories participating in the ELPAT program for Round No. 001 are presented in Table 5 [10]. The relative standard deviation values ranged from 10.0 to 14.4%. Seven different analytical methods were employed by the 22 reference laboratories (Table 6).

CONCLUSION

Dust performance evaluation materials meeting target and homogeneity criteria were successfully prepared from real-world dust materials. This success was indicated by the performance of the laboratories participating in the EPA round-robin study and the laboratories participating in the ELPAT program.

TABLE 3--Estimates of sample-to-sample variation based on EPA round-robin study.

		Methods				
Matrix level	Statistics	MW/AAS	HP/AAS	MW/ICP	HP/ICP	Lab XRF
Low dust	Mean, µg/g	114	108	98	98	93
	Sample Std Dev. (%)	<0.1	<0.1	<0.1	8.9	<0.1
High Dust	Mean, µg/g	4850	4680	4280	4400	2480
	Sample Std Dev. (%)	<0.1	3.5	<0.1	<0.1	<0.1

Note: MW = microwave digestion, HP = hotplate digestion
      AAS = atomic absorption spectrometry
      ICP = plasma emission spectrometry
      XRF = X-ray fluorescence

TABLE 4--RTI/NIOSH final verification analysis results.

Dust Wipe	Revised Target Values (µg/wipe)	Proposed Acceptable Range (±30% of target) (µg/wipe)	RTI Final Verification Values, n=15 (µg/wipe)	RSD (%)	NIOSH Verification Values, n=10 (µg/wipe)	RSD (%)
Level 1	46	32.2 to 59.8	35±2.8	8.1	36.5±2.3	6.2
Level 2	120	84 to 156	154±7.6	4.9	168.6±6.1	3.6
Level 3	780	546 to 1,014	932±62	6.6	908±54	5.9
Level 4	3,800	2,660 to 4,940	4,830±274	5.7	4,595±146	3.2

TABLE 5--ELPAT program summary statistics of reference laboratories for round 001.

Sample Type	Sample	Number of Labs	Mean, ug/wipe	S.D.	RSD (%)
Dust wipes	1	22	868.1	86.9	10.0
	2	22	4397.4	489	11.1
	3	22	168.1	17.4	10.3
	4	22	37.7	5.42	14.4

TABLE 6 -- ELPAT program methods of digestion for reference laboratories for round 001.

No. of Reference Labs	Digestion Method
16	NIOSH 7082 (nitric acid/hydrogen peroxide - hotplate) [7]
1	Modified ashing technique [11]
1	Microwave using nitric acid and hydrogen peroxide
1	EPA SW846-3050-7420 hotplate - modified [12]
1	EPA/AREAL microwave using nitric and hydrochloric acids [7]
1	NIOSH 7300 -- (nitric acid/perchloric acid - hotplate) [13]
1	Leach overnight with 20% nitric - hotplate

REFERENCES

[1]   Agency for Toxic Substances and Disease Registry. The Nature and Extent of Lead Poisoning in Children in the United States: A Report to Congress, U.S. Department of Health and Human Services. 1988.

[2]   Grand, L.D. and J.M. Davis. Effects of Low Level Lead Exposure on Pediatric Neurobehavioral Development: Current Findings and Future Direction. In: Smith, M.A., L.D. Grant, and A.I. Sors, eds. Lead Exposure and Child Development: An International Assessment. London. Kluwer Academic Publishers. pp. 49-115, 1989.

[3]   Goyer, R.A. Toxic Effects of Metals. In: Klassen, C.D., M.O. Amdur, and J. Doull, eds., Casarett and Doull's Toxicology, Third Edition, Macmillan, New York. 1986.

[4]   Abbritti, G., G. Muzi, C. Cicioni, M.P. Accattoli, T. Fiordi, and P. Morucci. Effects of Low Doses of lead on Children's Health. In: Caroli, S., G.V. Iyenzar, and H. Muntau, eds., Bioelements: Health Aspects, Ann. Inst. Super. Sanita. 25(3): 437-488, 1989.

[5]   Williams, E.E., P.M. Grohse, J.D. Neefus, and W.F. Gutknecht. A Report on the Lead Reference Materials Workshop. EPA 747-R-93-008, U.S. Environmental Protection Agency, Washington, DC, 1991.

[6]   Lead-Based Paint: Interim Guidelines for Hazard Identification and Abatement in Public and Indian Housing. U.S. Department of Housing and Urban Development, Washington, DC, April 1990.

[7]   Binstock, D.A., D.L. Hardison, P.M. Grohse, and W.F. Gutknecht. Standard Operating Procedures for Lead in Paint by Hotplate- or Microwave-based Acid Digestion and Atomic Absorption or Inductively Coupled Plasma Emission Spectrometry. EPA 600/8-91/213. U.S. Environmental Protection Agency, Research Triangle Park, NC 1991, 19 pp. Available from NTIS, Springfield, VA; NTIS PB92-114172.

[8]   Research Triangle Institute. Environmental Lead Laboratory Accreditation Program. Report on Preparation of Round 92-01 ELPAT Samples for the American Industrial Hygiene Association, April 1993.

[9]   Williams, E.E., D.A. Binstock, E.D. Estes, J.D. Neefus, L.E. Myers, and W. F. Gutknecht. Preparation and evaluation of lead-containing paint and dust method evaluation materials. In: Proceedings of the Symposium of Lead Poisoning in Children: Exposure, Abatement and Program Issues, American Chemical Society, Washington, DC, 1992.

[10]   Schlecht, P. and J. Grofe (Column Editors). ELPAT Program Report, Background and Current Status. Applied Occupational Environmental Hygiene Journal, 8(8):681-681, 1993.

[11]   Hausknecht, K.A., E.A. Ryan, and L.P. Leonard. Determination of Lead in Paint Chips Using a Modified Ashing Procedure and Atomic Absorption Spectrophotometry. At. Spectroscopy, 3(2):53-55, 1982.

[12]   Office of Solid Waste and Emergency Response. Test Methods for Evaluating Solid Wastes, SW 846, Third Edition, November 1986. Method 3050, Issued September 1986. Method 7420 Lead (Atomic Absorption, Direct Aspiration), Issued September 1986. U.S. Environmental Protection Agency, Washington, DC.

[13]   National Institute for Occupational Safety and Health. NIOSH Manual of Analytical Methods, Third Edition, 1984. NIOSH Method 7300, Issued May 1985.

Peter A. Pella[1], James R. DeVoe[2], and Anthony F. Marlow[3]

DEVELOPMENT OF NIST STANDARD REFERENCE MATERIALS FOR LEAD IN BLOOD, PAINT, HOUSEHOLD DUST, SOIL, AND SIMULATED BONE

REFERENCE: Pella, P. A., DeVoe, J. R., and Marlow, A. F., "Development of NIST Standard Reference Materials for Lead in Blood, Paint, Household Dust, Soil, and Simulated Bone," Lead in Paint, Soil and Dust: Health Risks, Exposure Studies, Control Measures, Measurement Methods, and Quality Assurance, ASTM STP 1226, Michael E. Beard and S. D. Allen Iske, Eds., American Society for Testing and Materials, Philadelphia, 1995.

ABSTRACT: The growing number of laboratories performing chemical analysis of environmental lead has prompted an increased demand for reference materials. The use of reference materials for benchmarking the accuracy of analytical methods is important for establishing measurement quality for within and between laboratories. This paper describes the development of a variety of NIST Standard Reference Materials and other reference materials such as lead in blood, lead-based paint films, a series of powdered lead-based paints containing different lead levels, lead in household dust, and lead in simulated human tibia.

KEYWORDS: Blood, Environmental samples, Lead, Paint, Soils, Standard Reference Materials.

[1]Research Chemist, Atomic and Molecular Spectrometry Group, Inorganic Analytical Research Division, National Institute of Standards and Technology, Gaithersburg, Maryland 20899

[2]Chief, Inorganic Analytical Research Division, National Institute of Standards and Technology, Gaithersburg, Maryland 20899

[3]Physical Science Technician, Atomic and Molecular Spectrometry, Inorganic Analytical Research Division, National Institute of Standards and Technology, Gaithersburg, MD 20899

The adverse health effects related to exposure to lead in the environment are receiving increased attention. This is evident from the recent growth in the number of federal, state, and local government programs designed to implement controls to reduce exposure. This increased awareness has placed a great demand on analytical techniques used for measurement of lead in such samples as blood, lead-based paint, household dust, and soils. Since it is important to produce measurements of high quality, reference materials of known lead content are needed to not only establish a benchma:k for measurement accuracy, but also to provide a means for implementing quality assurance practices. Furthermore, use of a reference material makes it possible to intercompare methods and accelerates the development of new ones. This paper presents an overview of the development of NIST Standard Reference Materials and other reference materials prepared in collaboration with other government agencies.

Lead in Blood-SRM 955a

SRM 955a was developed in 1991 in cooperation with the Centers for Disease Control (CDC). It is intended primarily for use in evaluating the accuracy of lead measurements in blood, and in validating secondary reference materials that are used in many laboratory performance evaluation programs. A unit of SRM 955a consists of four vials of frozen bovine blood, one each of four different lead concentrations (i.e., 5.01 ±0.09, 13.53 ±0.13, 30.63 ±0.32, and 54.43 ±0.38 µg/dL, respectively; as shown in Figure 1). Each vial contains about 2 mL of blood which was prepared and collected at CDC. The lead values were certified at NIST by a high accuracy method based on isotope dilution mass spectrometry (IDMS). The uncertainties stated above reflect the combined effects of measurement imprecision and variability of actual lead concentration among vials. The source of blood for this reference material was two cows that had been fed gelatin capsules containing lead nitrate. The blood was analyzed for the proper range of lead by atomic absorption spectrometry, and blended under clean conditions to produce four pools at the desired lead concentrations. The four pools were then treated with tripotassium EDTA as an anticoagulant, and dispensed into polyethylene vials, and frozen for storage at -20 °C. This material is currently available for purchase through NIST.

Prior to announcing the availability of SRM 955a, a round robin analysis program was conducted to assess the status of blood lead analyses at selected state and clinical laboratories. The participants were asked to analyze the four levels of this SRM in duplicate and send the results

National Institute of Standards & Technology
Certificate of Analysis
Standard Reference Material 955a
Lead in Blood

Standard Reference Material (SRM) 955a is intended primarily for use in evaluating the accuracy of lead determinations in blood and for use in validating working or secondary reference materials for lead-in-blood analysis. A unit of SRM 955a consists of four vials of frozen bovine blood, one each of four different lead concentrations. Each vial contains approximately 2 mL of blood.

CERTIFIED CONCENTRATION VALUES: The certified concentration values of lead were determined using isotope dilution, inductively coupled plasma mass spectrometry (IDMS). The certified values of lead and their associated uncertainties are given below. The uncertainties are 95%/95% statistical tolerance intervals and reflect the combined effects of measurement imprecision and variability of actual lead concentration among vials. The intervals are constructed so that at a confidence level of 95%, they will include the concentrations for 95% of all vials of SRM 955a.

Lead Concentration at 22 °C

Vial No.	µg/dL	µmol/L
955a-1	5.01 ± 0.09	0.242 ± 0.004
955a-2	13.53 ± 0.13	0.653 ± 0.006
955a-3	30.63 ± 0.32	1.478 ± 0.015
955a-4	54.43 ± 0.38	2.627 ± 0.018

NOTICE AND WARNINGS TO USERS

SRM 955a IS INTENDED FOR "IN VITRO" DIAGNOSTIC USE ONLY.

Expiration of Certification: This certification expires one year from the date of shipment from NIST. NIST will continuously monitor this SRM and should any of the certified values change before the expiration of the certification, purchasers will be notified by NIST. Please return the attached registration form to facilitate notification.

Use: Before use, a frozen sample should be allowed to thaw at room temperature (22 °C). The sample should be mixed by gently rolling, not shaking, the vial to remix any water that may have separated on freezing. Shaking will cause bubbles to form at the top of the sample.

For a certified concentration to be applicable to an analytical determination, a minimum sample of 100 µL must be used.

Storage: The SRM should be kept in their original vials and stored frozen at -20 °C. The vials should be stored in the box and aluminized bag supplied. Frost-free freezers should not be used because of temperature fluctuations.

The IDMS analyses were performed by K.E. Murphy and P.J. Paulsen of the Inorganic Analytical Research Division (IARD) and, density determinations, by J.R. Moody, IARD. Confirmatory analyses using graphite furnace atomic absorption spectrometry (levels 3 and 4) and laser-excited atomic fluorescence spectrometry (levels 1 and 2) were done by R.D. Elms, G.C. Turk and M.S. Epstein, IARD.

The technical and support aspects concerning the preparation, certification, and issuance of this SRM were coordinated through the Standard Reference Materials Program by R. Alvarez.

Gaithersburg, MD 20899
December 4, 1991

William P. Reed, Chief
Standard Reference Materials Program

Figure 1 - Certificate for SRM 955a, Lead in Blood (Page 1 of 2)

Statistical analysis of the experimental data was provided by S.B. Schiller of the NIST Statistical Engineering Division.

The overall direction and coordination of the analyses were under the chairmanship of R.D. Vocke, Inorganic Analytical Research Division.

PREPARATION AND ANALYSIS: This SRM was prepared in collaboration with the Division of Environmental Health Laboratory Sciences, National Center for Environmental Health and Injury Control, Centers for Disease Control (CDC). D.C. Paschal, E.W. Gunter, and D.T. Miller were responsible for its preparation. The source of blood for this reference material was two cows that had been fed gelatin capsules containing lead nitrate at the CDC livestock facility in Lawrenceville, Georgia. At CDC, the blood was collected, analyzed for lead by an atomic absorption method, and blended under clean conditions to produce four pools at the desired lead concentrations. The four pools were treated with tripotassium EDTA at a concentration of approximately 1.5 mg/mL, and dispensed into polyethylene vials. The bottles were then stored at -20 °C. Twenty vials were selected randomly from each of the four pools to test for homogeneity (1). Two 100-μL aliquots were taken from each vial, diluted with a matrix modifier, and analyzed in duplicate. The results indicated satisfactory homogeneity for each vialed lot within the limits of precision of the method; and, the vials were shipped frozen to NIST.

At NIST, ten randomly selected vials at each concentration level were analyzed by a high accuracy method based on isotope dilution, inductively coupled plasma mass spectrometry. In this method, the entire contents of a vial was weighed, spiked, and then analyzed, and the results, in ng/g, converted to μg/dL by using the density of the material. The density at 22 °C of all four concentration levels is 1.050 ± 0.002 g/mL. Because IDMS methods are inherently more accurate for the determination of lead in blood than other analytical methods, the certified concentrations are the means of the IDMS results.

REFERENCES

(1) Miller, D.T.; Paschal, D.C.; Gunter, E.W.; Stroud, P.E.; D'Angelo, J. Determination of Lead in Blood Using Electrothermal Atomisation Atomic Absorption Spectrometry with a L'vov Platform and Matrix Modifier. Analyst 112, 1701-1704 (1987).

-2-

Figure 1 - Certificate for SRM 955a Lead in Blood (Page 2 of 2)

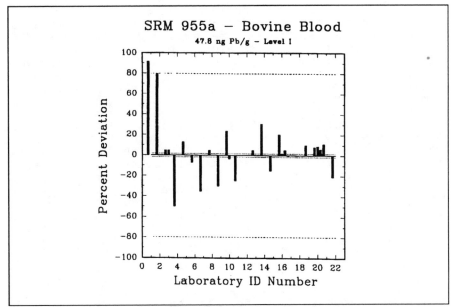

Figure 2 - Interlaboratory Performance

back to NIST for evaluation. The three principal methods of
lead analysis used in U.S. clinical laboratories were
represented, with the majority of laboratories evenly
divided between electrothermal atomization atomic absorption
spectrometry and anodic stripping voltammetry. A few of the
laboratories used an older, third method, Delves-cup flame
atomic absorption spectrometry, to analyze their samples.
While these methods are generally capable of a moderate
sample throughput, they require accurate standards spanning
the levels of interest in order to achieve an acceptable
level of accuracy. With the nonavailability of SRM 955 for
benchmarking clinical lead analyses, there was concern that
the analytical challenges posed by the new regulations might
be difficult to meet.

Figure 2 summarizes the data from the round robin for the
lowest level (5.01 µg Pb/dL). The distribution of results
is probably a reasonable reflection of the state of clinical
lead measurements at better clinical laboratories. Shown in
this diagram are bars representing a laboratory's positive
or negative deviation from the certified value. Some
laboratories analyzed the round robin material on more than
one instrument, and these data are represented by a
clustering of bars around a laboratory ID number. The
dashed lines that are barely distinguishable to either side
of the zero percent deviation line show the NIST uncertainty
interval for this standard. The interval has been

constructed so that at a confidence level of 95%, it will include the concentrations of 95% of all vials of SRM 955a. The dashed lines at the extreme upper and lower edges of the figure are the target uncertainties of laboratories participating in the Blood Level Reference System program of CDC and represent deviations of ±4 µg Pb at a concentration of 5.01 µg Pd/dL. These dashed lines also represent the limits for compliance at this level for laboratory certification under the current Clinical Laboratory Improvement Amendments (CLIA) regulations. The data clearly show that nearly all the laboratories were within 40% of the correct value, and thus were compliant with CLIA regulation. The data furthermore suggest that the blank (in this case Pb, contamination introduced during handling and analysis) is not a limiting factor for blood lead analyses. This is in contrast to a similar study conducted during the early 1970s [2] where it was shown that the analytical blank was the principle limitation in clinical blood lead analyses. Of the five laboratories that responded to that survey, all reported values for the lowest level that were too high were high in some cases by as much as a factor of four.

As the concentration levels and blood sample size for testing continue to decrease, the challenges to measurement quality will increase. Clearly, highly accurate and well characterized reference materials play a pivotal role in resolving such difficulties.

Lead Paint Film for Portable, X-Ray Fluorescence Analyzers-SRM 2579

Portable, hand-held, x-ray fluorescence analyzers are currently used in the field for determining the lead content of painted surfaces in old housing. A set of lead paint reference films was developed for checking the performance of these portable units. This SRM consists of a set of five (7.6 cm x 10.2 cm each) mylar sheets (each 0.2 mm thick), four of which are coated with a single, paint layer (about 0.04 mm thick) of certified lead content (Figure 3). The fifth consists of a lead-free lacquer layer on mylar sheet as a blank. Prototypes of these films were made and sent to the instrument manufacturers for comment. Each sheet is color coded according to lead level and is covered with a clear, thin plastic laminate to protect the paint layer. The painted mylar sheets were prepared by an automated coating process in which liquid paint fed from a reservoir was allowed to spread at a controlled thickness on the substrate in one continuous operation. Known amounts of a lead chromate concentrate were diluted with a paint vehicle to obtain the desired lead concentrations. The painted sheets from the various production runs were first overcoated and then cut into final dimensions for use as an SRM.

National Institute of Standards & Technology

Certificate of Analysis

Standard Reference Material 2579

Lead Paint Film on Mylar Sheet for
Portable X-ray Fluorescence Analyzers

This Standard Reference Material (SRM) is intended for checking the calibration of portable, hand-held, x-ray fluorescence analyzers when testing for lead in paint coatings on interior and exterior building surfaces.

SRM 2579 consists of a set of five 7.62 x 10.16 cm (3 in x 4 in) mylar sheets, four of which are coated with a single, uniform paint layer. Each paint layer has a different lead content which is color coded. The paint layer and the mylar sheet are 0.04 mm and 0.2 mm thick respectively. The fifth sheet is coated with a lead-free lacquer layer on mylar sheet of the same thickness as the lead paint samples and is included as a blank. All sheets are overcoated with a clear thin plastic laminate to protect the paint or lacquer layer from abrasion.

The certified values for lead for each level on the paint sheets are given in Table 1 in units of mg/cm^2. These values are based on measurements by isotope-dilution thermal ionization mass spectrometry and x-ray fluorescence spectrometry.

Notice to Users: Proper use of this SRM requires that the color-coded side face the x-ray source. The blank level SRM has a clear glossy transparent side which should face the x-ray source. For best results, the size of the x-ray beam from the field unit should irradiate an area of the SRM which is at least 2.5 cm in diameter, and is centered on the sheet. The certification of this SRM is valid for two years from the date of purchase, as long as the surface is not abraded.

Use: This SRM must be stored in the container provided at all times when not in use in the field. It is also recommended that this SRM be stored indoors at ambient room temperature when not in use in the field.

Financial support for this SRM was provided by the U.S. Department of Housing and Urban Development, Office of Lead Based Paint Abatement and Poisoning Prevention, R.J. Moroney, contract manager.

The fabrication of the SRM was under the direction of M. McKnight of the NIST Building Materials Division. The coordination of the technical measurements for its certification was accomplished under the direction of P.A. Pella and J.R. DeVoe, of the NIST Inorganic Analytical Research Division.

Statistical design and evaluation of the experimental data were performed by S.B. Schiller and E.S. Lagergren of the NIST Statistical Engineering Division.

The technical and support aspects involved in the preparation, certification, and issuance of this SRM were coordinated through the Standard Reference Materials Program by J.S. Kane.

Gaithersburg, MD 20899   William P. Reed, Chief
July 27, 1992   Standard Reference Materials Program

(over)

Figure 3 - Certificate for SRM 2579 Lead Paint Film (Page 1 of 2)

Preparation: The paint layers on mylar sheet were prepared by an automated coating process by Munsell Color, Newburgh, New York. Known concentrations of a lead chromate pigment (United Technologies/Inmont) were dispersed in a commercial paint vehicle to prepare the lead paints. The nominal concentration in weight percent of lead in the paints used to prepare the various levels was: Level I-18%; Level II-10%; Level III-6%; and Level IV-2%. A lead-free organic tint was added by Munsell to each paint mixture to give the desired color. The thin protective overlay of the paint layers including the NIST SRM label was applied by Dickard Widder Industries, Maspeth, NY.

Homogeneity: The non-uniformity of the lead layer both across the width and along the length of the material was characterized with laboratory x-ray fluorescence spectrometry using the lead $L\alpha$ x-ray line. The non-uniformity measured is the largest contributor to the analytical uncertainty given in Table 1. The attenuation of the lead $L\alpha$ x-rays used for homogeneity testing due to the protective overlay does not exceed 2 % relative, while that of the K x-rays commonly used for field measurement is negligible.

Table 1

Certified Values

Level	Color Code	Lead Concentration, mg/cm^2	[1] Estimated Uncertainty, mg/cm^2
I	Yellow	3.53	0.24
II	Orange	1.63	0.08
III	Red	1.02	0.04
IV	Green	0.29	0.01
Blank	Clear	<0.0001	

[1] The uncertainty includes both random and systematic components. The systematic component accounts for the variation in mean lead concentration over the width of the paint film. The random component is a distribution-free 95% confidence, 95% tolerance interval on the residuals after removal of the systematic trend. In the absence of systematic error, this interval will contain 95% of the true lead concentrations with 95% confidence.

Isotopic Composition: The isotopic composition in atom percent of the lead in the SRM is: ^{208}Pb 51.61%, ^{207}Pb 20.80%, ^{206}Pb 26.27%, ^{204}Pb 1.32%. The uncertainty for the ^{208}Pb, ^{207}Pb and ^{206}Pb isotopic abundance is estimated at 0.05% relative, while the uncertainty for the ^{204} lead Pb is 0.15% relative. These uncertainty estimates are 95% confidence intervals plus an allowance for systematic uncertainty. The atomic weight of the lead in the pigment is therefore 207.1901. The isotopic composition and atomic weight values are not certified, but are given for information only.

NIST Analysts

1. A. Marlow
2. K.E. Murphy
3. P.A. Pella
4. R.D. Vocke
5. R.L. Watters, Jr.

Cooperating Analysts

- J.I.H. Patterson, A. Fischberg, Princeton Gamma-Tech, Inc., Princeton, New Jersey.
- R. Boyce, Scitec Corporation, Kennewick, Washington.
- G.D. Stafford, Warrington, Inc., Austin, Texas.

-2-

Figure 3-Certificate for SRM 2579 Lead Paint Film (Page 2 of 2)

The certified lead levels in areal density units are 3.53 ±0.24, 1.63 ±0.08, 1.02 ±0.04, and 0.29 ±0.01 mg/cm². These correspond to weight per unit weight values of 79.27, 39.36, 25.44, and 7.41 mg Pb per g of paint film, respectively. These target levels were specifically chosen to bracket those levels most frequently encountered in the field. Since there was a small but significant radial non-uniformity of lead across the paint layers in each of the levels, representative samples of these SRMs were measured by laboratory x-ray fluorescence to derive tolerance intervals for obtaining the uncertainties in the certified values. The derived tolerance intervals in units of x-ray counts were converted to concentration units by means of a calibration line between x-ray counts and concentrations measured by IDMS. For this purpose, six samples previously measured by XRF were also measured by IDMS (each 2.5 cm x 2.5 cm) representing the two lowest, two in the middle range, and two highest x-ray counts for each level.

From each calibration line, a median value of x-ray counts was used to derive a robust central lead value together with conservative estimates of uncertainty for each level. The certified values stated above for each level plus or minus its tolerance interval will contain 95% of the true lead concentrations with 95% confidence.

Because the certified values for this SRM must be expressed in appropriate units of mass per unit area for use with x-ray analyzers, it was necessary to accurately measure the area of each of the six samples measured by IDMS for conversion to the proper units. The area of each sample was measured with a high precision microscope stage. When the lead concentrations of the samples measured by IDMS were converted from a weight per unit weight basis to a weight per unit area, the relative standard deviation of the averages increased by 0.5% in all levels, and is a reflection of the uncertainty of measurement of the area of each sample. During acceptance testing of these SRMs by XRF, we found variability of the 1.02 mg/cm² level samples exceeded the specification limit of 4% relative. In order to not compromise the tolerance limits for the certified value for this level, we decided to measure all samples within this level using a modified energy-dispersive x-ray spectrometer to eliminate those samples which fell outside the error limits.

Powdered Lead-Based Paints

In addition to measuring paint directly on interior surfaces, paint samples are often removed from a site for chemical analysis. In 1973, NIST issued SRM 1579, a powdered lead-based paint collected from interior surfaces of old dwellings undergoing renovation. The paint for this SRM was collected in the field by first softening it with a hand torch and then scraping it from plaster and wood substrates. The material was collected in plastic bags as a heterogeneous mixture of many different kinds of paints. In the laboratory, non-paint matter was removed and the paint mixture ground in a disk mill to produce a material suitable for further grinding to a smaller particle size in a jet mill. After a first pass through the jet mill, the resultant material was sieved to remove a coarse, non-grindable fraction. Two more passes through the jet mill gave a fine powder passing a 325 mesh (45μm) screen. Since this SRM has been in stock for nearly twenty years, a recertification of the lead value was performed. Reanalysis using IDMS has indicated a small but statistically significant bias in the original certified value. The original value was 11.87 ±0.04%, and the recertified value is 11.995 ±0.031%. The SRM is now called SRM 1579a (as shown in Figure 4).

Three additional powdered lead-based paints are currently being developed by NIST and EPA having target values of 0.05, 0.5, and 5.0 wt. percent lead. These values were established in accordance with guidelines presented at an EPA Reference Material Workshop [1]. The paint material for these proposed SRMs is being collected by EPA from painted interior surfaces in the form of paint chips, and then shipped in plastic bags to NIST for additional testing and final processing. The raw material that has been collected so far is somewhat heterogeneous covering a wide range of lead levels, such that it is difficult to get a reliable estimate of the lead content of the paint material in each bag without thorough grinding and mixing. Therefore, the bags of raw material are kept segregated, and the lead level in each bag is measured after the material is ground. The individual bags of ground material are then sorted according to lead level and then mixed and blended to prepare the desired target levels.

The processing of the paint material can be described as follows. The raw material from a each bag (nominally of the same lead level) is first passed through a vibrating coarse sieve to remove extraneous matter such as large particles of dirt, pieces of metal, and glass. Each cleaned paint material is then placed in a separate plastic bag and labelled to retain its original identification throughout the processing steps. This procedure, however, does not remove painted or unpainted plaster fragments so that this type of material will be present to some extent in the final SRM and will elevate the calcium concentration somewhat.

National Institute of Standards & Technology

Certificate of Analysis

Standard Reference Material 1579a

Powdered Lead Based Paint

This Standard Reference Material (SRM) is intended for use in the calibration of apparatus and the evaluation of methods used in the determination of lead in paint. SRM 1579a is intended to mimic or resemble the paint on interior surfaces of old housing (see section on Collection). It consists of 35 grams of a fine homogeneous powder of which 99+ percent passes a 45 μm (No. 325) sieve. The certified value is given below and is based on analysis of at least a 100 milligram sample of the as-received material.

Lead Content: 11.995 ± 0.031   Weight Percent

The certified value is based on measurements by isotope dilution mass spectrometry (IDMS). The uncertainty given is the 95% confidence interval of the certified value.

The overall direction and coordination of the technical measurements leading to this certificate were performed by R.D. Vocke of the Inorganic Analytical Research Division.

Statistical calculations were carried out by S.B. Schiller of the Statistical Engineering Division.

The technical and support aspects involved in the preparation, certification, and issuance of this Standard Reference Material were coordinated through the Standard Reference Materials Program by J.S. Kane.

Preparation, Testing, and Analysis

Collection

The paint for this Standard Reference Material was collected by the staff of the Philadelphia Department of Public Health from the interior surfaces of dwellings undergoing renovation. The paint was softened with a hand torch, scraped from the plaster and wood substrates, and collected in plastic bags as a heterogeneous mixture of many different kinds of paints. In the laboratory, non-paint matter such as bits of metal, plastic, glass, and wood were removed and the paint mixture was ground in a disk mill to produce a material suitable for feeding into a jet mill. The paint was comminuted in a jet mill operating at 6.895 x 10^5 Pa (100 psig) air pressure, then sieved through a 149 μm (No. 100) vibrating screen to remove the coarse, non-grindable fraction. Two additional passes through the jet mill at 6.68-7.37 x 10^5 Pa (97-107 psig) gave fine powder with 99.31 weight percent passing through a 45 μm (No. 325) sieve.

Homogeneity

Sample homogeneity was ascertained by X-ray fluorescence analysis for lead content on 17 samples chosen at random from the total lot. A statistical analysis of the data from 136 observations showed the bottle-to-bottle variability among the samples to be no greater than 0.02 percent lead. No within-bottle variation with respect to lead was detected.

Gaithersburg, MD 20899   William P. Reed, Chief
February 3, 1992   Standard Reference Materials Program

(over)

Figure 4 - SRM 1579a Powdered Lead Based Paint Certificate(Page 1 of 2)

Analysis

The IDMS analyses were performed by E.S. Beary, K.E. Murphy, P.J. Paulsen and R.D. Vocke of the Inorganic Analytical Research Division.

Certification of this Standard Reference Material in 1973 employed polarographic and atomic absorption spectrometric analyses, which have been described in detail in NIST Special Publication 260-45. [1]. Reanalysis using isotope dilution thermal ionization mass spectrometry has indicated a very small but statistically significant low bias in the original certified value due to incomplete dissolution. The material has therefore been recertified as SRM 1579a.

References

1. Development of NBS Standard Reference Material: No. 1579 Powdered Lead-Based Paint, B. Greifer, E.J. Maienthal, T.C. Rains and S.D. Rasberry 1973 NBS Special Publcation 260-45.

-2-

Figure 4 - SRM 1579a Powdered Lead Based Paint Certificate(Page 2 of 2)

The cleaned material is then coarsely ground in a large
blender to produce a particle size suitable for further
grinding in a ball-mill. The ball-milling results in a fine
powder having the consistency of flour. Each bag containing
the ball-milled material is weighed, sampled and measured by
energy-dispersive X-ray fluorescence (EDXRF) to determine
which bags are to be combined and blended to produce an SRM
of the desired lead level. The blending operations for the
0.05% and 0.5% levels are currently in progress and will
soon be ready for bottling. The final bottled material will
be tested for homogeneity by XRF and certified by IDMS and
ICP/OES.

Household Dust

Household dust has been identified as a readily available
source of lead poisoning to young children, especially when
lead-containing soil from the surroundings of a dwelling is
tracked indoors. Our first efforts in this area of SRM
development are directed toward producing a household dust
SRM for benchmarking the accuracy of laboratory based bulk
chemical analysis methods using a minimum sample size of
about 100 mg. The initial target value for this SRM will be
about 100-200 µg/g of lead. We also plan to certify other
toxic elements which are present at trace levels such as
mercury, cadmium, chromium, arsenic, and nickel. The source
of the EPA collected material for producing this SRM will be
disposable household vacuum cleaner bags containing dust
from various interior dwellings. They will be sent to NIST
after radiation sterilization for testing of lead levels and
for processing the material.

A pilot study has been conducted to determine the lead
content of various sieved fractions from vacuum bags
previously radiation sterilized. A coarse screen was used to
manually separate the dust from the fibrous and extraneous
material which comprises most of the volume of the vacuum
bag. The resultant dust material from each of eight bags was
then passed through a series of sieves where 500 µm, 250 µm,
100 µm, and 50 µm particle size fractions were collected.
The lead content of the fractions was then measured by
EDXRF. Accuracy of the X-ray fluorescence method was
verified by ICP/MS. For most of the bags , the apparent
lead concentration increased as the particle size fraction
collected decreased. Preliminary SEM analysis showed that
the mean diameter of the lead-bearing particles is about 1
µm. Because the lead bearing particles are small, many of
them are adhered to larger particles. This means that even
though the household vacuum cleaner may not retain particles
of this size, the representation of lead in the bulk mass
from the small particles is assured. From these studies, it
appears that a 100 µm sieve represents a good compromise
between having the necessary homogeneity of the material and
adequate yield of the dust material. Since composition of

the major inorganic constituents has not significantly changed between sieved fractions, this SRM should be representative of that material routinely encountered in the field. Studies of the particle size effect for the other toxic elements will be determined to the extent that compositional variation will be measured as a function of size fraction for a representative sampling of the material.

For producing the SRM, the contents of each bag will be sieved through a vibrating screen to remove the fibrous and extraneous material. Then the sieved dust fraction will be passed through a finer screen such that particles no larger than 100 μm will be retained for the SRM. The collected material in each bag will then be measured for lead level by EDXRF whose accuracy is verified by ICP/MS. These measurements will then determine which bags will be mixed to produce the final material for mixing and blending. The homogeneity for lead will be tested by XRF and if acceptable, the certification of lead and other toxic elements will be performed by IDMS, optical methods, and neutron activation analysis.

Paint-on-Wall Test Samples

A new project which we have initiated with EPA involves production of actual wall sections containing leaded paint. These sections will be measured for lead content in both mass per unit area and mass per unit mass. The level of lead will be close to the abatement decision level. These materials will not be SRMs but will be made available to manufacturers and users of chemical test kits and portable X-ray fluorescence instruments for purposes of measurement evaluation. One material, collected by EPA, will consist of sections of a fiberboard wall (15 cm x 20 cm) taken from old housing. The wall sections contain a lead-based paint layer overcoated with non-leaded paint. Validation of the lead content of these materials will be done by X-ray fluorescence and by ICP/OES. The EPA is also attempting to find other sources of painted substrates such as wood containing lead-based paint layers which are close to the abatement level and intended for the same purpose.

Simulated Human Tibia

It has long been known that the cumulative effects of lead exposure is preserved in mineralized tissues such as bone. Several groups have reported on the development of systems for measuring lead in bone that is based on the principle of x-ray fluorescence for in-vivo measurement of bone lead concentrations. Measurements of lead in human tibia or finger bone have been employed for monitoring accumulative lifetime exposure to lead and for assessing the efficacy of various chemical therapies for removing lead from patients. These in vivo measurements are currently performed by XRF using either K-shell or L-shell x-ray excitation conditions. There is, however, a lack of appropriate reference materials for assessing the comparability of results obtained from various XRF systems. For this reason we are working with the University of Maryland and NIEHS to produce a series of surrogate human tibia phantoms made of lead impregnated Plaster of Paris. The phantoms will be prepared at the University of Maryland in the form of the mid-shaft of a human tibia. There will be a set of eight phantoms with target values of blank (none added), 5, 10, 20, 50, 100, 200, and 300 µg of lead per gram of phantom. Four sets will be produced, one of which will be destructively tested. Of the remaining three, one will be circulated among the various research laboratories and two will be retained at NIST and serve as reference sets.

Care will be taken to minimize formation of voids during fabrication and will be checked by x-ray radiography. Destructive testing of one set of phantoms will be performed by taking cross sections along the length of each phantom in the set. One of the cross- sectional slices from each level in the set will be evaluated non-destructively for spatial inhomogeneity using x-ray microfluorescence analysis. Each of the cross sectional slices will then be ground to a fine powder and tested for bulk homogeneity for lead by XRF. If the uniformity of the material is acceptable, we plan to certify the lead content using IDMS.

SUMMARY

Measurement quality can be improved through the use of reference materials in a number of ways. They provide a means to accelerate the development of new methods of chemical analysis through valid intercomparison of results. They can establish a benchmark of accuracy for existing methods and thereby establish criteria for performance based testing regardless of the methods of chemical analysis that are used. Indeed, the very fact that a reference material exists establishes credibility of measurement methods. For example, if it is impossible to produce a reference material to a requisite level of accuracy due to factors involving homogeneity of composition or stability of analyte, then the methods of analysis become suspect.

REFERENCES

(1)
   Williams, E.E., Grohse, P.M., Neefus, J.D., Gutknecht,
   W.F., Lim, B., Breen, J.J., Harper, S., and von Lehmden,
   D., "A Report on the Lead Reference Materials Workshop,"
   EPA Report, No. 747-R-93-008, U.S. Environmental
   Protection Agency, Washington, DC, May 13-14, 1991.

(2)
   Murphy, T.J., "The Role of The Analytical Blank in
   Accurate Trace Analysis.," NBS Spec. Pb. 422, pp. 509-539
   (1976).

Harold A. Vincent,[1] Dawn M. Boyer,[2] Robert W. Elias[3]

QUALITY ASSURANCE DOUBLE-BLIND SAMPLE APPLICATIONS IN THE DETERMINATION
OF LEAD IN URBAN DUSTS AND SOILS

REFERENCE: Vincent, H. A., Boyer, D. M., Elias, R. W., "Quality
Assurance Double-Blind Sample Applications in the Determination of Lead
in Urban Dusts and Soils," Lead in Paint, Soil and Dust: Health Risks,
Exposure Studies, Control Measures, Measurement Methods, and Quality
Assurance, ASTM STP 1226, Michael E. Beard and S.D. Allen Iske, Eds.,
American Society for Testing Materials, Philadelphia, 1995.

ABSTRACT: X-ray fluorescence analysis (XRF), atomic absorption
spectroscopy (AAS), and inductively coupled plasma – atomic emission
spectroscopy (ICP–AES) were used for the measurement of lead in samples
for the Urban Soil Lead Abatement Demonstration Project (USLADP).
     In addition to the usual quality control measures, soil and dust
audit samples were introduced into each laboratory's sample input system
such that the persons doing sample preparation or analytical
determinations were unaware that the samples were for quality
assessment. The samples were introduced as unknowns along with other
USLADP project soil and dust samples with their identification known
only to the laboratory quality assurance officer.
     Acceptance of lead analysis data for individual groups of samples,
without qualification, was based partially on whether the values for
lead in the double-blind audit samples were within value limits
calculated from the statistical treatment of multi-laboratory test data.

KEYWORDS: X-ray Fluorescence (XRF), Inductively Coupled Plasma – Atomic
Emission Spectroscopy (ICP–AES), Atomic Absorption Spectroscopy (AAS),
lead, soil, dust, quality control, double-blind, reference materials.

[1]Chemist, Quality Assurance Research Branch, EMSL–LV, USEPA, P.O.
Box 93478, Las Vegas, NV 89193–3478.

[2]Scientist, Lockheed Environmental Systems and Technologies, 975
Kelly Johnson Drive, Las Vegas, NV 89119–3705

[3]Health Scientist, Environmental Criteria and Assessment Office,
MD–52, USEPA, Research Triangle Park, NC 27111

The purpose of this paper is to describe the manner in which double-blind audit samples were used to provide some of the quality assurance for the determinations of lead in soil and dust samples during the Urban Soil Lead Abatement Demonstration Project (USLADP).

The USLADP, sometimes referred to as the Three Cities Project or Lead Free Kids Project, was coordinated by the U.S. Environmental Protection Agency (EPA) and was carried out, cooperatively, by the EPA, the Center for Disease Control (CDC), and health-related groups in each of the three localities. The project was designed to test whether removal of lead from the immediate environment of children would result in the lowering of their blood lead levels. It involved many lead determinations on soils, dusts, wet wipes, and blood samples.

The health groups in the three cities, Baltimore, Boston and Cincinnati, worked with local laboratories to provide most of the analytical information. The determinations of lead in soils and dusts were done using X-ray Fluorescence Spectroscopy (XRF), Inductively Coupled Plasma - Atomic Emssion Spectroscopy (ICP-AES), and Atomic Absorption Spectroscopy (AAS).

The EPA's Environmental Monitoring Systems Laboratory at Las Vegas (EMSL-LV) participated in the USLADP by furnishing quality assurance materials, analytical determinations of lead, and statistical interpretations of the data for the quality assurance materials. The materials included soil and dust samples that were prepared into splits to be transmitted to the laboratories performing analytical determinations for the project. The participating laboratories performed lead determination on these quality assurance samples variously in calibration, batch control, and as double-blind audit samples.

This paper focuses on the characterization, distribution, and interpretation of data for the double-blind samples as they were used to support the assurance that the analytical data for lead in project samples met acceptance criteria for this project. Data from several laboratories were used in defining the statistical relationships. The audit sample application results reported in this paper are from one laboratory and may or may not be typical of the total study. Many project data from the several laboratories are still being analyzed.

EXPERIMENTAL

Characterization of Audit Samples

The collection, preparation, characterization and distribution of the audit materials has been described [1,2]. For each bulk audit sample material, lead was determined in at least 50 bulk sample splits by XRF in order to establish homogeneity. The samples were remixed and resplit if certain statistical criteria were exceeded, e.g. the variances of values for lead between sample split groups were significantly different than the variances for lead values within a split group. Preliminary lead values, based on XRF calibration, were assigned at that time.

A Kevex model 7000 XRF instrument was used for determining lead
and otherwise characterizing the audit samples for appropriateness as
quality assurance materials. This instrument is an energy—dispersive
system with a lithium—drifted silicon detector and an air—cooled,
rhodium—target X—ray tube with a silver secondary target for excitation.
The X—ray tube was operated at 35 kV and 3 milliamperes. An X—ray
fluorescence spectrum was acquired for each determination. X—ray count
integrations under the characteristic lines were done for both the lead
L—alpha and L—beta lines and the silver Compton and Rayleigh lines. The
procedure has been described in detail previously [2].

Measurements for lead in three quality control samples were made
with each batch. Analysis of those data yields information about
reproducibility at different lead concentration levels. Each of these
QC samples was used repetitively and occupied the same position in the
instrumental multi—sample sample holder throughout the work. Between
batch runs, each QC sample was removed, tumbled within the sample
container, and replaced to the same position in the Kevex instrument
sample holder.

Two of the quality control samples used with each XRF batch run
were from USLADP project bulk soil samples that were analyzed
extensively for lead using both ICP—AES and AAS techniques to establish
lead values and the homogeneity for lead. To create the high
concentration sample, one of these bulk samples was spiked with lead
oxide to create a control sample at approximately 18,000 mg/kg. NIST
1648, Urban Dust, was also used as a control sample during most of the
work. It is feasible to use primary reference materials, such as SRM's,
in XRF work because of the non—destructive nature of the technique.

It was common for the USLADP project laboratories to screen
project soil and dust samples to pass a 60 mesh screen before submitting
them for chemical analysis. They were subsampled within the chemistry
laboratory followed by final lead determination by one of the three
techniques mentioned above. It was important that the audit samples
resemble "real" unknown samples in order to avoid any bias. Generally,
laboratory personnel who prepared and subsampled incoming materials were
different to those who made the instrumental measurements. The
instrument operators should not have seen the condition of the incoming
samples.

The dust audit samples differed from the soil audit samples, and
other soil reference samples that were available, mostly in terms of the
particle sizes of their solid components. The dusts tended to have a
larger proportion of the finer—sized particles than did the soils.
After indoor carpet fibers and other indoor household components were
removed by sieving, the resultant dust powders were similar in the
components to the soils occurring in the same locality.

Distribution and use of Audit samples

Each participating laboratory provided EMSL—LV with sample
containers used by that laboratory for sample collection and input to
the laboratory. Splits of the audit samples were packaged in those

containers by the EMSL–LV team and transmitted to the Quality Assurance Officer (QAO) for the laboratory. The QAO in turn submitted the samples to the laboratory as part of the routine USLADP project input. These double–blind audit samples were inserted within project groups at the rate of approximately two per batch of 20 samples.

20 gram splits of the soil materials were furnished, while the split sizes for the dusts ranged from 50 mg to 2 grams.

Each laboratory was responsible for the calibration of its own instruments although a series of soil and dust reference samples was provided for use in quality control. These samples were used later in an interlaboratory study of calibration. When used as quality control samples, the reference samples were run with each batch to establish acceptance of the calibration for that batch. NIST 1648, Urban Dust Standard Reference Material (SRM), was also available to the laboratories to yield SRM traceability of the quality control data.

For each laboratory, only the QAO knew which samples were audit samples. The QAO did not know the lead content of the audit samples. The laboratory identification of the samples submitted in this manner was given by the laboratory QAO to the project Quality Assurance Officer at EPA's Research Triangle Park (RTP) laboratory, who had been advised as to the lead content of the audit samples.

The project QAO received analytical information early enough from each of the participating laboratories that if the audit sample values indicated that a severe problem existed in the lead analysis, warning and/or instructions to repeat the lead determinations could be given.

Deciding whether the groups of analytical data must carry qualifications or 'flags' regarding quality, is a longer–term task but can be made for each batch based on the audit sample data. This latter activity required that some special interpretations of interlaboratory test data be employed in establishing decision criteria.

The purpose of the interlaboratory calibration study was to be able to correct project data from each participating laboratory to a common base for overall project data comparison studies. All laboratories providing lead determinations for the project, plus the EMSL–LV laboratory, analyzed 20 dust and soil samples. The 20 included those identified in this paper. Correction factors for data from each laboratory resulted from the statistical treatment of the interlaboratory study data and will be used for the EPA integrated project report.

Calculation and Interpretation of Audit Sample Data

During the early time period of the USLADP project, the only multi–determination information available for the audit samples was the original XRF data provided by a single laboratory, EMSL–LV. A computer program called BIWEIGHT was applied to the data. That program employed 'biweight' statistical principles [3] to define acceptance windows and resulted in some very narrow acceptance ranges at different

concentration levels (Fig. 1). It was recognized that these limits were
too confining to apply to a multi-laboratory set of data.

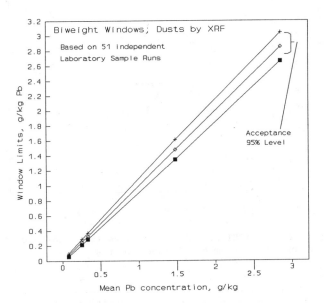

Figure 1 Original BIWEIGHT acceptance windows for
lead in audit samples over the 0–3000 mg/kg range.

The BIWEIGHT program used is a robust modification of Gaussian
statistics that puts more weighting on data points as they occur closer
to the median value. It is especially suitable for application to data
sets originating from several laboratories and when there is a need for
comparability between all data sets.

Calculations using data from XRF determinations of lead in dusts,
performed independently by four laboratories, show much wider acceptance
ranges than when using single laboratory data (Fig. 2). These
calculations can be contrasted with similar ones for lead in soils by
XRF at comparable concentration levels (Fig. 3).

Acceptance limits based on optical spectroscopic lead
determinations for the same materials were calculated (Fig. 4). These
acceptance limits differed from those calculated from XRF data due to
bias between the methods. Since the limits for data from one technique
could not appropriately be applied to data from another, it was
necessary to delineate one set of acceptance limits for the project
since participating laboratories could opt to use any of the three
methods for the determination of lead.

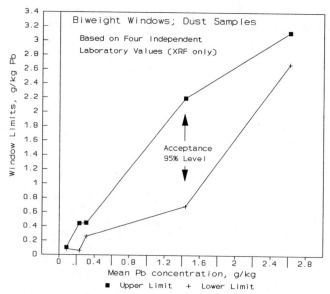

Figure 2   BIWEIGHT acceptance windows for lead in dusts based on values from 4 XRF laboratories.

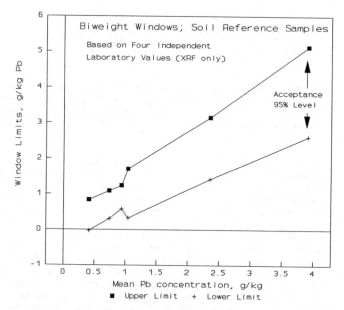

Figure 3   BIWEIGHT acceptance windows for lead in soils based on XRF results from 4 laboratories.

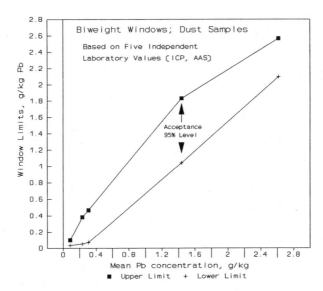

Figure 4 BIWEIGHT windows for dust analyses using optical spectral data only.

It was expected that the use of a larger number of data groups in the calculation of the BIWEIGHT windows would result in better definition of acceptance limits over the wide concentration range covered with the calibration and reference materials.

Data for lead in these dust and soil samples became available from several laboratories, including some not participating in the project sample analysis, but which were using the same analytical techniques (I.E. XRF,ICP—AES and AAS). The plot of acceptance windows versus dust lead concentrations (Fig. 5), using data from nine laboratories and all three methods, does not appear to represent a smooth function. This may be due to the dusts being different from each other in elemental composition other than lead and posing different technical problems for each measurement technique.

Because of the differences for limits at different lead concentrations and with different measurement systems, the data were studied on an individual sample basis to determine the influence on acceptance limits from the number of laboratory values and the kind of data used.

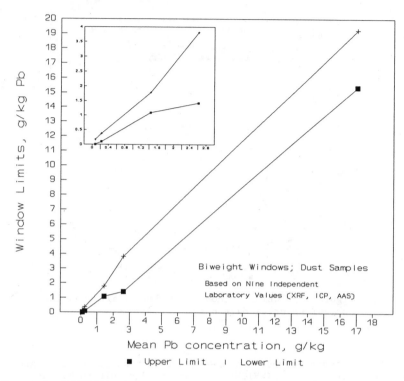

Figure 5 BIWEIGHT windows calculated using lead data from nine independent laboratories.

Acceptance window limits were calculated for individual soil and dust samples with varying numbers of laboratory values used (Figs. 6-8). The lead concentrations in these samples vary from approximately 300 mg per kilogram to 7000. It is apparent that windows established with five data sets exhibit only small changes upon using additional values. For most of the samples studied, little differences were found between window limits using any combination of five laboratory data sets out of the thirteen sets available.

The BIWEIGHT program yields calculated windows for 95% and 99% confidence levels by default and can be used to give values for other levels by selection. The values are presented in this paper only at the 95% level to facilitate comprehension.

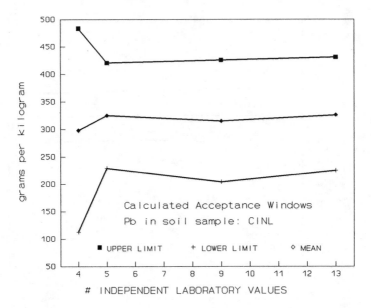

Figure 6 Calculated acceptance windows for lead in audit soil sample: CINLO.

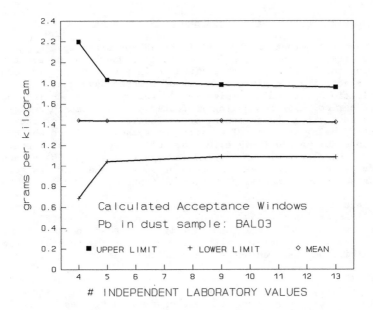

Figure 7 Calculated acceptance windows for dust audit sample BAL03 versus number of laboratory values used.

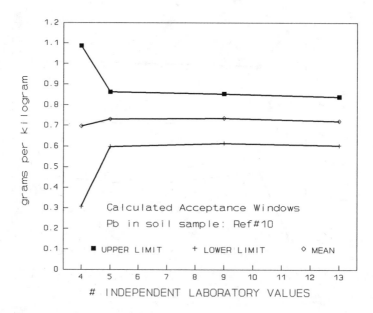

Figure 8 Calculation of acceptance windows for lead determination in RC reference soil sample #10 versus number of laboratory values used.

Audit Sample Results During Dust and Soil Analyses:

Lead determinations by one of the USLADP participating laboratories, were performed for the various double—blind audit samples according to the time periods delineated in Figure 9. The periods of analysis activity are given in terms of elapsed days that lead determinations for audit samples levels were performed during the project period. The scheduling indicated by days elapsed refers to the time elapsed since the beginning of collection of data for the laboratory being tracked. The different symbols indicate whether the batch under blind audit was a dust or soil group. It was intended that the audit samples would be matched in type to the group being analyzed. In order to have the ranges covered for some batches, it was necessary to have some audit samples of different types.

Lead determinations in the high lead level soil audit samples initially exceeded the 95% confidence acceptance windows(Fig. 10). Some of those values would fall between limits extended to the 99% confidence level. A soil audit sample, with about 315 mg Pb/kg, exhibits similar initial bias but is within the 95% confidence acceptance limits (Fig. 11).

A variety of audit samples were used during dust analyses. Acceptance limits are shown for some of them in figures 12 and 13. The project limits tend to be very wide compared to individual laboratory precision at the low concentration levels.

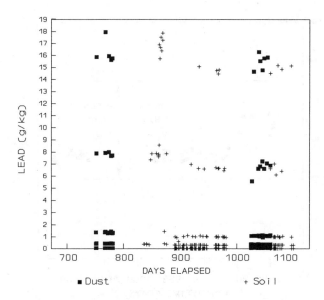

Figure 9 Lead values determined for audit dust and soil samples versus time with the project sample batch type indicated.

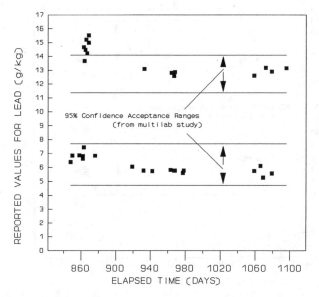

Figure 10 Lead determinations in audit soil samples during soil batch analyses.

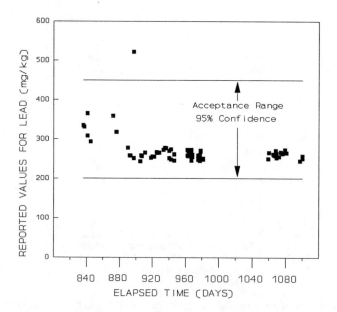

Figure 11 Lead determinations on low level audit soil samples versus time.

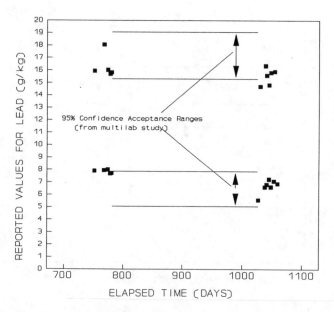

Figure 12 Lead determination in audit samples in dust batches versus time.

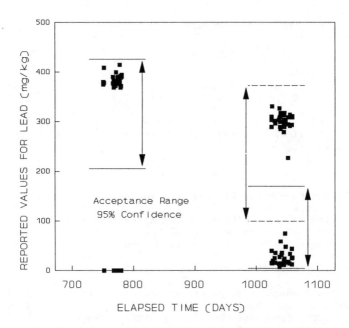

Figure 13 Lead determinations for three audit samples in dust batch groups versus time.

The final acceptance window limits for dust and soil audit samples were calculated from the multi-laboratory data but were adjusted to a project-common scale based on data from the USLADP interlaboratory calibration study. The acceptance windows for the 95% confidence level are shown for Dusts in Table 1 and for Soils in Table 2.

TABLE 1— 95% confidence windows for dust audit samples (mg/kg)

Sample	mean value*	lower limit	upper limit	Differential
BAL01	78	4	163	159
CIN02	233	93	372	279
BAL03	1438	1091	1786	695
CIN01	2617	1422	3812	2390
BOS01	17015	15362	19221	3859

*Mean values calculated from BIWEIGHT program may very slightly from classical means.

TABLE 2— 95% confidence windows for soil audit samples (mg/kg)

Sample	mean value*	lower limit	upper limit	Differential
CINLO	315	204	426	222
BALHI	1017	847	1187	340
BOSMI	6090	4742	7696	2954
CINHI	12729	11361	14096	2735

*Mean values calculated from BIWEIGHT program may very slightly from classical means.

SUMMARY

, Acceptance windows for lead determinations performed on soil and dust audit samples were established using data from several laboratories participating in the USLADP and using three different measurement techniques. The windows were established with the aid of the BIWEIGHT computer program. They were used to determine which groups of data associated with them in the batches, would be 'flagged' as possibly lesser quality data than those not flagged.

It isn't possible to guarantee that laboratory personnel will not recognize audit samples as such in the input mix, nor is it possible to determine from these data whether any kind of recognition by laboratory personnel led to the introduction of any bias.

Acceptance windows for dust audit samples were wider than for soil audit samples with similar concentrations. This may be due to the greater heterogeneity of the dusts and that lesser amounts of the dust materials were available for use as individual audit samples.

Reviews of program—wide audit data are continuing. The interpretation experience with the data of the one laboratory used for this paper will be valuable in the continuing work.

NOTICE

REFERENCES

[1]   Boyer, D.M., Hillman, D. C., Vincent, H.A., "Minimum Sample Size
      for the Analysis of Lead in Urban Dust by Energy Dispersive X-ray
      Fluorescence," Pittsburgh Conference, New Orleans, March 9-13,
      1992.

[2]   Vincent, H. A., Newberry,III, W. R., Hillman,D. C., Boyer, D. M.,
      Papp, M., Kohorst, K., "Preparation and Characterization of
      Quality Assurance Materials for XRF Measurements of Lead in Soil."
      Sixth Annual Waste Testing and Quality Assurance Symposium,
      Washington, D.C., July 16-20 1990.

[3]   Kafadar, K., "A Biweight Approach to the One-Sample Problem."
      Journal of the American Statistical Association(Theory and Methods
      Section), Volume 77, Number 378, pp. 416-424, June 1982.

Laboratory and Field Measurement Accreditation

John V. Scalera[1]

THE NATIONAL LEAD LABORATORY ACCREDITATION PROGRAM

REFERENCE: Scalera, J. V., "The National Lead Laboratory Accreditation Program," Lead in Paint, Soil, and Dust: Health Risks, Exposure Studies, Control Measures, Measurement Methods, and Quality Assurance, ASTM STP 1226, Michael E. Beard and S.D. Allen Iske, Eds., American Society for Testing Materials, Philadelphia, 1995.

ABSTRACT: The Environmental Protection Agency's Office of Pollution Prevention and Toxics (OPPT) has established the National Lead Laboratory Accreditation Program (NLLAP). The NLLAP has been established by OPPT in order to assure the public that laboratories which participate successfully in the NLLAP are capable of analyzing for lead in paint chips, dust and soil samples. In order to participate in the NLLAP, a laboratory must:

1. Participate quarterly in the Environmental Lead Proficiency Analytical Testing Program (ELPAT). ELPAT is a proficiency testing program run by the American Industrial Hygiene Association (AIHA) in cooperation with the National Institute of Occupational Safety and Health (NIOSH).

2. Under go a systems audit inclusive of on-site visits at least once every three years. The systems audit must be conducted by a public or private accrediting organization with a program recognized by EPA through a memorandum of understanding (MOU).

Laboratories accredited by laboratory accrediting organization participating in the NLLAP will be recognized by EPA as capable of analyzing for lead in samples of paint chips, dust and soil.

KEYWORDS: lead laboratory, NLLAP, paint chips, dust, accreditation, proficiency

---

[1]Chemist, TS-798, Office of Pollution Prevention and Toxics, U.S. Environmental Protection Agency, 401 M. Street., Southwest, Washington DC., 20460

INTRODUCTION

Under Title X, Section 405(b)[1] of the 1992 Lead-Based Paint Hazard Reduction Act, the Environmental Protection Agency (EPA) is responsible for assuring the public there are laboratories which are capable of analyzing samples of paint chips, dust and soil which may be contaminated with lead. Specific regulatory requirements which EPA is responsible for include:

The determination if effective voluntary laboratory accreditation programs are in place and operating on a nationwide basis for laboratories analyzing for lead in paint chips (film), soil and dust samples.

The establishment of a laboratory certification program for laboratories which demonstrate an ability to accurately test paint films, dust and soil samples for lead in the absence of an effective voluntary laboratory accreditation program.

In an effort to meet these regulatory requirements, the EPA Office of Pollution Prevention and Toxics (OPPT), is establishing the National Lead Laboratory Accreditation Program (NLLAP). Under the NLLAP, EPA will not directly accredit laboratories but will rely upon the expertise of laboratory accreditation organizations. The laboratory accrediting organizations can be private, state, or local entities.

As a part of the NLLAP, the EPA OPPT has established a set of minimum requirements for laboratory accrediting organizations participating in the program. These requirements which are discussed below, include the use of a minimum set of "Laboratory Quality System Requirements" for laboratories wishing to participate in the NLLAP. Laboratories which are accredited by laboratory accrediting organizations participating in the NLLAP, will in turn be recognized by EPA as capable of analyzing for lead in samples of paint chips, dust and/or soil.

BASIC NLLAP STRUCTURE

The basic program structure for the NLLAP is based upon "International Standards Organization/International Electrochemical Commission (ISO) Guide 25: General Requirements for the Competence of Calibration and Testing Laboratories"[2], "ISO Guide 58: Calibration and Testing Laboratory Accreditation Systems-General Requirements for Operation and Recognition"[3] and recommendations made by the Special Committee on Laboratory Accreditation established by the Federal Interagency Lead-Based Paint Task Force[4] (EPA report "Laboratory Accreditation Program

Guidelines: Measurement of Lead in Paint, Dust, and Soil,"
EPA 747-R-92-001, March 1992). The Committee
recommendations which were incorporated into the NLLAP
include the development of a program which consists of two
basic components, a proficiency testing program and a
laboratory systems audit inclusive of on-site visits. Based
upon committee recommendations, the NLLAP does not dictate
any single set of methods to be utilized for the analysis of
lead, but allows the choice of the methodology to be
utilized as an option left up to the laboratory performing
the analysis.

Concerning the recommendations of proficiency testing and
system audits, laboratories who wish to participate in the
NLLAP must:

> 1. Participate in the Environmental Lead Proficiency
> Analytical Testing Program (ELPAT).
>
> 2. Undergo a systems audit inclusive of on-site
> visits.

The ELPAT Program

ELPAT is a proficiency testing program administered by
the American Industrial Hygiene Association (AIHA) in
cooperation with the National Institute for Occupational
Safety and Health (NIOSH) and the EPA/OPPT. The proficiency
testing samples used in the ELPAT program consist of
variable levels of lead in samples consisting of paint
films/chips, dust, and soil matrices. The materials used to
produce the proficiency testing samples are from "real-
world" sources. In example, the source for paint chips
samples are buildings scraped down of their deteriorating
paint. Dust proficiency testing samples are filter papers
spiked with household dust. For every test round, four
samples at variable concentrations are provided per matrix
tested. Laboratories may request to participate in the
proficiency testing of one or two matrices only, their
accreditation being limited to the matrices they've been
tested for. Proficiency testing, which initiated in
December of 1992, is conducted on a quarterly basis. AIHA
is responsible for the production and distribution of the
ELPAT samples. NIOSH conducts the statistical evaluation of
the results submitted by participating laboratories, and
provides a final determination if the laboratory has
successfully analyzed the samples based on the performance
of a selected group of reference laboratories.   On a
quarterly basis, NIOSH submits to EPA the ELPAT results as
well as a performance rating of the laboratories
participating in ELPAT on a state by state basis. NIOSH
ELPAT performance criteria are based on accumulated results
over four rounds (one year). The acceptable range is based
upon consensus values from reference laboratories. A

sample result is considered acceptable if it lies within 3 standard deviations of the mean value obtained by selected reference laboratories for that sample.   A laboratory's performance is rated proficient if:

(1)   Three-fourths (75%) or more of the accumulated results over four rounds are acceptable; or

(2)   for the last two rounds, all samples are analyzed and the results are 100% acceptable.

System Audits

System audits performed for the NLLAP must be conducted by a public or private accrediting organization with a program recognized by EPA through a memorandum of understanding (MOU). The EPA OPPT has stated requirements for laboratory accrediting organizations wishing to participate in the NLLAP in a model MOU which is available from the National Lead Information Center Clearinghouse (phone number 1-800-424-LEAD).   The general requirements for laboratory accreditation organizations participating in the NLLAP are stated in "ISO Guide 58:   Calibration and Testing Laboratory Accreditation Systems-General Requirements for Operation and Recognition." Some specific requirements for laboratory accrediting organizations are stated in the NLLAP MOU model and include:

1.   Submit to EPA/OPPT for review, the organizational quality manual and related documents which describe the quality system currently in place.   The quality manual and/or related organizational documents must state all requirements for laboratory's seeking accreditation. The quality manual and/or related documents must specify organizational procedures for the removal of a laboratory's accreditation based on the laboratory's failure to maintain the conditions specified in the accreditation requirements.   In the event that a laboratory loses its accreditation status, EPA NLLAP officials must be notified in writing within five working days of the action by the laboratory accreditation organization.

2.   Establishment and implementation of a training program and continuing education program for assessors using the most current revision, including amendments of the EPA developed curriculum guidance document entitled "Pb-Based Paint Laboratory Accreditation: Curricula Recommendations For Assessor Training Programs-- Revision 1.0"[5] or their own curricula which addresses the areas covered in the EPA guidance document.   Requirements for qualifications for beginning assessor candidates and experienced assessors

are to meet those stated in the EPA curriculum guidance document mentioned above. The accrediting organization has the option to utilize the assessor training program of another accrediting organization recognized by the NLLAP.

3. Perform a systems audit on applicant laboratories inclusive of an on-site assessment applying their general and environmental program requirements which must be inclusive of the minimum requirements stated in the most recent edition of the NLLAP "Laboratory Quality System Requirements." The NLLAP "Laboratory Quality System Requirements" can be found as Appendix A of the NLLAP MOU model. Some areas addressed by the "Laboratory Quality System Requirements" are addressed latter in a following section.

4. Require that all laboratories applying for accreditation perform successfully (rated proficient or "P" by the National Institute for Occupational Safety and Health (NIOSH)) in the Environmental Lead Proficiency Analytical Testing Program (ELPAT) as administered by American Industrial Hygiene Association (AIHA) and NIOSH. Laboratories must participate in the ELPAT program on a quarterly basis as new rounds of proficiency testing samples are made available. The accrediting organization is responsible to make arrangements with NIOSH in order to secure the ELPAT data of participating laboratories.

5. Reevaluate laboratories accredited by it for lead analysis at a minimum of once every three years. This reevaluation would include a systems audit that includes an on-site visit. Laboratories which have been cited as having performed inadequately based on customer complaints, or poor performance in the ELPAT program are to be subject to more frequent reevaluation.

6. Upon approval of an accredited laboratory, provide to designated personnel of the EPA NLLAP accreditation information including the date the accreditation is effective, the accreditation expiration date and the matrices which the laboratory is accredited for. The accreditation organization shall also provide a continual update of the laboratory's accreditation standing over time as reassessments and performance evaluation reviews are conducted as well as any other information relevant to supporting an accreditation decision. Within 45 days after the accreditation of a laboratory, EPA NLLAP personnel are to be provided by the accrediting organization with the date the accreditation is in effect and the expiration date of the accreditation. A list of all current accredited

laboratories is to be supplied to EPA NLLAP personnel
at least once every three months.

7.   Maintain records for a period of ten years of the
terms of accreditation of each accredited laboratory
including all complaints received from customers of the
accredited laboratory. This information is to be
available upon request to EPA.

8.   The delegation of any responsibilities of
laboratory assessment to only organizations which are
recognized under the NLLAP.

9.   Participate in meetings with EPA at least once
every two years in an effort to help provide a formal
evaluation of NLLAP.

EPA is responsible for conducting evaluations of NLLAP
accrediting organizations at least once every three years,
more frequently if needed, based on complaints concerning
the organizations performance or significant changes in the
organization's program. These subsequent evaluations will
also be based upon the requirements stated for laboratory
accrediting organizations stated previously. These
evaluations will be the responsibility of OPPT's Chemical
Management Division (CMD), Technical Programs Branch.

Laboratory Quality System Requirements--As stated
previously, the laboratory accrediting organizations
participating in the NLLAP must perform system audits using
as a minimum the Laboratory Quality System Requirements of
the NLLAP. At their option, accrediting organizations may
require more stringent requirements for their accreditation
program. Areas addressed in the Laboratory Quality System
Requirements include laboratory:

- Quality Systems

- Personnel Qualifications and Training

- Reagents and Standards

- Analytical Instrumentation

- Analytical Methods

- Data Reduction, Validation and Reporting

- Quality Control Practices

- Documentation and Record Keeping

NLLAP SUPPORT DOCUMENTATION

In support of the NLLAP, the following documents have been produced by the OPPT. Information on how to obtain copies of these documents can be obtained from the National Lead Information Center Clearinghouse by calling toll free 1-800-424-LEAD.

1. "Pb-Based Paint Laboratory Operations Guidelines: Analysis of Pb in Paint, Dust and Soil (Revision 1.0)"[6]

This document provides laboratories with guidelines for operating a laboratory facility capable of analyzing for lead in paint, dust and soil matrices at levels of concern.

2. "Pb-Based Paint Laboratory Accreditation: Curricula Recommendations for Assessor Training Program (Revision 1.0)

This document provides laboratory accrediting organizations with an example curriculum which can be used to train their assessors in the area of conducting system audits as a part of the NLLAP.

3. NLLAP Memorandum of Understanding (MOU) Model

This document provides the model MOU to be used between EPA/OPPT and the laboratory accrediting organizations participating in the NLLAP. The document states requirements for laboratory accrediting organizations and provides the required "Laboratory Quality System Requirements" for laboratories participating in the NLLAP. Laboratory accreditation organizations recognized under the NLLAP will be required to evaluate participating laboratories based on, as a minimum, the "Laboratory Quality System Requirements."

MANAGEMENT AND IMPLEMENTATION

The NLLAP is managed as a part of the OPPT's Chemical Management Division's (CMD) Lead Program. The responsibility for implementing and support of the program lies with CMD personnel. It is the responsibility of CMD's Technical Programs Branch (TPB), to forward recommendations to the Director of OPPT concerning the recognition of any interested laboratory accrediting organization through the entering into a memoranda of understanding. Recommendations will be based upon the evaluation of the quality manual and related documents, including assessor training curricula, of candidate laboratory accreditation organizations seeking initial recognition or **to** maintain recognition by EPA as a part of the NLLAP. It is also the responsibility of TPB personnel to reevaluate the programs of recognized NLLAP laboratory accrediting organizations based upon the program requirements at least once every three years, providing recommendations to the Director of OPPT as to the renewal of the memoranda of understanding.

CURRENT PROGRAM STATUS AND RECOMMENDED LABORATORIES

At this time, over 200 laboratories are participating in the ELPAT Program. To date, the majority of the laboratories participating in ELPAT have analyzed proficiency testing samples consisting of all three matrices, paint chips, dust and soils. The most common instrumental methods of analysis being used are Flame Atomic Absorption Spectrometry and Inductively Coupled Plasma Atomic Emission Spectrometry. Based on the ELPAT Round 2 results, depending upon the matrix, 87 to 90 percent of the laboratories were rated as "proficient" based upon their performance.

Until the spring of 1994, EPA will make available to the public the current list of laboratories which have performed successfully in the ELPAT Program. Those laboratories which have undergone a systems audit under the NLLAP, will also be identified as being recognized by EPA under the NLLAP. This list, which is updated quarterly, can be obtained from National Lead Information Center Clearinghouse by calling 1-800-424-LEAD. In the spring of 1994, the ELPAT list of laboratories will be replaced by a list of laboratories which are recognized by the NLLAP, having successfully participated in the ELPAT Program and having under gone a systems audit by an accrediting organization participating in the NLLAP.

It is anticipated EPA will have entered into a memoranda of understanding with laboratory accrediting organizations as a part of the NLLAP this summer. Laboratory system audits conducted on behalf of the NLLAP are expected to be initiated this summer.

Under Title X, Section 405(b), EPA has the responsibility of periodically evaluating the effectiveness of the NLLAP. If the Agency finds the NLLAP ineffective in assuring the public laboratories are capable in the analyzing lead in paint chips, dust and soil samples, EPA is required to establish a federal certification program independent of the private sector.

REFERENCES

[1] U.S. Congress. "Title X, Residential Lead-Based Paint Hazard Reduction Act", H.R. Bill 5334, 1992

[2] International Standards Organization/International Electrochemical Commission. "ISO/IEC Guide 25: General Requirements for the Competence of Calibration and Testing Laboratories", Geneva, 1990

[3] International Standards Organization/International Electrochemical Commission, "ISO/IEC Guide 58: Calibration and Testing Laboratory Accreditation Systems-General Requirements For Operation and Recognition", Geneva, 1993

[4] U.S. EPA. "Laboratory Accreditation Program Guidelines: Measurement of Lead in Paint, Dust, and Soil.", EPA-747-R-92-001, 1992.

[5] U.S. EPA. "Pb-Based Paint Laboratory Accreditation: Curricula Recommendation for Assessor Training Programs (Revision 1.0)", EPA 747-R-92-005, 1993

[6] U.S. EPA. "Pb-Based Paint Laboratory Operations Guidelines: Analysis of Pb in Paint, Dust and Soil (Revision 1.0)", EPA-747-R-92-006, 1993.

Peter S. Unger[1]

THE A2LA LABORATORY ACCREDITATION PROCESS

REFERENCE: Unger, P. S., "The A2LA Laboratory Accreditation Process", Lead in Paint, Soil and Dust: Health Risks, Exposure Studies, Control Measures, Measurement Methods, and Quality Assurance, ASTM STP 1226, Michael E. Beard and S. D. Allen Iske, Eds., American Society for Testing and Materials, Philadelphia, 1995.

ABSTRACT: The acccreditation of lead (Pb) testing laboratories by the American Association for Laboratory Accreditation (A2LA) has been recognized by the U.S. Environmental Protection Agency under its National Lead Laboratory Accreditation Program (NLLAP). The A2LA program involves on-site assessment and successful participation in proficiency testing.

KEY WORDS: laboratory accreditation, assessment, proficiency testing

1. INTRODUCTION

A lead laboratory accreditation program has been developed under the regulatory authority of the U. S. Environmental Protection Agency. Requirements of the Department of Housing and Urban Development (HUD) and the Consumer Product Safety Commission (CPSC) were also considered in implementing the program. The EPA program for assessing laboratories is implemented by third party laboratory accreditation organizations. Currently both the American Association for Laboratory Accreditation (A2LA) and the American Industrial Hygiene Association (AIHA) are recognized by the USEPA as accreditors of lead testing laboratories.

The A2LA Program offers the lead testing program with a broader scope of accreditation and includes organizations engaged in other kinds of environmental assessment activities.

The A2LA Program is designed to accredit laboratories that conduct assessment activities associated with determining the presence of lead in environmental samples and the extent of this contamination. The assessment involves field testing, sample collection, and laboratory analysis in association with lead contamination originating from lead-containing paint and other sources of lead. The program and the attendant accreditation is available to organizations that conduct any or all of these activities. The lead of concern is usually found in several matrices which include air, building debris, dust, paint residue (chips), soil, and water. The main test technologies include:

Atomic Absorption Spectroscopy - Flame (AAS-Flame);

Atomic Absorption Spectroscopy - Furnace (AAS-Furnace);

Inductively Coupled Atomic Emission Spectroscopy (ICP-AES); and

X-Ray Fluorescence Spectroscopy (XRF).

---

1   Vice President
     American Association for Laboratory Accreditation
     656 Quince Orchard Road, Suite 620
     Gaithersburg, MD 20878-1409

The lead testing area is currently undergoing extensive research and regulatory scrutiny which has resulted in a number of efforts to develop methods capable of providing valid analytical procedures for the analysis of lead contamination. A number of these methods are in the final draft stages. This A2LA program endorses the use of these methods as appropriate to the matrix of interest. The methods acceptable for use under this program are listed below. These methods will be superseded by either adoption of the respective final version or when research or best practice indicates that a specific method is no longer acceptable for use. The U.S. Environmental Protection Agency (USEPA) has developed measurement protocols for several different lead measurement methods (40 Code of Federal Regulations (CFR): 50, 136, 141, 261; and Solid Waste (SW) 846 3rd Ed.) and has several draft methods undergoing final development. ASTM has developed measurement protocols for several different lead measurement methods and has a number a draft methods under development. The National Institute of Occupational Safety and Health (NIOSH) has developed measurement protocols for the analysis of airborne lead and dust lead measurement methods. A2LA provides accreditation for any of these methods.

There are strong opinions about the applicability of some of the procedures to certain types of sample matrices or types. A2LA does not intend to recommend which procedures are to be used in particular situations except to require that the methods chosen (from the A2LA acceptable methods list) be followed in detail. The application of the method must also remain consistent with its scope. A2LA will attest to the competence of laboratories performing to the state of the art.

An important aspect is the choice of the methods which are to be used to analyze for lead in environmental samples. Method choice will depend on a number of variables such as sample matrix, concentration range, necessary sample preparation, detection limit, dynamic range, precision, potential interferences, ease of use, and cost. There are seven sources of environmental samples that may be contaminated with lead: air, building debris, dust, paint (unapplied), paint residue, soil, and water. The choice of methods is limited to those methods of demonstrated performance or that are undergoing validation/development and are currently regarded as the best available technology and/or method. These methods are identified in the following section of this paper.

2. METHODS LIST

I. SAMPLE PREPARATION.

- EPA SOP, September 1991. Standard Operating Procedure for Lead in Paint by Hotplate- or Microwave-based Acid Digestions and Atomic Absorption or Inductively Couple Plasma Emission Spectroscopy, EPA 600/8-91/213; NTIS PB92-114172.

- EPA SW-846 3rd Ed. Method No. 3050A: Acid Digestion of Sediments, Sludges, and Soils.

- EPA SW-846 3rd Ed. Method No. 3051: Microwave Assisted Acid Digestion of Sediments, Sludges, Soils, and Oils.

- NIOSH Method No. 7082: Lead (in air).

- NIOSH Method No. 7105: Lead (in air).

- NIOSH Method No. 7300: Elements (in air).

- ASTM ES031: Practice for the Preparation of Soil for Subsequent Analysis by Atomic Spectrometry.

- ASTM ES033: Practice for the Preparation of Airborne Particulate Lead Samples Collected During Abatement and Construction Activities for Subsequent Analysis by Atomic Spectrometry.

- ASTM ES036: Practice for Hot Plate Digestion of Dust Wipe Samples for the Determination of Lead by Atomic Spectrometry.

- ASTM ES037: Practice for the Preparation of Dried Paint Samples for Subsequent Lead Analysis by Atomic Spectrometry.

II. LABORATORY SAMPLE ANALYSIS.

- EPA SOP, September 1991. Standard Operating Procedure for Lead in Paint by Hotplate- or Microwave-based Acid Digestions and Atomic Absorption or Inductively Couple Plasma Emission Spectroscopy, EPA 600/8-91/213; NTIS PB92-114172.

- EPA SW-846 3rd Ed. Method No. 6010A: Inductively Coupled Plasma Atomic Emission Spectroscopy (ICP-AES).

- EPA SW-846 3rd Ed. Method No. 7420: Lead [Atomic Absorption, Direct Aspiration (FAA)].

- EPA SW-846 3rd Ed. Method No. 7421: Lead [Atomic Absorption, Furnace Technique (GFAA)].

- NIOSH Method No. 7082: Lead [in air (FAA)].

- NIOSH Method No. 7105: Lead [in air (GFAA)].

- NIOSH Method No. 7300: Lead [in air (ICP-AES)].

- ASTM E1613: Method for the Analysis of Digested Samples for Lead by Inductively Coupled Plasma Atomic Emission Spectrometry (ICP-AES), Flame Atomic Absorption (FAAS) or Graphite Furnace.

For NIOSH references see DHHS (NIOSH) Pub. No. 84-100, 3rd Edition, Peter Eller, Editor, phone: 513-841-4256.

III. FIELD SAMPLE ANALYSIS

[The X-ray Fluorescence procedures are a screening technique and do not provide quantitative data at the action level for applied paint coatings.]

- EPA SOP September 1991. Standard Operating Procedures for Measurement of Lead in Paint Using the Scitec Map-3 X-ray Fluorescence Spectrometer, EPA 600/8-91/214.

- EPA SOP September 1993. Standard Operating Procedure for the Field Analysis of Lead in Paint, Bulk Dust, and Soil by Ultrasonic, Acid Digestion and Colorimetric Measurement, EPA 600/R-93/200.

- ASTM E1553: Practice for Collection of Airborne Particulate Lead During Abatement and Construction Activities.

IV. SAMPLE COLLECTION TECHNIQUES

[Quality system documentation covering chain-of-custody, sampling procedures and training of samplers is included.].

- NIOSH Method (11 May 92) No. 0700: Lead in Surface Wipe Samples

- HUD Paint Chip/Residue Sample Collection Procedure* **

- HUD Dust Sample Collection Procedure'*

- HUD Soil Sampling Procedure'*

* The sampling procedures described here are based on guidance provided in the Office of Public and Indian Housing, Department of Housing and Urban Development, Lead-Based Paint: Interim Guidelines for Hazard Identification and Abatement in Public and Indian Housing, September 1990.

** Federal Register Notice, Vol. 57, No. 125, Monday, June 29, 1992, Department of Housing and Urban Development, NOFA for Lead-Based Paint (LBP) Risk Assessments, page 28926.

- ASTM ES028: Practice for the Field Collection of Paint Film Samples for Lead Determination.

- ASTM ES029: Practice for the Field Collection of Soil Samples In and Around Buildings for Lead Determination.

- ASTM ES030: Practice for the Field Collection of Dust Samples Using a Wipe Sampling Method for Lead Determination.

3. GENERAL CRITERIA

A2LA uses as the basis for all of its accreditations the world recognized ISO/IEC Guide 25-1990, "General Requirements for the Competence of Calibration and Testing Laboratories" (available from ANSI 212-642-4900). These requirements have become the standard guide throughout the world and finding a laboratory competent to meet these requirements has become the basis for mutual recognition agreements with accreditation systems in other countries. A2LA currently has in force six agreements with systems in Australia, Canada, Hong Kong, New Zealand, and the Netherlands.

Several testing technologies are available and should be selected as appropriate to the sample type and associated action level. HUD, EPA and CPSC have legislative and regulatory responsibilities which they must exercise in dealing with the problems associated with the use of paint, removal and disposal of lead based paint, paint residue, building debris and contaminated soil, and the A2LA program must take these into consideration.

Accredited organizations are permitted to advertise the fact that they are accredited. Their scope of accreditation is specific, and users are encouraged to ask to see the scope of accreditation to review those specifics before employing an accredited laboratory. The A2LA Directory includes the scope of testing for each laboratory, and users may always contact the Association for specifics of a laboratory's competence.

The general criteria for accreditation of laboratories and/or field testing organizations are contained in Part A of the A2LA green booklet entitled, General Requirements for Accreditation. These are the ISO/IEC Guide 25 Requirements. All provisions except paragraph 5.2(f) of Guide 25 apply under this program.

The general criteria for field testing activities exclude sections 7 and 14 of Guide 25. For the environmental lead program, references to the laboratory in the general requirements for accreditation shall mean laboratory and/or field testing organizations as appropriate.

To summarize the general requirements for accreditation, each organization, as appropriate to their activity, shall have:

- a recognizable organization and management structure;

- a documented quality system with periodic audits and reviews and quality control and quality assurance procedures appropriate for the testing technologies or sample collection procedures employed;

- trained and competent personnel;

- calibrated testing and measuring equipment;

- test methods and/or standard operating procedures available and understood;

- controlled accommodation and environment as necessary;

- specimens (samples) handled carefully and chain-of-custody procedures included as necessary;

- records and certificates and reports reflecting the proper conduct of the sample collection or testing;

- subcontractors, outside support and services of adequate quality to meet the requirements of ISO Guide 25; and

- a formal complaints handling procedure and related documentation.

4. SPECIFIC CRITERIA

Specific criteria are an elaboration on or interpretation of the general criteria plus those additional requirements applicable to a certain field of testing, testing technology, type of test, or specific test. The numbering system for each section below corresponds to the numbering system in Guide 25. The specific criteria applicable to the Environmental Lead Program are as follows:

4. Organization and management. No additions to Guide 25.

5. Quality system, audit and review. The laboratory and/or field testing organization shall comply with the quality system provisions (section 5) of Guide 25. In addition, the organizations shall comply with the quality control (QC) procedures required by applicable federal or state environmental or public health agencies when testing specific matrices.

Standard curves shall be prepared to adequately cover the expected concentration ranges of the samples using at least 3 calibration standards and one blank, unless otherwise specified by the method employed. New curves shall be prepared whenever an out-of-control condition is indicated and after new reagents are prepared.

Field testing devices shall be calibrated as required by the testing procedure. In the absence of a requirement in the testing procedure, calibration shall be in accordance with the manufacturer's specification.

Control chart data or the equivalent shall be maintained for each routine analysis or testing activity. A documented corrective action plan shall be implemented when analytical results fail to meet QC criteria. Records shall indicate what corrective action has been taken when results fail to meet QC criteria.

Supervisory personnel shall review the data calculations and QC results. Deviations or deficiencies in QC shall be reported to management, and such reports shall be recorded. QC data shall be retrievable for all analytical and/or testing results. Method detection limits shall be determined and documented.

The laboratory shall conduct routine analyses of reagents, water used for dilutions, and solvents used for extractions to document the absence of contamination. Trip, field, and laboratory blanks shall be routinely analyzed as needed.

The laboratory and/or field testing organization shall have QC procedures (SOPs) specific to each test technology addressing, as appropriate the use of:

- reagent/method blank analyses;

- trip and field blanks;

- replicate/duplicate analyses;

- spiked and blank sample analysis;

- blind samples;

- surrogate standards;

- quality control samples;

- control charts;

- calibration standards and devices;

- reference material samples; and

- internal standards.

The following minimum QC sample analysis program shall be practiced in the laboratory:

- one QC check standard (instrument check solution) in 20 samples tested; the lab should repeat all samples if QC check standard is outside $\pm$ 10%;

- one blank in 20 (or per batch) both field and/or (reagent) laboratory;

- one spike in 20 (or per batch). The spike must be prepared from a standard stock which is different from the calibration standard stock, and should have a lead concentration that is within the range of the samples to be run;

- one (matrix) duplicate or (matrix) spiked duplicate in 20 (or per batch) independently prepared samples run as blinds; and

- one reference control sample (consists of a representative matrix spiked with the target analytes) in 20 (or per batch). This reference material is a secondary reference material whose concentration is traceable to a primary reference material.

Realistic sample matrices are to be used for the reference materials.

6. _Personnel_. The laboratory and/or field testing organization shall comply with all staff/personnel provisions (section 6) of Guide 25. In addition, the laboratory and/or field testing organization shall have documented evidence of analyst/tester proficiency for each test method performed. Persons in each senior technical position shall have a bachelor's degree in one of the applied sciences as a minimum educational requirement. Each analyst/tester accountable for performing tasks in any of the following areas shall meet the associated specified minimum experience requirements:

- general chemistry and instrumentation -- six months;

- atomic absorption -- one year;

- atomic emission spectrometry -- one year;

- x-ray fluorescence spectroscopy -- two years;

- field testing -- six months; and

- sample collection -- six months.

7. _Accommodation and environment_. The laboratory (this section does not apply to field testing) shall comply with the environment provisions (section 7) of Guide 25. In addition, the laboratory environment shall:

- use distilled/demineralized water that it can demonstrate to be free of interferents at detection limits;

- routinely check and record the conductivity of distilled/demineralized water (for a continuous system check should be per batch or daily);

- provide exhaust hoods for volatile materials [per 29 CFR (Code of Federal Regulations) 1910.1450, Occupational Exposure to Toxic Substances in Laboratories];

- provide contamination-free work areas (as necessary);

- provide adequate facilities for storage of samples, extracts, reagents, solvents, reference materials, and standards to preserve their identity, concentration, purity, and stability;

- have written detailed procedures and facilities in place for collection, storage, and disposal of chemical wastes (40 CFR 261);

- appropriately store corrosive, reactive, or explosive chemicals safely in conformance with 29 CFR 1910; and

- provide adequate separation of activities to ensure that no activity has an adverse effect on analyses.

While specific safety criteria are not an aspect of laboratory accreditation, laboratory personnel should apply general and customary safety practices as a part of good laboratory procedures. Each laboratory must have a safety and chemical hygiene plan [per OSHA (Occupational Safety and Health) rule 29 CFR 1910], as part of their standard operating procedures. Where safety practices are included in an approved method, they must be strictly followed.

8. _Equipment and reference materials_. The laboratory and field testing organization shall comply with the equipment and reference

materials provisions (section 8) of Guide 25. Equipment used for lead based paint testing shall meet the following minimums:

For analytical balances/pan balances:

- analytical balances shall be capable of weighing to 0.1 mg.;

- records of balance calibration shall be kept for at least two ranges (no more than two decades apart) using weights that conform to at least Class 3 tolerances (ASTM E 617-1990);

- records showing daily functional/calibration checks for analytical balances and monthly for other balances shall be maintained; and

- the balances shall undergo metrological calibration at least annually.

For pH meters:

- the laboratory shall use a clean pH meter with properly maintained electrodes suitable for the test performed with scale graduations at least 0.1 pH units (calibrated to $\pm$ 0.1 pH units for each use period);

- either a thermometer or a temperature sensor for temperature compensation shall be in use. Automatic temperature compensators which are an integral part of the apparatus are acceptable.

- a magnetic stirrer with clean PTFE-coated spin bar shall be utilized when making pH measurements;

- records shall be kept showing daily, or before each use, calibration, whichever is less frequent. Verify the absence of electronic drift by analyzing a reference buffer as a sample at least every 20th sample or at least once per batch; and

- aliquots of standard pH 4 & pH 7, or pH 7 & pH 10 shall be used only once.

For labware and sample collection devices:

- all such devices shall be cleaned in a manner appropriate for the analytical procedures for which it is to be used.

For ovens:

- thermometers shall be graduated in increments no larger than 1°C.;

- if oven temperature cannot be read without opening the door, the bulb of the thermometer shall be immersed in a sand bath; and

- oven temperature shall be adequately monitored (e.g., beginning and end of each use cycle).

For hot plates:

- maintain temperature at the center of the hot plate such that the surface temperature is 140°C. Note: An uncovered beaker containing 50 ml of a liquid such as an oil located in the center of the hot plate can be maintained at a temperature no higher than 140°C.

For microwaves ovens:

- calibrate the power available for heating weekly. This quality control function is performed to determine that the microwave has not started to degrade and that absolute power settings (watts) may be compared from one microwave unit to another. This power evaluation is accomplished by measuring the temperature rise in 1 kg (1.0 liter) of water exposed to microwave radiation for a fixed period of time. Water is placed in a teflon beaker and stirred before measuring the temperature. The beaker is circulated continuously through the field for 2 minutes with the unit at full power. The beaker is removed, the water vigorously stirred, and the final temperature recorded. The final reading is the maximum temperature reading after the energy exposure. These measurements should be accurate to ± 0.1°C and made within 30 sec of the end of heating. The absorbed power is determined by the following relationship:

$$P = \frac{(K)\ (CP)\ (m)\ (T)}{t}\ ;$$

Where:

P = the apparent power absorbed by the sample in watts (W), [W=joule per sec].

K = the conversion factor for thermal capacity or specific heat (cal per gm per degree C) of water.

Cp = the heat capacity, thermal capacity, or specific heat (cal per gm per degree C) of water.

m = the mass of the water sample in grams.

T = T_f, the final temperature minus the T_i, the initial temperature in degrees C.

t = time in seconds (s).

Using 2 minutes and 1 Kg of distilled water, the calibration equation simplifies to: P = (T) (34.87). The power in Watts can now be related to the percent power setting of the microwave unit. The microwave is then calibrated by simply plotting the percent power rating versus the experimentally determined Watts.

For thermometers:

- the laboratory shall have access to a NIST (NBS)-traceable thermometer for use in verifying working thermometers;

- the calibration of working mercury-in-glass thermometers shall be checked at least annually against a NIST (NBS)-traceable certified thermometer; and

- the calibration of dial-type thermometers shall be checked at least quarterly against a NIST(NBS)-traceable thermometer.

For autopipetors/dilutors:

- the apparatus shall have sufficient sensitivity for the intended use; and

- records shall be kept showing delivery volumes are checked gravimetrically at least monthly.

9. Measurement traceability and calibration. The laboratory and\or field testing organization shall comply with the measurement traceability and calibration provisions (section 9) of the general criteria. In addition, the organizations shall as appropriate:

● document the frequency, conditions, and standards used to establish calibration of all analytical/testing methodology; and

● verify and document all working standards versus primary (reference) standards.

10. <u>Calibration and test methods</u>. The laboratory and/or testing organization shall comply with the calibration and test method provisions (section 10) of Guide 25. In addition, the organizations shall:

● use approved (EPA, HUD, ASTM, NIOSH accepted and/or draft methods as appropriate) methodologies in their entirety as required for each test or analysis performed;

● have procedures for making and controlling revisions to in-house SOPs (use revised SOPs only after written authorization by senior technical personnel);

● have documented procedures for data collecting and reducing, reporting and record keeping;

● have documented validation procedures to apply at appropriate levels of all measurement processes;

● have documented procedures to check the validity of reported analysis values;

● have documented procedures for correcting erroneously reported results;

● have quality control procedures documented and available to the analysts/testers;

● use reagent grade or higher purity chemicals to prepare standards;

● use primary standard & QC reference materials;

● prepare fresh analytical standards at a frequency consistent with good laboratory practices unless otherwise stated in the method (frequency is a function of concentration and type of matrix); generally, the lower the concentration the less stable the standard)

● properly label reference materials/reagents with concentrations, date of preparation, expiration date and the identity of the person preparing the reagent; and

● have standards preparation documentation such as a preparations record book.

11. <u>Handling of calibration and test items</u>. The laboratory and/or testing organization shall comply with the handling provisions (section 11) of Guide 25. In addition, the organizations shall:

● have documented procedures for collection, shipping, receipt and storage of samples as appropriate.

● give samples an unambiguous sample number when collected and/or logged.

● maintain a permanent record for sample collection and log-in data;

● store samples in such a way as to maintain their identity, integrity, stability, and concentration; and

● follow documented chain-of-custody procedures, when required.

The organization shall have a sample custodian who shall be responsible for the sample control/logging. The procedures involved include the control, identity, preservation, and condition of samples, and sample handling, storage, and disbursement for analysis. The laboratory shall have a person responsible for ensuring that all analyses are performed within any USEPA/HUD or method-specified holding times, where appropriate.

12. Records. Test records shall be protected from loss, damage, misuse or deterioration and shall be retained for an appropriate period in a manner that permits retrieval when required. Test records that are created and/or retained on magnetic media (e.g., computer disks) or photographic media (e.g., microfiche) shall be stored in a manner that protects them from the hazards that affect such media and provision shall be made for the printing of such records when required. Note: It is not possible to define a particular retention period that is suitable for all laboratories' and/or field testing organizations circumstances. The minimum appropriate period will be based upon the nature of the organization's work, and its regulatory, legal, and contractual obligations. The organization shall have:

● a system that provides for retrievability and traceability of the sample source, the methodology of analysis/testing, results (including calibration and instrument checks), the person performing the analysis, and the date; and

● a secure archive area where records are held for appropriate periods of time and where access, deposit and removal of records are controlled and documented.

The organization shall comply with all the records provisions (section 12) of Guide 25. In addition, the organization shall establish and maintain a records system ensuring that:

● all observations and calculations are recorded in a permanent manner (such as laboratory/field notebooks, pro-forma work sheets, or magnetic media) at the time they are made and that the units of measurement in which observations are recorded are stated;

● original records are uniquely identified and traceable to the tests or test items to which they refer and to any test reports based upon them;

● records are traceable, retrievable, and legible and include sufficient information and explanation such that they can be readily interpreted by staff other than those responsible for their generation;

● records contain sufficient information to permit identification of possible sources of error and to permit, where feasible and necessary, satisfactory repetition of the test under the original conditions;

● records contain sufficient details of any significant departures from test specifications or other specified procedures including authorizations for such departures;

● records are checked for data transcription or calculation errors;

● records identify the person or persons responsible for their generation and those responsible for checking data transcriptions and calculations; and

• corrections or amendments to test records are made in a manner that does not obliterate the original data and are signed or initialled by the person responsible.

13. <u>Certificates and reports</u>. Test reports shall include a signature of the analyst/tester who conducted the test and shall conform to the documentation requirements listed in attachment B of program requirements document.

14. <u>Sub-contracting of calibration or testing</u>. No additions to Guide 25.

15. <u>Outside support and supplies</u>. No additions to Guide 25.

16. <u>Complaints</u>. No additions to Guide 25.

5. PROFICIENCY TESTING [PERFORMANCE EVALUATION] REQUIREMENTS

To be accredited under this program, enrollment and proficient performance in the Environmental Lead Proficiency Analytical Testing (ELPAT) Program administered by AIHA and NIOSH/EPA is required. Sample sets for one of more of three matrices (paint chips, soil and dust wipes) are supplied on a quarterly basis. Four concentration levels are required for each of three matrices: paint chips, soil, and dust wipes. NIOSH supplies the results of participating laboratories directly to A2LA.

Any laboratory performing field testing and/or sampling shall be required to participate in suitable proficiency testing programs as they become available.

The listing of any accredited laboratory is not continued in the yearly A2LA <u>Directory of Accredited Laboratories</u> unless all relevant proficiency test data requirements have been met.

<u>Initial Accreditation</u>. Applicant laboratories shall attain a rating of "proficient" under ELPAT for each matrix for lead (Pb) in which it seeks accreditation before accreditation can be initially granted.

<u>Maintaining Accreditation</u>. Accredited laboratories must continue to participate in <u>all</u> rounds of ELPAT for all matrices for which the laboratory is accredited. To maintain full accreditation, each accredited laboratory must be at least 75% (12 of 16 test samples) "proficient" over the 4 most recent rounds for each matrix.

<u>Loss of Accreditation</u>. If a laboratory obtains less than 75% "proficient" for the previous four rounds in any matrix for which it is already accredited, the laboratory's scope of accreditation shall be revised to delete that particular matrix. A2LA shall issue a revised scope of accreditation to the laboratory with a copy to USEPA NLLAP officials within five (5) working days of receipt of NIOSH ELPAT report results.

<u>Restoring Accreditation</u>. Accreditation for a specific matrix (i.e., paint chips, soil, or dust wipes) may be restored if the laboratory's performance on the next ELPAT round is 100% (no outliers) and there are no more than 25% (4 of 16 test samples) cumulative outliers over the 4 most recent rounds. Accreditation may also be restored if the laboratory performs at a level of zero outliers on the next two ELPAT rounds.

6. A2LA OBLIGATIONS UNDER NLLAP

<u>Notification of Accreditation Action.</u> When a laboratory loses its accreditation under this environmental lead(Pb) program, A2LA

shall notify in writing the authorized official of the USEPA National
Lead Laboratory Accreditation Program within five (5) working days
the result of such loss of accreditation.

Notification of Organizational Changes. A2LA shall also notify
in writing the authorized official of the USEPA National Lead
Laboratory Accreditation Program within thirty (30) days of any
decision to implement major changes in organizational policies or
management of A2LA which could affect the NLLAP.

Assessor Qualifications. A2LA environmental lead (Pb) assessors
shall have attained at least a bachelors degree in chemistry or a
related science and have at least 3 years of non-academic analytical
laboratory experience of which at least 2 years shall be metals
analysis experience. In addition to the current policy and
procedures for selection, orientation, training and evaluation that
all assessors must complete (as stated in the A2LA Assessor
Acceptability Guide), A2LA shall have a training program for novice
environmental lead (Pb) assessors and continuing education program
for all environmental lead (Pb) assessors based on the most current
version, including amendments, of the USEPA developed curriculum
guidance document entitled, Pb-Based Paint Laboratory Accreditation:
Curricula Recommendations for Assessor Training Programs. The A2LA
training curricula now consists of a two-day lead (Pb) technical
requirements and a five-day assessor course both with written
examinations, which have been reviewed and approved by USEPA. All
novice environmental lead (Pb) assessors shall pass both examinations
before being used on an assessment. A2LA veteran assessors, other
wise meeting the qualifications stated above and under contract
before June 1, 1993, must also attend the two-day course and pass the
examination before being used as an assessor for laboratories
requesting accreditation under the environmental lead (Pb) program.

7. CONDITIONS FOR ACCREDITATION

To attain and maintain accreditation, an applicant must agree to:

- Afford accommodation and cooperation as is necessary to enable
  A2LA to verify compliance with the requirements for
  accreditation including provision for examination of
  documentation and access to all calibration and testing areas,
  records and personnel for the purposes of assessment,
  surveillance, reassessment and resolution of complaints;

- Comply at all times with the criteria, requirements (including
  participation in proficiency testing as required), and
  conditions for accreditation;

- Claim that it is accredited only in respect of services for
  which it has been granted accreditation and which are carried
  out in accordance with these conditions;

- Pay such fees as shall be determined by A2LA;

- Not use its accreditation in such a manner as to bring A2LA into
  disrepute and not make any statement relevant to its
  accreditation which A2LA may consider misleading or
  unauthorized;

- Upon suspension, withdrawal or expiration of its accreditation
  (however determined) discontinue its use of all advertising
  matter that contains reference thereto and return any
  certificates of accreditation to A2LA;

- Not use its accreditation to imply product approval by A2LA
  unless permitted by a specific program;

- Endeavor to ensure that no certificate or report, nor any part thereof, is used in a misleading manner;

- In making reference to its accreditation status in communication media such as advertising, brochures or other documents, comply with the requirements of A2LA;

- Inform A2LA headquarters without delay of changes in any aspect of the laboratory's status or operation that affects the laboratory's legal, commercial or organizational status; organization or management (e.g., managerial staff); policies or procedures, where appropriate; premises; personnel, equipment, facilities, working environment or other resources, where significant; authorized signatories; or such other matters that may affect the laboratory's capability, or scope of accredited activities, or compliance with the criteria, requirements and conditions for accreditation; and

- Carry out any adjustments to its procedures in response to due notice of any intended changes by A2LA to the criteria, requirements, or conditions for accreditation, in such time as in the opinion of A2LA is reasonable.

In order to apply, the applicant laboratory's AUTHORIZED REPRESENTATIVE, must agree to the above conditions for accreditation and must attest that all statements made on their application are correct to the best of their knowledge and belief. An accredited laboratory's AUTHORIZED REPRESENTATIVE is responsible for ensuring that all of the relevant conditions for accreditation are met.

8. A2LA ACCREDITATION PROCESS

Application

A laboratory applies for accreditation by obtaining the application package from A2LA headquarters and completing appropriate application sheets. All applicants must agree to a set of conditions for accreditation (see Part 6), pay the appropriate fees set by the A2LA Board of Directors, and provide detailed supporting information on:

- Scope of testing in terms of field(s) of testing, testing technologies, test methods, and relevant standards;
- Organization structure; and
- Proficiency testing.

Accreditation is available for testing laboratories (tests) and calibration laboratories (calibrations). For tests, the scope of accreditation is normally identified in terms of standard test methods prepared by national, international, and professional standards writing bodies. If a laboratory desires accreditation only for a superseded version of a standard test method, the date of the version used is identified in its scope of accreditation. When the date is not identified in their scope of accreditation, laboratories are expected to be competent in the use of the current version within one year of the date of publication of the standard test method. For calibrations, the scope of accreditation is described typically in terms of the measurement parameter, range of measurement and best attainable uncertainties. In some cases, a laboratory's capability will be described in terms of types of tests, testing technologies, or other descriptive text when it is not appropriate or practical to identify specific tests or calibrations.

If a laboratory wishes accreditation for the use of its own methods, then it must provide the following information before assessment:

- Origin of method;
- Departures from standard;
- Reason for departures;
- Effects of departures; and
- Comparison with the standard methods they replace.

Accreditation will only be granted for tests or types of tests publicly available to all interested laboratories.

On-site Assessment

Once the application information is completed and the appropriate fees are paid, A2LA headquarters staff identifies and tentatively assigns one or more assessors to conduct an on-site assessment. Assessors are selected on the basis of their testing or calibration expertise so as to be better able to provide guidance to the laboratories. They do not represent their employers (if so affiliated) while conducting assessments for A2LA. The laboratory has the right to ask for another assessor if it objects to the original assignment. A2LA assessors are drawn from the ranks of the recently retired, consultants, industry, academia, government agencies, and from the laboratory community. Assessors work under contract to A2LA. Assessments may last from one to several days. More than one assessor may be required.

Assessors are given an assessor guide and checklists to follow in performing an assessment. These documents are intended to ensure that assessments are conducted as uniformly and completely as possible among the assessors and from laboratory to laboratory.

Before the assessment is conducted, the assessor team requests copies of the quality manual and related documentation (i.e., SOPs related to Guide 25 requirements) in order to prepare for the assessment. The quality manual and related documentation must be reviewed by the assessor team before the on-site assessment can begin. This review is done ideally before the assessment is scheduled. Upon review of submitted documentation, the assessor(s) may ask the laboratory to implement corrective action to fill any documentation gaps required by Guide 25 before scheduling the assessment. The assessment generally involves:

- An entry briefing with laboratory management;
- Review of quality documentation, sample handling, and records;
- Interviews with technical staff;
- Demonstration of selected tests or calibrations including, as applicable, tests or calibrations at representative field locations;
- Examination of equipment and calibration records;
- A written report of assessor findings; and
- An exit briefing including the specific identification of any deficiencies.

The objective of an assessment is to establish whether or not a laboratory complies with the A2LA requirements for accreditation and can competently perform the types of tests or calibrations for which accreditation is sought. However, when accreditation is required to demonstrate compliance with additional criteria which may be imposed by other authorities, such as in the case of U.S. EPA, the A2LA assessment will include such additional criteria. Assessors also provide advice, based on observations or in response to questions in order to help the laboratory improve its performance.

Deficiencies

At the conclusion of an assessment, the assessor prepares a report of findings, identifying deficiencies (i.e., deviations from the criteria or standard procedures for which accreditation is requested) which, in the opinion of the assessor, the laboratory must correct in order to be accredited. The assessor holds an exit briefing with top management of the laboratory, going over the findings and presenting the list of deficiencies (deficiency report). The authorized representative of the laboratory (or designee) is asked to sign the deficiency report to attest that the deficiency report has been reviewed with the assessor. The signature does not imply that the laboratory representative concurs that the individual item(s) constitute a deficiency. The laboratory is requested to respond within one month after the date of the exit briefing detailing either its corrective action or why it does not believe that a deficiency exists. If the laboratory fails to respond in writing within four months after the date of the exit briefing, it may be treated as a new applicant subject to new fees and reassessment should it wish to pursue accreditation after that time.

It is entirely possible that the laboratory will disagree with the findings that one or more items are deficiencies. In that case, the laboratory is requested to explain in its response why it disagrees with the assessor.

A laboratory that fails to respond to all its deficiencies within six months of being assessed shall be subject to being reassessed at its expense. Even if the laboratory responds within six months, A2LA staff has the option to ask for reassessment of a laboratory before an initial accreditation vote is taken based on the amount, extent and nature of the deficiencies. The Accreditation Council also has the option to require reassessment of a laboratory before an affirmative accreditation decision can be rendered.

Accreditation Anniversary Date

The anniversary date of a laboratory's accreditation is established 75 to 105 days after the last day of the final on-site assessment before an initial accreditation decision, regardless of the length of time required to correct deficiencies. This date remains the same throughout the laboratory's enrollment

Accreditation Decisions

Before an accreditation decision ballot is initiated, staff shall review the deficiency response, including objective evidence of completed corrective action, for adequacy and completeness. If staff has any doubt about the adequacy or completeness of any part of the deficiency response, the response is submitted to the assessor(s). Since all deficiencies must be resolved before accreditation can be extended, staff shall ask the laboratory for further written response in those cases where staff recognizes that an affirmative vote is not likely because of incomplete corrective action in response to deficiencies or obvious lack of supporting evidence that corrective action has been completely implemented.

Staff selects a "Panel of Three" from the Accreditation Council members rotating the mix of each Panel for every vote in order to evenly spread the workload. All votes are also sent to either the Accreditation Council Chairman or one of the Vice Chairmen for voting. The "Panel of Three" selection takes into account as much as possible each member's technical expertise with the laboratory testing or calibration to be evaluated. In order to avoid potential conflicts of interest that some Council members have with certain votes, ballots are prepared so as not to reveal the identity of the laboratory. At least three ballots (either affirmative or abstain) of the four ballots distributed must be received before accreditation can be granted.

Staff shall notify the laboratory asking for further written response based on the specific justification for one or more negative votes received from the Panel and Chairman (or Vice Chairman). If further written response still does not satisfy the negative voter(s), a reassessment may be proposed or required. If a reassessment is requested by more than one voter, the laboratory is asked to accept a reassessment. If the laboratory refuses the proposed reassessment, the whole Council is balloted. If two-thirds of those voting agree to a reassessment, accreditation is denied until a reassessment and satisfactory laboratory response(s) to all deficiencies are completed.

Adverse Accreditation Decisions

Any decision which would deny or revoke a laboratory's complete accreditation, must be agreed upon by a two-thirds vote of the whole Council.

If accreditation is granted, the A2LA staff prepares and forwards a certificate and scope of accreditation to the laboratory for each enrolled field of testing and special program. The laboratory should keep every scope of accreditation available to show clients or potential clients the testing technologies and test methods for which it is accredited. A2LA staff also uses the scopes of accreditation to respond to inquiries and to prepare the A2LA Directory of Accredited Laboratories.

Annual Review

Accreditation is for two years. However, after the first year of accreditation, each laboratory must pay annual fees and submit updated information on its organization, facilities, key personnel, and results of any proficiency testing.

Reassessments

A2LA conducts a full on-site reassessment of all accredited laboratories every two years. Reassessments are also conducted when evaluations and submissions from the laboratory or its clients indicate significant technical changes in the capability of the laboratory have occurred.

Each accredited laboratory is sent a renewal questionnaire, well in advance of the expiration date of its accreditation, to allow sufficient time to complete the renewal process. A successful on-site reassessment must be completed before accreditation is extended for another two years.

Adding to the Scope of Accreditation

A laboratory may request an expansion to its scope of accreditation at any time. Such a request must be submitted in writing to A2LA headquarters. Each request is handled on a case-by-case basis. Unless the previous assessor can verify the competence of the laboratory to perform the additional tests or calibrations, another on-site assessment is normally required. If the additional tests or calibrations require a new technology, another assessment is definitely required.

Laboratory Reference to A2LA Accredited Status

Since accreditation is issued in a number of fields of testing and testing technologies, it is the ethical responsibility of accredited laboratories to describe their accredited status in a manner that does not imply accreditation in areas that are outside their actual scope of accreditation. This may be accomplished through adherence to the following guidelines:

- Where the A2LA name and/or logo is used on general literature such as letterheads and business cards, it shall always be accompanied by at least the word "accredited".

- When the A2LA name and/or logo is used on a business solicitation document such as a proposal or quotation form, the laboratory has the responsibility to distinguish between those proposed tests that fall within the laboratory's scope of accreditation and those that do not. This may conveniently and satisfactorily be done by attaching a copy of its current A2LA Scope of Accreditation sheet.

- Where test results are endorsed by a display of the A2LA accreditation logo, the field of testing must be stated. On endorsed reports where test results are reported within the field of testing where certification exists but in a testing technology that is not included in the scope, they must be so indicated. For example, if a laboratory is accredited in the Environmental Field for only wet chemistry and metals, any gas chromatographic data reported would need to be identified as not covered by the A2LA accreditation. This may be done by placing an asterisk after each such test result with a footnote stating, "This is not covered by our current A2LA accreditation."

- An accredited laboratory owns the right to release A2LA assessor reports and deficiency reports as long as the reports are reproduced in whole and not in part. A2LA holds the assessment information in confidence unless specifically requested in writing by the accredited laboratory to release this information to another party.

Every circumstance where the principle of accurate representation applies cannot be anticipated and dealt with in this document. Therefore, it is the responsibility of the accredited laboratory not to misrepresent its accredited status under any circumstances. If there are questions, the laboratory should submit intended uses of the logo and/or any other accreditation claims to A2LA Headquarters for advance approval.

Misuse of the A2LA Accreditation Logo

A2LA provides guidance to laboratories attaining accreditation for proper control on the use of its accreditation logo.

Incorrect references to A2LA or misleading use of the accreditation logo found in advertisement, catalogs, etc. shall be dealt with by suitable actions which could include legal or corrective action or publication of the transgression.

In cases of misuse of the accreditation logo by laboratories, A2LA shall take appropriate corrective action.

Suspension of Accreditation

The accreditation applicable to a specific laboratory may be suspended for a limited period, for example in the following cases:

- if ongoing surveillance shows non-compliance with the requirements of such a nature that immediate withdrawal is not considered necessary;

- if a case of improper use of the accreditation logo (e.g., misleading prints or advertisements are not solved by suitable retractions and appropriate remedial measures by the laboratory); and

- if there has been any other deviations from the requirements of the A2LA accreditation program (e.g., failure to pay the required fee or to submit annual review information within 60 calendar days after it is due).

A2LA shall confirm an official suspension in a certified letter (or equivalent means) to the laboratory's authorized representative, indicating the conditions under which the suspension will be removed. A2LA may publish notification of the suspension.

Upon fulfillment of the indicated conditions within the specified period, A2LA shall remove the suspension and notify the laboratory accordingly; otherwise, the accreditation is withdrawn.

Withdrawal of Accreditation

A2LA shall withdraw accreditation in the following cases:

- under the relevant provisions for suspension of accreditation;

- if surveillance indicates that deviations from relevant requirements are of a serious nature;

- when complaints are received relating to one or more of the laboratory's test reports and investigation reveals defects in the quality system;

- the A2LA accreditation logo is being improperly used;

- at the formal request of the laboratory;

- if the system rules are changed and the laboratory either will not or cannot ensure conformance to the new requirements;

- on any other grounds specifically provided for under these program requirements or formally agreed between A2LA and the laboratory; and

- when such action is necessary to protect the reputation of A2LA.

A2LA shall implement this action by informing the laboratory accordingly by certified letter or equivalent means. A2LA may publish notification of the withdrawal. Withdrawal of accreditation results in the laboratory's name being withdrawn from the A2LA Directory of Accredited Laboratories.

A laboratory may appeal to A2LA against a decision to withdraw or not to award accreditation.

Appeals Procedure

The A2LA staff shall advise the applicant of its right to challenge an adverse accreditation recommendation of the Accreditation Council. If not satisfied with the Council decision, the applicant may make a further appeal to the A2LA Board of Directors. All decisions by the Board are final. Details of the appeals procedure and the applicant's right to a hearing are contained in the A2LA Bylaws and operating procedures.

Confidentiality Policy

All information provided by applicants in connection with a request for an application package, an application for accreditation, an assessment or proficiency test is confidential. Such information is examined by a small group of A2LA staff, assessors, and Accreditation Council. All are made aware of its confidentiality. Such information shall not be released unless the applicant provides A2LA permission in writing to do so.

Documents necessary to convey information about accredited laboratories and their scopes of accreditation are not confidential.

In response to a question about whether or not a particular laboratory has applied for accreditation, A2LA simply responds by saying that the laboratory is not accredited. Staff should neither confirm nor deny whether a laboratory has ever applied for accreditation. If the laboratory itself is saying that it has applied for accreditation, it is the laboratory's responsibility to release the information regarding its applicant status. If the caller says that the laboratory claims it applied, staff shall take the name, address and phone number of the laboratory to check to see if the laboratory is misleading the client but staff still will not verify the laboratory's application.

If an inquiry is made about a laboratory whose accreditation has lapsed but is in the renewal process, staff can indicate that the laboratory is not now accredited but is in the process of renewal, if that is the case. If the renewal laboratory's accreditation has lapsed with no indication (return of renewal forms or payment) of pursuit of renewal, staff indicates simply that the laboratory is not accredited.

Should the laboratory insist that staff verify for a potential client that it has applied to A2LA, staff shall indicate that it has applied only if the laboratory makes such a request to A2LA in writing.

If A2LA finds that a laboratory is misrepresenting its applicant or accredited status, staff shall treat such information as a complaint by first informing the A2LA President. The President shall determine the appropriate action which would usually involve contacting the laboratory directly about the alleged misrepresentation.

Conflict of Interest Policy

Since its inception, A2LA has had a policy that actual or apparent conflicts of interest must be avoided as mandated by normal business ethics. Consistent with the principles set forth in ISO/IEC Guide 58, "Calibration and Testing Laboratory Accreditation Systems - - General Requirements for Operation and Recognition," A2LA believes that it is vital that its accreditation services be impartial and objective, uninfluenced by the private interests of individuals acting for A2LA. Accordingly, any person directly involved in actions relating to the A2LA accreditation process shall avoid direct participation in A2LA actions which may involve an actual or apparent conflict of interest.

The Chairman of the Board and the President shall, as promptly as possible, take all possible means to prevent or overcome any such actions that may conceivably be in violation of this policy.

Ronald H. Peters[1] and Harriotte A. Hurley[2]

THE AMERICAN INDUSTRIAL HYGIENE ASSOCIATION ENVIRONMENTAL LEAD LABORATORY ACCREDITATION PROGRAM (ELLAP)

REFERENCE: Peters, R. H. and Hurley, H. A., "The American Industrial Hygiene Association Environmental Lead Laboratory Accreditation Program (ELLAP)," Lead in Paint, Soil and Dust: Health Risks, Exposure Studies, Control Measures, Measurement Methods, and Quality Assurance, ASTM STP 1226, Michael E. Beard and S. D. Allen Iske, Eds., American Society for Testing and Materials, Philadelphia, 1995.

ABSTRACT: In 1973 the American Industrial Hygiene Association (AIHA) began accrediting laboratories analyzing industrial hygiene (IH) samples taken to evaluate worker exposure to toxic chemicals. There are now over 400 laboratories accredited by AIHA's IH laboratory accreditation program. In 1993 AIHA established the Environmental Lead Laboratory Accreditation Program (ELLAP) to accredit laboratories analyzing samples of paint chips, soil, and dust wipes for lead content. ELLAP accreditation requires proficiency in the AIHA Environmental Lead Proficiency Analytical Testing (ELPAT) program, a quarterly performance evaluation program which provides blind samples of paint chips, soil, and dust wipes. The ELPAT program was developed with assistance and support from NIOSH and the EPA. ELLAP accreditation also requires triennial site visits and compliance with detailed quality assurance criteria.

KEYWORDS: lead, American Industrial Hygiene Association, laboratory accreditation, proficiency testing, laboratory quality assurance

---

BACKGROUND

The American Industrial Hygiene Association (AIHA) is a not-for-profit professional organization of industrial

---

[1]National Director, Laboratory Services, and Vice President, Clayton Environmental Consultants, Inc., 1252 Quarry Lane, Pleasanton, CA 94566.

[2]Directory, Laboratory Services, Western Operations, Clayton Environmental Consultants, Inc., 1252 Quarry Lane, Pleasanton, CA 94566.

hygienists dedicated to protecting the health and safety of workers and the community. AIHA has over 10,000 members internationally and, in addition to its national organization, has seventy-five local sections that are organized by geographical area. Most of the work of AIHA is conducted by its forty-five volunteer committees that address a variety of different industrial hygiene (IH), safety, and management issues. Training courses are offered through the United States and abroad to provide continuing educational opportunities in basic and advanced topics. AIHA publishes the AIHA Journal, a peer-reviewed monthly periodical that presents articles on current IH research, practical applications, and other issues. AIHA administrative activities are handled by an active office staff located in Fairfax, VA, near Washington, D.C. AIHA staff includes technical professionals and governmental affairs specialists.

One of AIHA's most important activities is laboratory accreditation. AIHA currently administers two laboratory accreditation programs, three proficiency testing programs, and a quality assurance program for individuals involved in asbestos analysis.

In 1973 AIHA recognized the need to monitor laboratories analyzing IH samples, those samples taken to evaluate worker exposure to toxic chemicals in the workplace, and established the AIHA IH laboratory accreditation program. In cooperation with the National Institute for Occupational Safety and Health (NIOSH), AIHA developed the Proficiency Analytical Testing (PAT) program, a performance evaluation program which provides blind IH samples (solvents on charcoal tubes, metals on filters, free silica on filters, and asbestos on filters) on a quarterly basis. There are now over 400 accredited IH laboratories and over 1400 participants in the PAT program.

A quality assurance program for asbestos counters working at remote project sites was established in 1987. To be listed on AIHA's Asbestos Analysts Registry (AAR), an asbestos analyst must meet specific quality criteria and must maintain proficiency in the Asbestos Analytical Testing (AAT) Program, a performance evaluation program that requires the analysis of four air-generated asbestos samples on a quarterly basis. AIHA's Bulk Asbestos Program provides bulk building materials to laboratories desiring to monitor their asbestos identification performance. This proficiency testing program was established primarily for non-commercial laboratories that do not need to be accredited by the NIST NVLAP asbestos programs. There are over 1400 counters listed on the AAR and 176 participants in the Bulk Asbestos Program.

AIHA's accreditation programs are administered by volunteer committees with staff support. The AIHA Laboratory Accreditation Committee (LAC) manages the IH laboratory accreditation program, and the AIHA Asbestos Analysts Registry Group (AARG) handles the AAR, AAT, and the Bulk Asbestos Program.

ENVIRONMENTAL LEAD LABORATORY ACCREDITATION PROGRAM (ELLAP)

AIHA's newest entry in the laboratory accreditation arena is the AIHA Environmental Lead Laboratory Accreditation Program (ELLAP). The ELLAP was developed by the AIHA Environmental Lead Laboratory Accreditation Committee (ELLAC) through a process that included participation and sought input from experienced directors of IH, environmental, and state public health laboratories, the Environmental Protection Agency, NIOSH, HUD and NIST. The ELLAP includes comprehensive requirements that were designed to assure that personnel, facilities, equipment, and operating systems are capable of producing accurate and defensible data. The requirements of the program are outlined here. A detailed discussion of the program is contained in the ELLAP policies, which are available from AIHA and are included with each application for accreditation.

The information presented here reflects the current AIHA ELLAP requirements. The EPA's National Lead Laboratory Accreditation Program (NLLAP) may affect some of these requirements. Some of the areas which may be changed by the EPA NLLAP are indicated.

ELLAP REQUIREMENTS

The ELLAP requirements are organized into five major areas: site visits, proficiency testing, personnel, facilities, and quality assurance.

Site Visits

To provide assistance to the laboratory and to ensure that the laboratory is in compliance with ELLAP requirements, a site visit by a trained AIHA Site Visitor is required prior to accreditation and every three years thereafter. Routine visits are announced, but the policies provide for unannounced site visits for problem investigation and resolution. A checklist is used to facilitate consistency. A copy of the checklist is provided to the laboratory as part of the application form. The Site Visitor provides a sample which must be analyzed during the visit.

Laboratories that meet certain criteria may request that the initial site visit be waived. The criteria are: 1) the laboratory is accredited under the AIHA IH laboratory accreditation program or some other program that follows International Standards Organization (ISO) guidelines; 2) the laboratory is rated proficient in the ELPAT program; and 3) the laboratory has successfully completed a site assessment that covered metals within the prior three years. Laboratories that meet these criteria are also eligible for interim accreditation, which may be granted for a nine month period while the laboratory is under evaluation for accreditation. If accreditation is not earned within the nine month period, the interim accreditation expires.

The Environmental Lead Proficiency Analytical Testing (ELPAT) Program

Evaluating the laboratory's proficiency at analyzing real world samples is a critical part of the ELLAP. As a performance evaluation tool, the Environmental Lead Proficiency Analytical Testing (ELPAT) Program was established through a Cooperative Research and Development Agreement (CRADA) between NIOSH and AIHA with support from the USEPA through a Memorandum of Understanding (MOU) between NIOSH and the EPA. ELPAT provides quarterly proficiency testing samples of paint chips, soil, and dust wipes in varying concentration levels. The samples are produced by Research Triangle Institute under contract with AIHA. The samples are generated from lead-contaminated materials obtained from such sources as abatement projects, industrial sites, and vacuum cleaner bags.

The first ELPAT round was conducted in December of 1992. The program is now in the fourth round with over 200 participants. AIHA administers the ELPAT program, and NIOSH handles the statistical analysis.

Personnel

Three positions are defined by the ELLAP: Technical Manager, Quality Assurance Coordinator, and Analyst. There are specific requirements for each position. The Technical Manager, the individual who directs the activities of the laboratory, must have a baccalaureate degree in chemistry or a related science, must possess at least two years non-academic experience in analytical chemistry, and must have at least six months experience in metals analysis. The requirements for the Quality Assurance Coordinator (QAC) allow for a degreed or non-degreed individual. If the QAC has a degree in a basic science, he/she must possess at least one year of non-academic analytical chemistry experience and training in statistics. If the QAC is not degreed, he/she must have a minimum of four years analytical chemistry experience and training in statistics. The requirements for analysts are performance based and, other than the completion of an internal or external training course in metals analysis, no specific criteria exist. The laboratory must be able to demonstrate that the analyst is capable of producing reliable results through successful analysis of Standard Reference Materials (SRMs), proficiency testing samples, or quality control (QC) samples.

The EPA NLLAP criteria differ from those recommended by AIHA. The Technical Manager must have a minimum of three years laboratory experience, at least two of which must be in metals analysis. The criteria for analysts are not performance based, but require specific minimum lengths of time of laboratory experience. The time requirement varies depending on the analytical responsibility of the position.

Facilities

Unlike other sections of the ELLAP policies, the facilities section contains the only non-mandatory recommendations. These non-mandatory recommendations are indicated in the policies by using the word "should" and as opposed to shall. Recommendations are included for electrical services, lighting and temperature control to meet instrument and/or sample requirements. The policies address the organization, the physical facility, safety, and equipment.

The ELLAP accredits organizations, not individuals. Single site accreditations are offered and laboratories with multiple locations must apply for separate accreditations for each site. Mobile laboratories are allowed to seek accreditation, but must meet the same requirements as fixed facilities. The laboratory must have an active and identifiable lead analysis capability at the location seeking accreditation.

The policies require that a laboratory have the space, contamination control practices, ventilation, safety and health policies, and equipment to safely and effectively perform lead analyses.

Space must be sufficient for sample receipt and processing, as well as storage and containment for chemicals, compressed gases, and glassware. The adequacy of such will be assessed by the site visitor.

Contamination control can be accomplished through physical facilities design, operating procedures and housekeeping practices. Lunch areas, if provided, must be separate from the laboratory. Consumption of food or beverages and smoking are not permitted in laboratory areas. Work surfaces must be non-porous or have a non-porous coating to minimize surface contamination.

Housekeeping practices must be sufficient to prevent contamination of samples and work surfaces. Wipe sampling must be conducted at least quarterly to determine surface levels of lead in the laboratory.

The laboratory ventilation system must be adequate for controlling chemical exposures of laboratory employees, consistent with the requirements of the OSHA laboratory standard or applicable state standards. Laboratory fume hoods must be maintained and face velocities must be measured and recorded at least annually.

Although this program is not intended to address safety concerns, there are requirements for procedures to minimize employee and environmental exposures, and to reduce fire and safety hazards. Laboratories are expected to follow all applicable federal, state and local regulations regarding environmental contamination, waste disposal and safety and health. As part of the application for accreditation, the

Technical Manager must provide a written statement that a system for the proper disposal of samples is in place, and that the laboratory complies with OSHA Standard "Occupational Exposures to Hazardous Chemicals in Laboratories", or the equivalent state standard. The site visitor will not perform a safety inspection of the laboratory but will verify that a written Chemical Hygiene Plan exists for the laboratory operation.

Equipment requirements are performance based. Successful analysis of proficiency testing samples may be used to demonstrate the suitability of an instrument in performing that analysis. Specific instrumentation is not required. An equipment log must be maintained for each major instrument, including records of in-house preventive maintenance and service. Specific requirements for equipment calibration are covered in the quality assurance program section.

Quality Assurance

There are many detailed quality assurance requirements, covering all aspects of laboratory operations, including documentation of the QA program, sample handling, analysis, data validation, reporting, and sample disposal.

Documentation of the Quality Assurance Program

All laboratories seeking accreditation must have a quality assurance (QA) program in place, which is detailed in a written QA manual. The QA manual must meet the QA/QC requirements of the approved methods used, and must include or address sixteen required program components. To offer flexibility, these program components may be contained in the quality assurance manual and related support documents, including standard operating procedures.

In defining these requirements, the ELLAC incorporated program components of the AIHA Industrial Hygiene Laboratory Accreditation Program, the ISO Guides and the EPA Interim Guidelines and Specifications for the Preparation of Quality Assurance Program Plans. The sixteen program components which must be addressed are:

- A Title Page
- A Table of Contents
- Organization and Responsibility
- Quality Assurance Objectives and Policies
- Personnel Qualifications and Training
- Sampling Materials
- Chain-of-Custody and Sample Receiving Procedures
- Reagents and Standards
- Equipment Calibration and Maintenance Procedures
- Analytical Methods
- Data Reduction, Validation and Reporting

- Internal Quality Control Procedures
- Performance and System Audits
- Corrective Action
- Quality Assurance Reports
- Documentation and Recordkeeping
- Sample Retention and Disposal

The QA Manual must be submitted upon initial application and with each subsequent reaccreditation application. This manual must be updated whenever necessary and reviewed and approved by management at least annually. The document must reflect the actual operating, and quality control programs in force in the laboratory, and must be accessible to all laboratory personnel.

The organization of the quality assurance program and accountability of individuals must be defined. At a minimum, this must include the responsibilities and accountability of the technical manager, quality assurance coordinator and lead (Pb) analysts.

The objectives of the quality assurance program and policies of the organization must be clearly stated.

Qualification criteria and training requirements for laboratory personnel must be defined. Analysts must complete an external or internal training program in lead or applicable metals analysis, prior to performing analyses on client-submitted samples. The training must be documented in laboratory records, and include a description of the content and duration of the program.

Sampling Materials

Information regarding sampling materials, sampling containers, preservatives, and shipping instructions must be available to clients through the laboratory. This does not require the laboratory to provide these materials. However, the laboratory must be knowledgeable in appropriate sample collection, preservation and shipping requirements. The laboratory should request that clients submit field blanks with samples, where applicable, as is the case with wipe samples.

Chain-of-Custody/Sample Receiving Procedures

The laboratory must have a written description of the chain-of-custody and sample receiving procedures followed in the laboratory.

A sample log must be used to record the receipt of all samples. This log must contain, at a minimum: a unique laboratory identification system to identify each sample and/or batch of samples received by the laboratory; the date received; and the Client identification.

The acceptability of sample condition at time of receipt, and the name of individual receiving samples for laboratory must be recorded. Sample rejection criteria must be stated in the sample receiving procedures, as well as provisions for advising field personnel of problems with samples.

It is anticipated that the EPA NLLAP will also require that the analysis requested, the storage location of samples, and comments, be recorded in the sample log.

Within the laboratory, each sample must be identified by a unique laboratory number.

Procedures must be in place to document the custody of samples and data from sample collection through receipt, storage, analysis and reporting of data.

Reagents and Standards

Reagents and standards must be of the grade or quality specified by the analytical methods in use in the laboratory.

Reagents and standards must be inspected, dated and initialed upon receipt. Standards must have an expiration date assigned, and must not be used beyond that date.

Purchased calibration standards must be traceable to NIST standards. Standard and reagent preparation must be documented and must include the date of preparation, the concentration and/or purity of parent material, the assigned expiration date, and preparer's initials.

It is anticipated that the EPA NLLAP may also require verification of standard concentrations upon receipt and periodically thereafter.

Calibration and Maintenance Procedures

Instrument calibration and maintenance procedures, and the frequency of such must be stated. ELLAP does not have specific acceptance criteria for instrument performance and calibration checks. However, ELLAP does require that laboratories have defined their own acceptance criteria for these checks. It is expected that the EPA NLLAP will specify acceptance limits.

Instruments must be subjected to performance checks prior to use. Such checks may include evaluation of instrument sensitivity, noise levels and absorbance or emission levels versus historical values.

With the exception of ICP, a minimum of three calibration standards which bracket the sample concentrations and a blank must be analyzed each day of use to construct a calibration curve. Acceptance criteria in terms of the relative percent difference (RPD) of response factors or correlation coefficient must be stated.

For ICP analyses, a minimum of a single point standardization must be performed each day of use, with linearity confirmed by the analysis of a standard at the high end of the standardization range. In addition, an interference check standard must be analyzed each day.

Instrument calibration must be verified each day of use by analysis of a reference standard independently prepared from a source other than that of the calibration standard. The EPA NLLAP will most likely require NIST traceability of all calibration standards, however, this may be accomplished through in-house analysis.

Continuing calibration verification standards and continuing calibration blanks must be analyzed in accordance with the specified test method. THE EPA NLLAP may require continuing calibration verification standards and blanks after every 10 samples.

Records must be maintained which document preventive maintenance and repairs to instruments. Problem or service descriptions, dates and types of repair, and person performing repair must be recorded. Equipment which is out of calibration or defective must be taken out of service until repaired.

Each instrument in the laboratory must have a manufacturer's instrument operation manual or equivalent, available for determining standard operating conditions and use.

Because of the importance of ancillary equipment, calibration and maintenance procedures must be specified and records maintained for microwaves, balances, and mechanical pipets if used for lead analyses.

Analytical Methods

Analyses must be conducted using those methods mandated by legal requirements, recognized published methods or methods developed and validated by the laboratory. Methods may not be used for sample analysis until competence for each particular matrix has been demonstrated.

Procedures recommended by EPA, NIOSH, ASTM, AOAC, APHA or others may be appropriate, if the laboratory can demonstrate acceptable performance for each particular matrix. The ELLAP policies provide examples of methods which may be acceptable.

Alternate procedures and/or modifications of methods may be used if they have been validated by the laboratory. The EPA NLLAP requires the laboratory to have written method validation procedures with elements defined by the EPA.

Analytical methods must be available to all analysts in the form of standard operating procedures or SOPs. The SOPs must be dated and approved for use by the Technical Manager, and the SOP adoption and revision process must be defined.

The EPA NLLAP has specified eleven required program components for SOPs. They permit amendment of SOPs by attachments in order to address all required elements.

Linear calibration ranges must be established and routinely verified for each method in use by the laboratory. Method detection limits (MDLs) must be established and statistically verified at least annually for each method. For methods with stated MDLs, demonstration of ability to achieve such MDLs is required.

Data Reduction and Validation

Laboratories must establish and maintain a data review process beginning at sample receipt and extending through the report process.

The data reduction and review process must include, but not be limited to: comparison of quality control data against established acceptance limits; computation verification; transcription of data; and adherence to the procedures established in the laboratory's SOPs.

The review process must be documented and laboratory records must document all analyses in detail. Acceptable data recording and correction procedures are contained in the ELLAP policies.

Reporting

Final test reports must include the following information: the name and address of the laboratory; a unique report identification; the client name and address; sample description and identification; the date received by the laboratory; the test method; sample results; detection limit; modification to the test method, if applicable; signature by the technical manager or his/her designee; and the date of issue. Test report corrections or additions must be documented. Concentration below laboratory reporting limits must be reported as not detected, (ND) or less that (<) and reference the reporting limit. The reporting of zero concentration results is unacceptable.

The EPA NLLAP has very specific and detailed report content requirements similar to CLP reports, and AIHA was unsuccessful in having this requirement eliminated. Reports must include calibration data, raw data, and quality control data. The amount of information provided to the client is based on the request of the client, however, the laboratory is required to generate and keep the required information on file in a final test report. For single sample lot submissions of fewer than 50 samples, this information does not need to be kept on file in a final test report, but it must be maintained and be accessible, to be assembled on request.

Internal Quality Control Procedures

The required elements of the intra-laboratory quality
control program include the evaluation of accuracy,
precision and contamination control.

Accuracy studies are performed to determine how close a
measurement comes to an actual or a theoretical value.
Accuracy can be expressed as percent recovery and be
evaluated by the analysis of matrix spike samples or
reference samples. A matrix spike is an aliquot of a sample
fortified with a known quantity of the analyte of interest
and subjected to the entire analytical procedure.

Precision is a measure of the reproducibility of analyses.
Precision is commonly expressed as standard deviation or
relative percent difference and can be evaluated by the
analysis of replicate samples. Replicate sample analyses
are one or more analyses on separate aliquots of samples to
evaluate method precision. Most commonly, two replicate
analyses, (defined as a duplicate analysis) are performed.

Method blanks provide a measure of contamination
attributable to laboratory equipment, collection medium and
reagents. A method blank contains representative collection
medium and all reagents used to prepare and analyze samples,
and it is subjected to all preparation steps and processed
with samples. Procedures for cleaning glassware to reduce
chemical contamination must be specified by the laboratory.

Soil and Paint Chip Samples

Matrix spiked samples for either soil or paint chip samples
must be analyzed with a minimum frequency of ten percent
(10%) of the samples for each matrix per batch of samples.
A batch refers to a group of samples of the same matrix
which are processed at a single time. If there are fewer
than 10 samples in a batch, at least one spiked sample per
batch must be analyzed.

Duplicate samples must also be analyzed with a minimum
frequency of ten percent (10%) for each batch of samples.
Again, if there are fewer than 10 samples in a batch, at
least one duplicate sample must be analyzed. In the event
the analyte is not detected in the sample, replicate matrix
spike samples may be analyzed to evaluate precision.

For paint and soil samples, a method blank would include
only reagents and would be synonymous with a reagent blank.
Method blanks must be analyzed with a minimum frequency of
five percent (5%) for each batch of samples. Fewer than 20
samples in a batch, require at least one method blank.
Method blanks must not be used to correct sample results.

Dust Wipe Samples

When analyzing dust wipe samples, matrix spike samples
cannot be prepared since the entire dust wipe sample is

digested prior to analysis. Instead, method spikes and method spike duplicates samples are prepared by adding a known amount of lead containing dust to blank collection media. Method spike and method spike duplicate samples must be analyzed with a minimum frequency of ten percent (10%) for each batch of samples.

A method blank for dust wipe samples must include unused wipe sample collection medium in addition to all reagents. Method blanks must be analyzed with a minimum frequency of five percent (5%) of the samples for each batch of samples. As is the case with paint and soil samples, method blanks must not be used to correct sample results. It is recommended that field blanks be submitted by clients to determine any lead contribution from the actual media used for sample collection.

External Reference or Control Samples Analysis

A reference or control sample must be analyzed with every batch of samples. The concentration of the control sample must be within the working range of the method and must not require extensive pretreatment, dilution or concentration prior to analysis. Sources of these samples include but are not limited to: NIST Standard Reference Materials, ELPAT samples, commercially available reference samples, samples prepared by other laboratories or samples prepared in-house.

Acceptance limits must be defined by the laboratory. ELLAP requires only one reference or control sample per batch, while the EPA NLLAP requires analysis at a rate of 5% of the samples in each batch and has specified acceptance limits.

Acceptance Limits

As with instrument performance and calibration checks, ELLAP does not define specific acceptance limits. Unless specific acceptance limits are established by a method, acceptance limits must be established for each method based upon statistical evaluation of the data generated by the analysis of quality control samples. The laboratory's calculation procedures for statistically derived acceptance limits must be documented. It should be noted that some methods have listed acceptance criteria for applicable analytes based upon determinations by a single laboratory, the compilation of data from many laboratories, or limits that are assumed or expected. Laboratories should realize that these limits may be too broad to define accurate acceptance criteria for their particular laboratory conditions. These limits are best used as guidelines during the initial phases of method use and are superseded when the laboratory has collected sufficient self-generated data for proper statistical evaluation. The EPA NLLAP has defined interim acceptance limits of $\pm 25\%$ for recovery of matrix spikes, $\pm 20\%$ of known value for laboratory control samples, and 25% RPD for duplicate samples. These limits must be used until laboratories have generated sufficient data to statistically derive their own acceptance limits.

Control charts or a quality control database must be used to record quality control data and compare quality control data with acceptance limits.

Performance and System Audits

The laboratory must describe its policy regarding participation in proficiency testing programs or collaborative or comparative studies. At a minimum, accredited laboratories must participate in ELPAT for all matrices accepted by the laboratory for analysis. Proficiency test samples must be analyzed in a manner similar to client samples.

Quality assurance audits must be conducted at least annually by the quality assurance coordinator. The QA coordinator must provide reports to laboratory management at least quarterly, regarding quality assurance problems, corrective action and quality assurance audits.

Corrective Action

Laboratories must take corrective action whenever quality control data are outside acceptance limits. No data may be reported until the cause of the problem is determined and corrected, or until the laboratory demonstrates that the cause was a random event and no longer affects data. Laboratories must keep records of all out-of-control events, the determined cause or causes and the corrective action taken. Laboratories are required to respond to client quality complaints and maintain records of corrective action.

Documentation and Record Keeping

The document and record retention policies of the laboratory must be stated and must include the manner and duration of record retention. All laboratory records must be maintained for a period of at least five years. EPA NLLAP is requiring maintenance of all records for at least ten years.

Computer records are satisfactory without hard copy files, provided hard copies can be generated as needed and data edits are documented within the computer files. Computer back up procedures are required.

Sample Retention and Disposal

The sample retention and disposal policies of the laboratory must be stated and include the manner and duration of sample retention and disposal.

Laboratories must dispose of samples according to federal,

state and local regulations. The application for accreditation requires that the Technical Manager provide a written statement that a system for the proper disposal of samples is in place. Disposal practices will not be evaluated by AIHA. However, the site visitor will verify that procedures are in place in the laboratory.

ACCREDITATION PROCESS

To become accredited under the AIHA ELLAP, a laboratory must first complete a comprehensive application that requires the laboratory to demonstrate that it is in compliance with the ELLAP requirements, which are provided as part of the application form. The AIHA office conducts an administrative review of the application and, if complete, forwards it to two ELLAC members for technical review. If additional information is needed by the Reviewer, the AIHA office requests it from the laboratory. Once the Reviewers are satisfied that the laboratory meets the criteria on paper, a Site Visit is authorized. The Site Visitor confirms that the submitted application represents the operating systems in place in the laboratory. Any discrepancies noted by the Site Visitor must be resolved before the laboratory is granted accreditation. After successful completion of the Site Visit, the ELLAC votes on whether or not to recommend accreditation of the laboratory to the AIHA Board of Directors. If accreditation is recommended, the AIHA Board reviews the recommendation. If the Board grants accreditation, a certificate of accreditation is issued.

Accreditation is based on the matrix. The laboratory may seek accreditation for one, two, or all three matrices; however, the ELLAP requires that the laboratory seek accreditation for each matrix analyzed in-house. The accreditation period is three years, after which the laboratory must apply for reaccreditation and undergo a reaccreditation site visit. If the laboratory desires, the ELLAP site visit may be combined with site visits for other programs, if the Site Visitor has completed the AIHA Site Visitor training program.

CONCLUSION

The ELLAP has well defined requirements for personnel, facilities, equipment, and quality assurance. These requirements were developed to minimize ambiguity, to increase the objectivity of laboratory evaluations and to specify the necessary elements for the generation of accurate and defensible data. Laboratories interested in this program should contact the ELLAP coordinator at the AIHA office (telephone number: 703-849-8888) for an application or copy of the ELLAP policies.

Author Index

Subject Index